FIELD BOOK OF AMERICAN TREES AND SHRUBS

A CONCISE DESCRIPTION OF THE CHARACTER AND COLOR OF SPECIES COMMON THROUGHOUT THE UNITED STATES, TOGETHER WITH MAPS SHOWING THEIR GENERAL DISTRIBUTION

By F. SCHUYLER MATHEWS

AUTHOR OF

THE FIELD BOOK OF AMERICAN WILD FLOWERS
FIELD BOOK OF WILD BIRDS AND THEIR MUSIC
FAMILIAR LIFE OF FIELD AND FOREST, FAMILIAR FEATURES OF THE ROADSIDE, ETC. ❖ ❖

MEMBER OF THE NEW ENGLAND BOTANICAL CLUB

WITH NUMEROUS REPRODUCTIONS OF WATER COLOR, CRAYON, AND PEN AND INK STUDIES FROM NATURE BY THE AUTHOR ❖ ❖ ❖ ❖

G. P. PUTNAM'S SONS
NEW YORK AND LONDON

FIELD BOOK OF TREES AND SHRUBS

Copyright, 1915, by
F. SCHUYLER MATHEWS

Twenty-fourth Impression

Made in the United States of America

To

MY FRIENDS

MARINUS W. AND MARY A. DOMINICK

EVER IN HELPFUL SYMPATHY WITH MY EFFORTS IN THE

FIELDS OF BOTANY AND ORNITHOLOGY

THIS LITTLE VOLUME IS

AFFECTIONATELY INSCRIBED

INTRODUCTION.

There is a very considerable number of native trees and shrubs of these United States many of which are not as well known as they should be. I do not refer, of course, to such common trees as the Sugar Maple, Fir, and American Elm, but to their less familiar relatives and to the numerous interesting shrubs which are far from uncommon throughout the land. This book is intended, therefore, not only to furnish the reader with a means for identifying such species, but to demonstrate certain truths relative to form and color which are more within the province of the artist than the botanist and which naturally do not appear in text-books on botany. A particular tree, for instance, possesses a typical figure and a tone of green different from that of its associates. There is no reason why these differences should not be described with as much exactness as possible.

Moreover, it is important to record the fact that Nature is manifold in her differences—there are no two things alike, yet there are salient types. It is best to know that the individuals of a species are not all run in the same mold, that botanical rules cannot circumscribe all truth, that what one sees may be very different from what another sees, that even expressed expert opinion upon a given species leads to polemics in botany the outcome of which we will do well to await with patience.

Types and Differences

Botany does not stand still, it moves. There used to be a score of species of *Crataegus*—to-day there are more than two hundred! I suppose nothing could more surely indicate the incomplete condition of recent botanical investigation than the unsettled status of our common blackberries; they are not yet perfectly understood, and for

Progressive Botany

that reason it seemed wisest to exclude them altogether from this book.

It would be well, on the other hand, to call attention to the recent exhaustive study of the Shadbushes by Professor K. M. Wiegand in *Rhodora*, and of the Birches by Professor M. L. Fernald in the *Am. Journal of Science*, although these treatises possibly do not constitute the last word which may be said in the two groups, they are splendid examples of thoroughness in the work of modern botanists. Not less illuminative of the painstaking character of recent investigation are Mr. Eggleston's revisions of *Crataegus* in *Gray's Manual* and *Britton and Brown's Flora*. These are certainly as reliable as anything is likely to be upon that most difficult and baffling group.

On Nomenclature I must repeat what I have already said in the *Field Book of American Wild Flowers* about nomenclature. The system followed here is that of Engler and Prantle, and the scientific names conform to the Vienna Code—at least it is intended that they should do so. It is deplorable that some American botanists do not abide by this internationally supported standard, but I presume they have their own excellent reasons for not doing so. In any event it is perfectly apparent that a difference like this promotes confusion and retards progress. Indeed progress is often retarded in all professions by just such unwillingness on the part of the individual to be subordinate. Meanwhile if we should pick up the works of, say, three botanical authors and find they contain as many different scientific names for one species, we think we are justified in indulging in a few expressions not altogether complimentary to two out of the three writers.

Accuracy in Form Very naturally this book would not have been written if it had not become apparent that there were yet many things to say about trees and shrubs which, up to the present time, have remained unsaid. For example, an examination of my descriptions of *Vaccinium* and *Gaylussacia* will show that the records of leaf-forms do not altogether agree with those given in other botanical works. I must therefore draw attention to the diagrams herewith and suggest to the

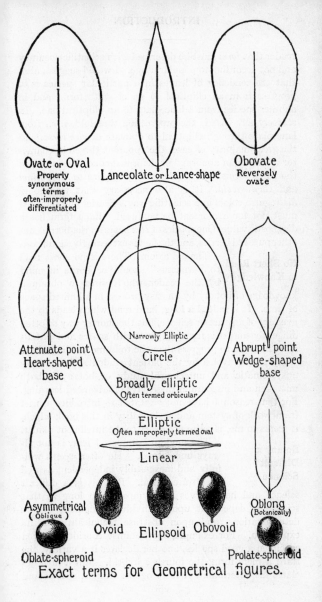

Ovate or Oval
Properly synonymous terms often improperly differentiated

Lanceolate or Lance-shape

Obovate
Reversely ovate

Attenuate point
Heart-shaped base

Narrowly Elliptic
Circle
Broadly elliptic
Often termed orbicular

Elliptic
Often improperly termed oval

Abrupt point
Wedge-shaped base

Linear

Asymmetrical
(Oblique)

Ovoid   Ellipsoid   Obovoid

Oblong
(Botanically)

Oblate-spheroid

Prolate-spheroid

Exact terms for Geometrical figures.

reader that *form* must be described with scientific accuracy and not according to popular usage. I would suggest, also, that the tendency of leaves in a particular species is to progress from an elliptical to an obovate form, and in another species from a lanceolate to an elliptical one. In scarcely any case is the progression threefold, *i. e.*, from lanceolate through elliptical to obovate or *vice versa*. In the great majority of cases the apparent threefold character is due to an abnormal or deformed condition in one of the three forms. This rule exactly applies to *Vaccinium* and *Gaylussacia*. It is also necessary that we should distinguish colors in a scientific way. Scarlet and pure red must not for a moment be confused. Each term has a diagnostic value. One species of *Ilex* bears scarlet berries, another pure red berries, and the fact is exceedingly significant.

No Short Road to Knowledge The old axiom "There is no short road to Parnassus" should be borne in mind by the reader who desires to obtain a knowledge of botany by an easy process in a limited space of time. It is indeed a long, hard road which leads to the mastery of any art or science, but the shorter way so often diligently sought is frequently set with snares and pitfalls more inimical to progress than the toilsome winding of the stony path traveled by the patient student. An entirely unsystematic and untechnical study of botany is both mistaken and insecure in these days of advanced learning. For that reason I have not hesitated to introduce a brief framework of system and technicality in this book which, it seems to me, is quite necessary to the intelligent reader.

Botany a Difficult Science The modern botanist, I fear, is not always understood. He often seems willfully and inexcusably independent as well as ultratechnical. But his is a difficult science and he deserves our sympathy so long as that science is dependent upon individual judgment for its determinations, and upon abstruse technicality for its expression. For example, one botanist considers a given specimen a good species, another declares it a variety, the third a mere form, the fourth a hybrid. Still a fifth declares his determination to recognize straight species and

viii

forms only and drops varietal rank altogether. Now must
we decide when doctors disagree! Again, such words as
endocarp, exocarp, homogamous, and heterogamous are
only an indication of the technicalities with which some
botanical descriptions fairly bristle. These are the stones
over which we stumble on our way to Parnassus. Nor do
our difficulties cease here, for, with a cheerful disregard of
exactness outside of his own profession, some misguided
botanist will use such a simple word as *innovation, purple*,
or *oval* according to his own ideas of usefulness and throw
us completely off the track. Oval and ovate are synonyms
in the absolute scientific sense, and ovoids and ellipsoids
are solids. There is no way of avoiding such facts, yet not
infrequently some careless writer confuses the plane with
the solid and one geometrical figure with another. It
would be an ungracious thing for me to call attention to
such irregularities without reminding the reader that the
science of botany cannot be held responsible for infractions
of the individual.

I have tried to follow, therefore, throughout these pages, both in text and drawings,
the consistent course of one whose initial
interest in botany is purely æsthetic, and

**Artistic and
Scientific
Accuracy**

whose aim is strict scientific accuracy in the presentation
of form, proportion, and color in trees and shrubs. An
occasional expression of opinion in reference to the validity
of a given species, however, should be taken as such, and
not construed as authoritative statement; but I have no
hesitation in recording a scientific inaccuracy even though
fixed custom may have accounted a term correct. An
asymmetrical leaf, for instance, is inconsistently called
oblique; the word oblique means "deviation from a
straight line." That does not apply to a lop-sided leaf.
The term asymmetrical does, it is more comprehensive.
The Venus di Milo's face is asymmetrical—out in its proportions, the word oblique would not properly apply.

It is not without hope that I may
stimulate an interest in our vanishing
woodlands that I describe in somewhat

**The Vanishing
Woodlands**

condensed form the character of the wood of various

timber trees. It is worth while knowing for what purposes this wood is used, and consequently what we are likely to lose when the lumber supply is ultimately exhausted. We have in this country 1694 timber owners who hold in fee simple 105,600,000 wooded acres, over one-twentieth of the land area of the United States from Canada to Mexico. The Commissioner of Corporations at Washington reveals this in his published maps. These few enormous holdings combined are two and one half times the area of New England and four-fifths times the size of France! The concentration in a few hands of one of the most important natural resources of this land, the commissioner says, is due to "lavish land grants" and loose, ill-enforced land laws. Now it does not follow that these landowners are obstructing any efforts by the people to save the timber lands because no such proper efforts are being made *in extenso*. The fact is, had not these few hands owned the lands nearly every acre of them would have been stripped and burned over for purposes of grazing and tilling long years ago. The owners, then, have proved to be conservators. But are they really such in the true sense of the word? No. Dollars actually hold the woods and when there are enough of them passing from hand to hand the trees will go. Why any of the natural resources of the land should be jeopardized by private ownership it is difficult to understand. The trouble, however, is less a matter of ownership than a lack of protective law.

Acknowledgments   In recording my grateful acknowledgments to those who have generously contributed in material ways to the making of this volume I wish to mention the late Maria L. Owen, whose interest in my work and whose letters about New England trees were a great encouragement, Mr. Joseph E. Harned who furnished me with extensive lists of the trees of Maryland and West Virginia, Professor Harvey M. Hall who answered many inquiries about conditions on the Pacific Slope, Professor Karl M. Wiegand who advised me on the subject of the Shadbushes, Dr. B. L. Robinson and Mr. Walter Deane to whom I have referred many problems and upon whose general advice I always implicitly rely, Professor Geo. B. Sudworth, the leading dendrologist of this country, whose advice and lists of distribution have been very useful, Professor Charles S. Sargent whose monumental work on the Silva of North America I have been glad constantly to consult, Mr. Carroll S. Mathews whose assistance in the work of technical compilation has been invaluable, and Miss Mary A. Day, librarian of the Gray Herbarium, whose ministrations to my need in books and data have so largely contributed to the successful accomplishment of my task.

I also wish to state that the excellent pressed specimens from the collection of Mr. Emile F. Williams deposited in the Gray Herbarium have furnished incomparable models for many of my sketches. Otherwise the drawing was out-of-door work executed in the presence of the trees themselves—that is, if I except those sketches made from typical Gray Herbarium specimens gathered from the further parts of the United States.

F. Schuyler Mathews.

Cambridge, Mass., Oct. 1, 1914.

A KEY FOR THE IDENTIFICATION OF SPECIES BY THE LEAVES.

I. EVERGREEN LEAVES. PINE FAMILY.

1.	Long, slim needles.	Pine, 2–21
2.	Short, flat, blunt needles.	Fir, 32–38; Hemlock, 40–42
3.	Short, sharp needles.	Spruce, 24–32; Cypress, 44; Sequoia, 45–46; Juniper, 52–53; Yew, 57–58
4.	Overlapping scales.	Sequoia, 45–46; Cedar, Cypress, etc., 48–50; Savin, etc., 53–56

II. DECIDUOUS LEAVES. PINE FAMILY.

1.	Slim, soft needles.	Larch, 21–24

III. SIMPLE ALTERNATE LEAVES.

1.	Toothless.	Ginkgo (cleft) 58; Willow (rarely toothless), 78–82; Corkwood, 97; Oak (cleft or uncleft or scolloped), 134–158; Osage Orange, 168; Buffalo-nut, Magnolia, etc., 170–176; Tulip Tree (cleft), 177; Strawberry Shrub, etc., 178–181; Bay, 184; Sassafras (cleft), 185–186; Cal. Laurel, Syringa (often few-toothed), etc., 186–189; Pear, Apple (rarely toothless), 197–198; Redbud, 269; Genista, etc., 272–273; Crowberry, 281; Smoke Tree, etc., 288; Winterberry, Mt. Holly, 293–294; Buckthorn (rarely toothless), 320; Hudsonia, etc., 327–330; Alt. leaved Dogwood, Tupelo, 336–338; Labrador Tea, Azalea, etc., 340–350; Andromeda, etc., 351–354; Heather, Huckleberry, 355–360; Blueberry, 360–363; Bumelia, Persimmon, etc., 367–372
2.	Toothed.	Willow, 61–82; Poplar (cleft), 82; Poplar, 84–92; Myrtles (rarely toothless), 93–96; Hazelnut, Birch, 109–134; Elm, etc., 160–168; Mulberry, 169–170; Barberry, 182; Hydrangea, etc., 190–192; Sycamore (cleft), etc., 194–197; Liquidambar (cleft), Pear, Apple, etc., 193–200; Shadbush, 202–210; Thorns (cleft), 212–252; Cherry, 254–265; Holly, 289–294; Burning Bush, etc., 296–298; Buckthorns, etc., 319–322; Lindens, etc., 322–327; Devil's Club, 332; Sw. Pepperbush, 339; Leucothoe, 350–351; Lyonia, etc., 355; Huckleberry (slightly) 356–359; Blueberry, etc., 362–364, 367; Sweet Leaf, 370; Silver-bell Tree, etc., 372; Baccharis, etc., 402–404.

KEY FOR THE IDENTIFICATION OF SPECIES

IV. SIMPLE OPPOSITE LEAVES.

1. Toothless. Shepherdia, Dogwood, 330–336;
Loiseleuria, Sheep Laurel, etc., 346–
348; Lilac, Fringe Tree, etc., 380–
382; Paulownia, Catalpa, etc.,
383–386; Honeysuckle, Symphoricarpos, 388–392; Viburnum, 398

2. Toothed. Maple, 298–314; Diervilla, 387;
Symphoricarpos, 391; Viburnum
(sometimes cleft), 392–399

V. COMPOUND ALTERNATE LEAVES.

1. Toothless. Acacia, Locust, etc., 265–270; Amorpha, Locust, etc., 273–278; Rhus.
284–286

2. Toothed. Butternut, Walnut, Hickory, 97–108;
Barberry, 182; Mt. Ash, 201–202;
Hop Tree, etc., 278–280; Rhus
(also toothless), 282–286; Horse
Chestnut, Buckeye (radiate), 315–
318; Angelica Tree, 331

VI. COMPOUND OPPOSITE LEAVES.

1. Toothless. Soapberry, 314; Ash, 374–376

2. Toothed. Ash-leaved Maple, 310; Ash, 372–379;
Swamp Privet, 380; Callicarpa,
383; Elder, 400

THE NAMES OF COLLECTORS OF SPECIMENS WHOSE INITIALS ARE RECORDED ON THE DRAWINGS

THE LEAF DRAWINGS ARE EXACT REPRODUCTIONS REDUCED TO TWO-THIRDS NATURAL SIZE

E. W. A.	Elizabeth W. Anderson, 127.
L. H. B.	Dean Liberty H. Bailey, 267.
C. F. B.	Charles F. Batchelder, 295.
W. H. B.	William H. Blanchard, 119.
E. P. B.	Eugene P. Bicknell, 231.
E. B.	Dr. Ezra Brainerd, 239, 251.
B. F. B.	Benjamin F. Bush, 249.
J. R. C.	Hon. Joseph R. Churchill, 55, 115, 175, 279, 291.
M. A. D.	Mary A. Day, 275, 295.
J. D.	J. Davis, 233, 241.
W. D.	Walter Deane, 55.
W. W. E.	Willard W. Eggleston, 219 to 249.
C. E. F.	Charles E. Faxon, 321.
M. L. F.	Prof. Merritt L. Fernald, 123, 233.
J. M. G.	Dr. Jesse M. Greenman, 127.
J. G. J.	Prof. John G. Jack, 231, 235, 245.
C. H. K.	Clarence H. Knowlton, 207, 209.
O. B. M.	O. B. Metcalfe, 171.
M. L. O.	Maria L. Owen, 283.
J. C. P.	John C. Parlin, 237.
B. L. R.	Dr. Benjamin L. Robinson, 123, 249, 259, 337.
E. F. W.	Emile F. Williams, 11, 95, 115, 127, 195, 245, 275.

ILLUSTRATIONS

AT END OF BOOK
COLORED

CRAYON

ILLUSTRATIONS

FIELD BOOK OF TREES AND SHRUBS

PINE FAMILY. *Pinaceae*

PINE FAMILY. *Pinaceae*.

One of the oldest Families in the world. Trees or shrubs with resinous sap and evergreen (excepting Larix) needle-like, awllike, or scalelike leaves. The flowers borne in scaly catkinlike clusters, mostly staminate and pistillate on the same tree. The fruit commonly a woody cone with few or many scales bearing winged or wingless seeds, or it is berrylike. The foliage generally a dark olive green, en masse.

White Pine
Soft Pine
Pinus Strobus

A handsome plumy-foliaged, straight-stemmed evergreen tree 50–75 and occasionally 180 feet high, with a trunk diameter of 2–5 feet; the dark, perpendicularly seamed gray brown bark in rough, rather small segments; the wide-spreading branches straight and horizontal.

The needles soft, slender, and delicate, three-sided, 3–4 inches long, light or dark bluish green, the inner side with a strong line of white bloom, producing a play of color when the wind stirs the branches, the sheaths deciduous, always in clusters of 5. Flowering in late spring. Staminate flowers oval, with 6–8 scales at the base, the pistillate flowers in long-stemmed, cylindrical catkins. The cones large, 4–6 inches long, narrow cylindrical, slightly curved, nodding, dark brown when ripe in the summer of the second year, scales broad wedge-shaped, thin at the top, and without spines or prickles. The winged seed smooth. The empty cones fall during the second winter.

The White Pine[1] is distributed in generally light sandy soil, from Newf. west to the south shore of Lake Winnipeg, northeastern Minn. eastern Ia. southern Mich. northern Ill. and northeastern O., and south along the Alleghany Mts. to northern Ga. (Tallulah Falls), and near the Atlantic coast to central N. J. This most useful and beautiful pine has furnished in the past the greatest amount of finished lumber for building purposes in the northern States; however, reckless, inexcusable waste and inordinate

[1] Planted by Lord Weymouth in Wiltshire, Eng., about 1720 and also named Weymouth Pine, for him.

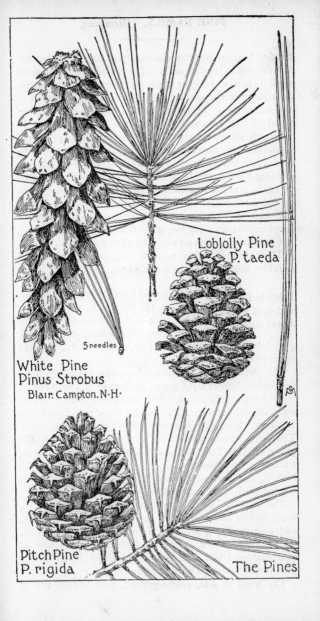

Loblolly Pine
P. taeda

5 needles

White Pine
Pinus Strobus
Blair. Campton. N·H·

Pitch Pine
P. rigida

The Pines

cutting have so depleted the supply of late years that unless the tree in the future should be planted on an extensive scale its lumber is never again likely to resume the prominent place in the market which it occupied a quarter of a century ago. At the present time, the clear-grained wood of the southern Cypress has superseded it. In favorable situations the White Pine in thirty years will attain a trunk diameter of 24 inches, and a height of 60 feet. The tender sapling is easily distinguished from that of other species; the bark is essentially smooth and often greenish, and the branches are slender and supple. Even on older trees with a ten-inch stem, the bark is smooth half-way up from the ground. Saplings are also variable in color; the prevailing hue of the foliage is light blue green, but occasionally it is an unmixed olive green.

The pale buff yellow wood is soft, easily worked, and durable; weight 24 lbs. to a cubic foot.

Loblolly Pine
Old-field Pine
Pinus taeda

A tall, straight tree 50–80 and in the forest often 150 feet high, with a trunk diameter of 4 feet. The long branches wide-spreading, the thick, rough bark gray brown, separating into thin, ruddy scales, in large segments.

The slender, rigid, three-sided needles extremely long, 6–9 inches, lighter olive green, in clusters of 3 or rarely 2, with elongated sheaths $\frac{3}{4}$–1 inch long when young. Flowering in early spring. The slender staminate flowers are two inches long, with commonly 10–13 overlapping scales. The large, attenuated ovoid cone 3–5 inches long, the scales thickened at the tip and terminating with a short, triangular, reflexed spine. It grows laterally on the branch, and persists through the second season. Seeds winged, with three rough ridges on the underside.

The Loblolly Pine is distributed from Cape May, N. J., south mostly along the coast to Fla. and the Gulf States, and west to Wood, Mineral, Hampshire, and Hardy Cos. W. Va. eastern Tex. (along the Colorado River), and to southeastern Okla. Ark. and southwestern Tenn. Common in old fields and barren sandy tracts.

The wood is soft, coarse-grained, and brittle, and is

extensively made into lumber; it is pale yellowish brown buff and nearly half as heavy again as White Pine. In the northern markets it is called Yellow Pine.

A rugged, picturesque tree with coarse, resinous wood, 40–50 and occasionally 75 feet high, with a trunk diameter of 3 feet. The coarse brown gray or dull **Pitch Pine** *Pinus rigida* brown bark deeply furrowed into broad flat-topped perpendicular ridges. The twigs very coarse, scaly, and gray brown. The heavy branches gnarled, often drooping, with tufted olive green foliage.

The yellowish olive green needles coarse, flattened, curved, and twisted, 2–4 inches long, with a short sheath, fine-toothed on the edge like a saw, and the surface marked by rows of fine white dots (under the glass). Growing in clusters of 3. Staminate flowers short with 6–8 scales. The small ovoid cone 2–3½ inches long, stemless, becoming almost hemispherical when open, borne laterally on the branches, single or in clusters, ripening in the autumn of the second season, often persisting (empty) on the tree for several years. The scales thickened at the tip and set with a stout recurved spine or prickle; this absolutely distinguishes the cone from that of the Red Pine.

The Pitch Pine grows in dry, sandy, or barren soil, and occasionally in swamps. It is distributed from the St. Johns River, N. B., west to the north shore of Lake Ontario and the lower Ottawa River, western N. Y. (Ithaca), northeastern Pa. eastern O. Ky. and Tenn. and southward along the Atlantic seaboard to Norfolk, Va., and along the Alleghany Mts. to Ga. where it ascends to an altitude of about 2800 feet. In New England it is common along the valley of the Merrimac but does not extend north to the White Mts. It is occasional in the valley of the Connecticut, also, as far north as the Passumpsic River, and is fairly common in the northern Champlain Valley. It is the chief pine in the "barrens" of N. J. and of Long Island, and is the only native pine of New England with three needles in a cluster.

The variable pale brown and deep buff wood is light, soft, brittle and durable, but coarse-grained and useful only for charcoal and fuel. Rarely it is manufactured into lumber and construction timber. It is not plentiful in the production of turpentine.

Pond Pine
Marsh Pine
Pinus serotina

Similar to the Pitch Pine; a southern species found in the swamps near the coast. Bark broken into broad, flat squarish plates. The dark green needles much longer, 5–9 inches long, with sheaths of proportionate length, also in clusters of 3. The cone likewise hemispherical when fully open, borne laterally and as a rule singly, but at maturity lacking prickles on the scales—these being very short and early deciduous.

The Pond Pine is common in the swamps from Va. to Fla. (St. John's River), and on the west coast of Fla. from Pensacola to Citrus Co. and probably farther south; but the range is imperfectly known. It is not very useful for timber, though it is used for masts and general construction. It also produces turpentine. Commercially it is not distinguished from *P. taeda*.

Table Mountain Pine
Prickly Pine
Pinus pungens

A rugged pine common in the Alleghanies, similar in outline and appearance—excepting color—to the Scotch Pine, commonly 30–40 and under advantageous conditions 60 feet high. The thick ruddy brown bark fissured into large, loose, scaly plates. The stout yellow green needles short, sharp-pointed, broad, flat, rigid, 2–3½ inches long, in clusters of twos and sometimes threes, crowded in confused masses on the twigs, the young sheaths about ½ inch long.

The ovoid cones about 3–4 inches long, with very thick scales armed each with a strong reflexed prickle about ¼ inch long. These rough, spiny cones remain for a year or more upon the tree and contribute very largely to its rugged appearance. They usually persist on the branches for 10–20 years, ripening slowly and discharging the seed through several seasons.

The Table Mountain Pine is distributed from western N. J. and central Pa. generally through the Alleghany Mts. to N. C. eastern and middle Tenn. and Ga. (Tallulah

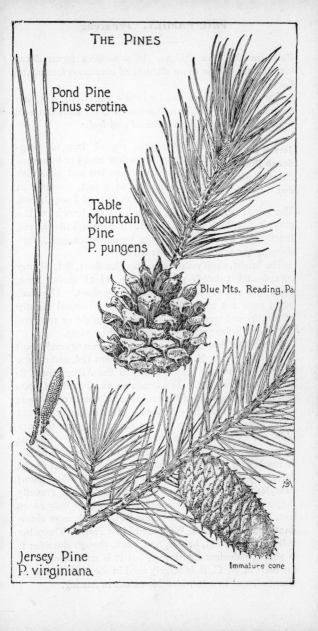

THE PINES

Pond Pine
Pinus serotina

Table
Mountain
Pine
P. pungens

Blue Mts. Reading. Pa.

Jersey Pine
P. virginiana

Immature cone

Falls, in the Blue Ridge). It sometimes forms dense forests, and climbs to an altitude of over 4000 feet in the Carolinas.

The pale buff brown wood is brittle, not strong, soft, and rather light. It is almost useless in the manufacture of lumber, but is made into charcoal and fuel.

Jersey Pine
Scrub Pine
Pinus virginiana

A picturesque, rugged tree of straggling, irregular outline 20–45 or in advantageous circumstances 100 feet high with a trunk diameter of 3 feet, common in the "barrens" of N. J. and Long Island. The rough trunk is a dull brown or sepia brown, with a grayish cast; bark with thin plates in perpendicular ridges, shortly and sharply severed, the branches scragged, often showing the tan-colored inner bark.

The bright, deep yellow green needles short, flat, slightly curved and twisted, $\frac{1}{16}$ inch wide, $1\frac{1}{2}$–$2\frac{1}{2}$ inches long, growing in clusters of 2, the sheaths very short. The small ovoid cone 1–2 inches long, the scales thickened slightly at the tip and terminated by a short straight or recurved awl-shaped spine; often persisting for four years.

The Jersey Pine is distributed over barren or sandy land from Long Island, N. Y., west to southern Ind. and middle Tenn. (Putnam Co.), and south to the Aiken River, S. C. and northern Ala. It ascends to an altitude of 3000 feet in the mountains of Va. and locally forms broad forests of tall trees on the hillside slopes. On the sandy barrens of N. J. its stunted growth, on a sunny day, with the sapphire sea as a background forms one of those picturesque objects which is no light challenge to the artist's brush. It reaches its best development in the valleys west of the Alleghany Mts., and is more or less common throughout Maryland. In N. C. it grows sparingly on the gravelly ridges of the Piedmont plateau to a height of only 20–40 feet, but on the spurs of the Blue Ridge much more abundantly, along with the White and Pitch Pines. The ocher yellow wood is soft, brittle, and weak, though durable; it is almost valueless for timber, but it is extensively used for fuel; in N. C. it is largely used in the manufacture of charcoal, and to a considerable extent in fencing.

A commonly low, scragged, picturesque
pine 15–25 feet or rarely 100 feet high with
a trunk diameter of 3 feet. Sometimes
it is a mere shrub. The shaggy bark is
a dark ruddy brown, grayish with age,
the scales rough and forming irregular
ridges with a scarcely perpendicular trend. The wide-
spreading branches (with slender, drooping, ruddy or
plum-colored twigs) of the larger tree form a symmetrical
figure slightly resembling the spruce; otherwise this pine
on sterile ground and in exposed situations becomes greatly
stunted or distorted.

*Gray Pine
Northern
Scrub Pine
Pinus Bank-
siana*

The needles are the shortest in the Pine Family, hence
they bear a remote resemblance to those of the fir or
spruce. They are $\frac{1}{2}$–$1\frac{1}{2}$ inches long, $\frac{1}{16}$ inch wide, rigid,
flat, bright warm yellow green, generally curved and
twisted, and grow in clusters of 2 diverging at a wide angle.
Flowering in May–June. The young whitish buff cones
inclined in the same direction as the branch are curved
and pointed at the tip, the old dark, brown cones without
prickles on the reflexed thickened scales, 1–2 inches long,
conic-oblong, remaining closed for several years, and persisting on the branch for sometimes ten years. The scales
of the young cones terminate in minute, rudimentary,
incurved prickles.

The Gray Pine is distributed over barren, sandy, or dry
soil from N. B. west through the Great Lake and Hudson
Bay region (south shore) to Great Bear Lake, the Mackenzie River, and the Rocky Mts., and south locally
through Me. northern N. H. (Lake Umbagog), northern
N. Y. Ind. Ill. and central Minn. There is an isolated
station of this pine on the summit of Welch Mt., 3500 feet
altitude, in Waterville, N. H., where it grows in low, shrubby
clumps; but on the banks of the Penobscot and at Lake
Umbagog it attains a height of about 60 feet, and on the
southeastern coast of Me. on Steel Harbor and Great Wass
Islands off Jonesport, on Mt. Desert Island, and near
Winter Harbor (Schoodic Peninsula), it reaches a height
of 20–30 feet.

Yellow Pine
Shortleaf Pine
North Carolina
Pine
Pinus echinata

A distinctively southern pine of im·posing proportions, 50–80 and sometimes in the southern forests 100 feet high, with a trunk diameter of 4½ feet. The bark, coarse, broken into large, squarish scales, and deep ruddy brown, in age grayish, yellowish beneath, the trunk very straight.

The needles are 2½–5 inches long, deep olive green, roundish, slender, and soft (the western form more rigid), with long sheaths; in clusters of 2 (sometimes 3). Flowering in May–June. The long ovoid cone is the smallest among the American pines—scarcely 2 inches long, about 1 inch thick before it opens, and has a very small weak prickle on the thickened tip of the scale, which is early deciduous.

The Yellow Pine is distributed from Staten Island, N. Y. south to Fla. (region of the Chattahoochee River), and west to southern Mo. eastern Kan. eastern Okla. and northeastern Tex.

The wood of this handsome pine is moderately coarse-grained, hard, and durable; its color is a beautiful gold ocher grading into pale buff yellow. It is largely used for the interior finish and flooring of buildings, and for ship building, and is next in value to the famous Georgia Pine, but is less strong, less ruddy in color, much lighter in weight, and not quite as hard. In 1894 approximately 60 million feet (board measure), were sawed in the State of N. C. alone, and since that year, the annual output has been greatly increased. It belongs rather to the upland forests, and appears much less common on the coastal plain.

Scotch Pine
Scotch Fir
Pinus
sylvestris

A long-lived rugged tree naturalized from Europe and prospering under cultivation at certain stations on the New England coast, 20–40 and in favorable situations over 100 feet high. Often the tree is low, with scragged, wide-spread, drooping branches and an irregular trunk, but not infrequently it is erect in habit with evenly balanced limbs, especially when in close association on forest tracts. The bark is grayish

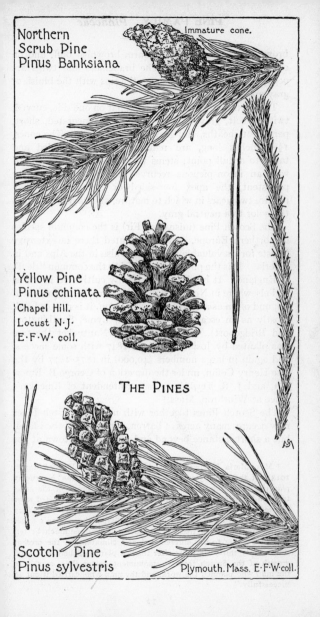

Northern
Scrub Pine
Pinus Banksiana

Immature cone.

Yellow Pine
Pinus echinata
Chapel Hill.
Locust N·J·
E·F·W· coll.

THE PINES

Scotch Pine
Pinus sylvestris

Plymouth. Mass. E·F·W·coll.

brown or on young trees a warm brownish buff, and on old ones a light brown. The branchlets and twigs are ocher yellow and thickly set at the tips with the bluish or gray green foliage.

The needles are 2–3 inches long, flat on one side, curved, twisted, soft, grayish blue green, with lacerated, short, persistent sheaths, and grow in clusters of 2. The cones, 1½–3 inches long, are remarkably angular-scaled and taper to a dull point; stems very short, the scale tipped with an inconspicuous recurved tubercle, deciduous or persistent, the apex four-sided or rhomboidal. They require two years in which to mature, and vary from a dull tan color to a neutral gray.

The Scotch Pine (misnamed Fir) is the common species of northern Europe, and is cultivated there in extensive forests for its valuable timber; it is also in the Alps and in Siberia. It is the pine which furnishes the common "deal" of England. It has been successfully cultivated in Mass. and elsewhere in New England, sometimes as an ornamental, and often as a useful tree. In Conn. it is rare or local, mostly as an escape (New London, Lyme, Southington, and Bridgeport). On the island of Nantucket the tree was planted by Josiah Sturgis in 1847 with some success, and again in large numbers (40,000) in 1875–1877 by the late Henry Coffin, under the direction of George B. Emerson, and J. S. Tewksbury, superintendent of Emerson's place at Winthrop, Mass.[1]

The Scotch Pines together with numerous Pitch Pines now occupy many acres of barren, sandy soil of the island, but a short distance beyond and south of the town at the

[1] Mrs. Maria L. Owen writes in the *Nantucket Mirror* (March, 1913), of the later planting, as follows: "While the Nantucket planting was going on Mr. Emerson set out a grove of the same trees on his own land at Winthrop, and the Tewksburys had some planted on their place, but all have died but one, which is now thirty feet or more in height, although it was no larger than a man's finger when imported. The trees in Nantucket have done much better, doubtless owing to the different soil and climate. At the present time, nearly thirty-six years after the last planting, there is a good growth of the Scotch trees—a monument better than marble to the man who planned the work, and the man who carried it out so successfully."

head of Miacomet Pond. They are approximately 10–20 feet high, and very scragged in appearance, but the plantation is one of the largest of the kind in this country, and a great boon to the island which, otherwise—excepting those few specimens planted within the town or on nearby farms—would be quite treeless. *Pinus rigida* (the Pitch Pine) is, however, the more abundant pine on the Island; it was also planted in 1847 by Sturgis

A handsome dark-foliaged tree 50–75 and occasionally 120 feet high with a trunk diameter of 4 feet. In Maine it not infrequently reaches a height of 100

Red Pine
Norway Pine
Pinus resinosa

feet. Bark a ruddy brown gray, red beneath, perpendicularly seamed, the scales smooth, thin, broad, and flat. The very coarse twigs smooth and tan red. The straight trunk is much lighter and ruddier in color than that of *Pinus Strobus* or *Pinus rigida*.

The large flexible needle deep dark green, straight, 3–6 inches long, flat on one side, rounded on the other, in clusters of 2, the dark brown sheaths long and persistent. Flowering in late May. The slender staminate flower spike $\frac{5}{8}$ inch long. The cone 2–2$\frac{1}{2}$ inches long, ovoid-conical, when open much broader, growing at a right angle with the branch; the scales thickened at the apex but without spines. The ripened cones persist on the tree all winter.

The Red Pine is common in sandy, light soil, and is distributed from Newf. west along the north shore of the Gulf of St. Lawrence to northern Ont. (North of Abittibi Lake), southern Man. (at the south shore of Lake Winnipeg), and southwest to Mass. R. I. and Conn. (Granby and Salisbury), Pa. (Chester Co.), northeastern O. (North of Cleveland), central Mich. northern Wis. and northeastern Minn. It is fairly common in the southern White Mts. but less common than *Pinus rigida* farther south in the vicinity of Manchester, N. H.

The wood is close-grained, strong, hard, and buff or pale tan yellow with nearly white sapwood. It is used for construction work, for piles, masts, and spars; weight

30 lbs. per cubic foot. The bark is occasionally used for tanning leather.

**Austrian Pine
Black Pine
Pinus Laricio
var. *austriaca***

A handsome tree 60–80 feet high, with a straight trunk, and branches conspicuously set in regular whorls (circles). A European species. The bark is grayish brown, and (as in the Red Pine) reddish beneath; scales coarse and broad, not set in well-marked perpendicular ridges; twigs tan yellow, stout, and rough scaly under the leaf-tufts.

The needles are 3–5 inches long, rigid, flat on one side, sharp-pointed, with a short persistent sheath, and dark olive green, the darkest of all the pines; growing in clusters of 2. The gray brown cones are 2¼–2¾ inches long, ovoid-conical, or quite ovoid when open; set at a right angle with the branchlet, ripening the second autumn, the empty cones persisting on the branches.

The Austrian Pine is cultivated in this country as an ornamental tree, and to a limited extent is used in the reforestation of denuded woodlands. It most resembles our native Red Pine, but the needle is far more rigid, and the winter twigs are also tan yellow, while those of the Red Pine are ruddy. The wood is soft, light, and very durable; it is used in Europe for building purposes, and it yields a large amount of turpentine.

**Long-leaved
Pine
Georgia Pine
Southern
Yellow Pine
*Pinus palustris***

A southern pine of large proportions with extremely hard and resinous wood of great economic value, 60–70 and under favorable conditions 100 feet high, with a trunk diameter of 4 feet. The trunk long, straight, and generally free from branches, bark in rather smooth, thin-scaled, red brown plates, the branches coarse and scaly.

The needles are extremely long, 10–15 inches, slender, flexible, and bright olive green, and grow in clusters of 3 from long sheaths; they are crowded at the tips of the branches. The staminate flowers are in conspicuous spikes 2¼–3 inches long, magenta red, and appear in March or April. The cones, growing terminally on the branches,

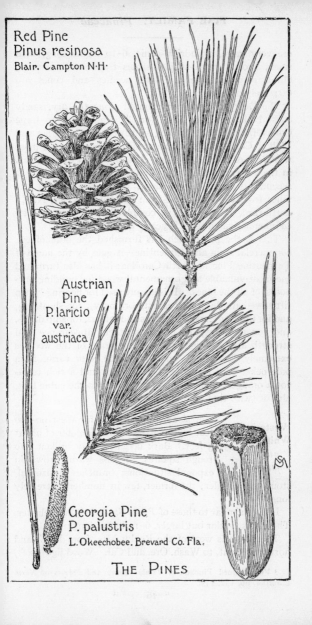

Red Pine
Pinus resinosa
Blair. Campton N·H·

Austrian
Pine
P. laricio
var.
austriaca

Georgia Pine
P. palustris
L. Okeechobee. Brevard Co. Fla.

THE PINES

are very large, cylindrical-conic, 6–10 inches long, with thick, broad, wedge-shaped scales tipped with a short, blunt, recurved prickle. Both needles and cones are extremely ornamental.

The Georgia Pine is distributed along the dry, sandy coastal plain region from Norfolk, Va., south to Cape Canaveral and Tampa Bay, southwest to Ala. (Clay and Walker Cos.), and northwestern Ga., then, after a lapse westward of about 100 miles, it reappears in eastern Tex. in the valleys of the Sabine and Trinity Rivers, where it reaches its finest development. It is rare beyond 150 miles from the coast, and from the Neuse River, N. C., northward, it has been so completely cut out, that its commercial value there is nearly destroyed.[1]

This is the pine which has furnished the bulk of our commercial rosin and turpentine—it goes by the name of Turpentine Pine in North Carolina; it has also furnished the most valuable and ornamental wood for building purposes, of all the pines. It is largely used for flooring (when rift-sawed its durability is extraordinary), for sheathing, and for interior (exposed) beams and rafters, for ship decks, and for a variety of purposes where appearance and strength are most important. The grain of the wood is extremely close, hard, and tough; the color varies from pale ocher to a translucent gold ocher and a rich terra-cotta orange. The weight is 45 pounds to the cubic foot, almost twice that of White Pine.

Western White Pine
Pinus monticola

A slender pine of the far West 90–100 feet high, with a trunk diameter of about 3 feet. Bark lavender gray broken into rough squares, or pale warm brown in exposed situations; branches horizontal, stout, and slender; the former, few in number, extremely long.

Leaves similar to those of *Pinus Strobus*—5 in a cluster. The cones similar but larger, 6–10 inches long.

The range is west of the Rocky Mts. from B. C. and northern Mont. to Wash. Ore. and Cal. Wood light, soft,

[1] *Vide* Gifford Pinchot in *Timber Trees and Forests of North Carolina*, pp. 132, 133.

---

pale brown, commercially of great value. This **pine** attains an age of 200–500 years.

The largest of the Pacific pines, 160–180 feet high with a trunk diameter of 6 feet. Bark gray brown broken perpendicularly into long irregular plates; limbs long, horizontal, and heavy.

Sugar Pine
Pinus Lambertiana

The leaves are similar to those of *Pinus Strobus*, 5 in a cluster, rather thick 2¾–4 inches long. The very large cones are 12–16 inches long, occasionally longer, madder purple within, the tips of the scales chestnut brown.

The range is through the mountains from the North Fork, Santiam River, Ore., south through the Coast and Cascade Ranges and the Sierras to southern and lower Cal. Wood similar to the foregoing, and not commercially distinguished from it.

The only pine having single needles; a small tree 25–40 feet high with a low scraggly habit. Bark rough, dark brown, scaly, irregularly furrowed.

Single-leaved Pine
Pinus monophylla

The leaves are yellow green with a whitish tinge, commonly single, very rarely double, stiff, curved, sharp-pointed, short, about 1½ inches long. Cones very rugged, short, often with contorted scales, russet brown.

The range is through the desert regions of Utah, Nev. Ariz. southeastern Cal. and south.

A rather small pine 35–60 feet high, with a trunk diameter of about 20 inches. A narrowly thick-crowned tree, with smooth gray white bark on the branches,

Foxtail Pine
Pinus Balfouriana

and cinnamon brown bark on the perpendicularly seamed trunk, broken into squarish plates.

The leaves bright grayish blue green crowded on the ends of the branchlets for 10–20 inches, 5 in a cluster, curved and close-pressed. Cones a deep plum purple within, the scales russet brown; irregularly ovoid.

The range is through Cal. from the Coast ranges in the north to the southern Sierras, generally at high elevations, on Scott and Eddy Mts. at Kearsage Pass at 12,000 feet elevation, and South to Cottonwood Creek, at an elevation of about 11,000 feet.

**Western
Yellow Pine
*Pinus
ponderosa***   A majestic, tall pine 125–140 or occasionally 180 feet high, with a trunk diameter of about 6 feet. Bark light russet red broken into thick broad plates with a scaly surface, the heavy branches sagging with upturned ends, forming a narrow crown. Bark on young trees dark red brown. The young ocherish green shoots have an orangelike odor when bruised.

The needles are deep yellow green, stout, 5–10 inches long, slightly rough, commonly 3 in a cluster (rarely 4–5 mostly on young saplings), in heavy clusters at the ends of the branches. Cones bright green or deep plum purple at maturity, $2\frac{3}{4}$–6 inches long, massive, the scale-tips very thick with stout recurved prickles.

The range is entirely west of the 100th meridian, from B. C. and Mont., south to western Neb. Tex. and Cal., also in Mex. The Rocky Mt. form, *Pinus ponderosa* var. *scopulorum*, has shorter needles.

The wood is hard, strong, light (29 lbs. to the cubic foot), and very variable in color—from pale yellow to gold ocher and terra cotta red. One of the most valuable lumber trees of the far West, reaching an age of 350–500 years.

**Lodgepole
Pine
*Pinus contorta***   A western pine of wide range, extending from the coast level to an altitude of 11,000 feet. A tree of varying characters, 20–50 or in its eastern range 100 feet high, with a trunk diameter of 2 feet. Bark thin, madder purple or red brown, deeply furrowed perpendicularly, and sharply broken horizontally; older or more eastern trees with a gray brown bark, the branches heavy, the trunk tall and slender.

The leaves lustrous deep yellow green, about 2 inches (1–$2\frac{3}{4}$) long, variable $\frac{1}{24}$–$\frac{1}{8}$ inch wide, curved, somewhat rigid. Cones ovoid, persistent, pale brown on the thickened scales which are tipped with recurved spines, and madder purple within.

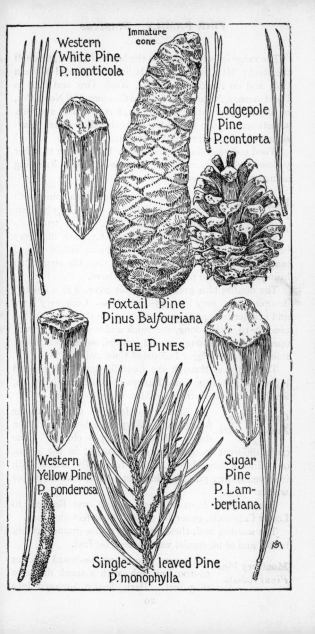

Western
White Pine
P. monticola

Immature
cone

Lodgepole
Pine
P. contorta

Foxtail Pine
Pinus Balfouriana

THE PINES

Western
Yellow Pine
P. ponderosa

Sugar
Pine
P. Lam-
bertiana

Single-   leaved Pine
P. monophylla

PINE FAMILY. *Pinaceae*

The range is from Alaska to the border of Mex., through the Rocky Mts. to the Black Hills, S. Dak. and western Col., and on the coast of B. C. Wash. Ore. and Cal. to Point Arenas, Mendocino Co. and Gasquet, Del Norte Co., mostly at an elevation of 500 feet, but in Wash. and Ore. sometimes at 3000 feet. It has been called *Pinus Murrayana*, in the eastern part of its range.

Wood coarse-grained, hard, ruddy light brown to ocher yellow, slightly heavier than *Pinus ponderosa*. Reaching an age of 100–200 years.

Digger Pine
Pinus sabiniana

A medium-sized California pine with a rarely straight, more commonly bent stem 50–75 feet high, and a trunk diameter of about 2 feet. Bark dull gray brown, scaly, with irregularly confluent ridges tinged madder purple. Foliage grayish and thin, the stem often branched or forked perpendicularly above.

The needles blue green or grayish green, 2 in a cluster, drooping, and very long, 8½–12 inches. Cone very large and heavier (except *Pinus Coulteri*) than that of any other pine, 7–10 inches long, the thick scales chestnut brown, opening slowly through several months, seeds sepia brown, relished by the Digger Indians of California.

The range is through the foothills, lower slopes, and higher valleys of the Coast Ranges and the Sierra Nevadas, south to the San Bernardino Mts. of southern Cal.

Coulter Pine
Pinus Coulteri

A similar species with stiffer, heavier foliage, and heavy branches which often droop. Needles 3 in a cluster. Cone quite different in appearance; the largest in the genus, 9–13 inches long, heavy, scales terrifically armed with incurved thorny points, pale ocher brown, madder purple within.

The range is from southern Cal. (Coast Ranges) to Lower California, generally at 3000–6000 feet elevation.

The wood of both these species is coarse-grained, ruddy brown and of no special value except for fuel.

Monterey Pine
Pinus radiata

A very interesting seaboard species 50–100 feet high, with a trunk diameter of 3 feet. Bark deeply furrowed into broad plates, ruddy or sepia brown. Branches large and spreading, forming on old trees a broad crown, with dense foliage.

The needles bright grass green, commonly 3 (sometimes 2) in a cluster, 4-6 inches long. Cones ovoid, persistent for 6-10 or more years, russet brown, madder purple within, thick-scaled, about 5 inches long, with age becoming imbedded in the branchlet as the latter grows; often shedding seed only after several years.

The range is from central Cal. (Point Ano Nuevo to Big Creek, north of Monterey), south especially near Cambria, and on the coast and islands as far as Santa Rosa and Santa Cruz Islands; also on Guadaloupe Island off Lower Cal. Very local.

A commonly small pine 20-30 but occasionally 75 feet high, with a trunk diameter of 20 inches. Bark dull light umber brown, thin, shallowly furrowed, or nearly smooth.

Knobcone Pine
Pinus attenuata

The needles yellow green, 3 in a cluster, slender, twisted, about 3½-5 inches long. Cones very long ovoid, curved, in clusters, light ocher brown, about 6 inches long, persisting on the branches for an indefinite period—perhaps 10-50 years.

The range is from southern Ore. to northern Cal., through the Coast and Cascade Ranges and the Sierra Nevadas. Common along the Sacramento River near Redding, Shasta Co., about 60 miles south of Mt. Shasta.

A conical, thinly soft-foliaged tree 30-50 and sometimes 90 feet high when growing in favorable situations, with a trunk diameter of 2 feet, the slender branches horizontal, or drooping in long sweeps.

Black Larch Tamarack Hackmatack
Larix laricina

Bark on younger trees quite smooth, on older ones rough, not perpendicularly seamed, ruddy brown, with thin, small, almost rounded scales. Twigs slender, smooth, terra cotta to tan color.

The needles are pale, bright blue green, ¾-1 inch long, triangular, soft, deciduous, very many in a cluster, turn-

ing ocher yellow in the autumn. Flowering in March–
April. The cone is very small, $\frac{1}{2}$–$\frac{3}{4}$ inch long, ovoid,
light chestnut brown, with few scales, remaining on the
tree throughout the winter, when the seeds are dropped;
the stalk is very short, stout, and incurved; a much smaller
cone than that of the European Larch.

The American Larch is distributed generally in low
lands or cold swamps from Newf. and Lab. south to
northern N. J. Pa. Ind. Ill. and central Minn., and west
to the Rocky Mts. and British Columbia, northwestward
it extends to Cape Churchill, Hudson Bay, Great Bear
Lake, and the Mackenzie River within the Arctic Circle.
The tree is called "Epinette Rouge" in Quebec, and by
the Indians of New York "Ka-neh-tens."—The leaves
fall. It is common in Me. N. H. and Vt. and grows
stunted and scattered on the slopes of Mt. Katahdin to
an altitude of 4000 feet. In the White Mts. it is found in
limited quantities in the swamps and about the ponds in
the principal valleys. The wood is very hard, coarse-
grained, and durable especially when in contact with the
ground. It is used chiefly for railroad ties, telegraph poles,
fence posts, etc., and sometimes for the interior finish of
buildings. The weight is about 39 lbs. to the cubic foot.
The Larch is picturesque, and its sparse, light, cool green
foliage is dainty and in sharp contrast with that of all other
trees; its extraordinary tall and thin figure, its narrow
pyramidal head, and its lacelike leaves all contribute to
make it a strikingly ornamental feature of parks and
gardens.

European   The European Larch is in common culti-
Larch   vation in this country in parks and gar-
Larix decidua   dens; it is a hardy tree well established
                      in the northeastern States. The twigs
are stouter and yellower than those of the American
Larch, the needles are longer, and the narrow cones are
fully an inch long, and have many scales. The branches
of this tree are somewhat more pendulous than those of
its American relative; it is by no means rare in some of
the eastern cities.

Twisted needles of
Knobcone
Pine
P. attenuata

Needles of
Monterey
Pine
P. radiata

Digger
Pine
Pinus
sabiniana
cone
and
needles.

Needles
also of
Coulter
Pine
P.
Coulteri

Cone
scale of
P. Coulteri

PINE FAMILY. *Pinaceae*

Western Larch
Larix occidentalis

An extremely tall western tree, often 80–100 and under favorable conditions at high altitudes, 200 or more feet high, with a trunk diameter of 3–4 feet. The mature tree is remarkable for its immensely tall stem, short branches, and sparse foliage; it is a slow grower, attaining a trunk diameter of only 20 inches in about 250 years.

The needles are like those of the eastern larch; the cones much larger, 1–1½ inches long, with many scales. *Larix occidentalis* is distributed in altitudes of 2000–7000 feet, from southern B. C. (south of latitude 53°) south through the Cascade Mts. to the Columbia River and to western Mon. and through the Blue Mts. of Wash. and Ore.

This is the tallest and most stately of all the larch trees; it attains its greatest height in northern Mont. and Ida. where it flourishes in the broad forests of the bottom lands as one of the most conspicuous trees. The light terra cotta brown wood is very heavy (46 lbs. or more to the cubic foot), hard, and durable, and is largely manufactured into lumber for the interior finish of buildings, etc.

Alpine Larch
Larix Lyallii

A much smaller western tree 40–50 and occasionally 70 feet high, growing only at high elevations, 4500–8000 feet. Branches pendulous. Bark light gray to dark brown.

The needles are four-sided, pale blue green, and 1–1½ inches long. The ovoid cones are very large, 1½–2 inches long, the many scales reddish plum purple.

The range of *Larix Lyallii* is through the mountains of the Northwest, in Mont. Ida. Ore. and Wash., and northward in adjacent territory. Distribution imperfectly known.

White Spruce
Cat Spruce
Skunk Spruce
Picea canadensis

A tall, handsome evergreen tree of the extreme North, 30–70 and in favorable situations 150 feet high, with a trunk diameter of 3–4 feet, resembling in contour and color the Balsam Fir. Branches numerous and somewhat pendulous. Bark reddish to grayish brown, on young trees nearly smooth, on older ones rough, with small, closely set scales; the twigs light tan yellow and smooth. Foliage unpleasantly odoriferous.

Needles bluish gray green, slender, four-sided, $\frac{1}{2}$–1 inch long, a trifle curved, sharp-pointed, with a slight bloom, and a disagreeable pungent odor when bruised, which is suggested by two of the common names, and which is an ample means for the identification of the tree. The cones are cylindrical-conic, $1\frac{1}{2}$–2 inches long, when mature papery-soft under pressure of the fingers, at first light green, finally light tan yellow, generally deciduous the first season, the scales thin and flexible, the edges rounded and not indented or jagged.

The White Spruce is distributed from Lab. Newf. and N. S., west through Que. Ont. and Man. to B. C., and through the northern sections of Me. N. H. Vt. N. Y. Mich. Wis. Minn. S. Dak. and Mont. to the Rocky Mts., and northward beyond all other trees to within 20 miles of the Arctic Sea. In Me. it is more frequent than the Red Spruce, in sandy soil as far south as Casco Bay; in N. H. it is abundant in the northern Connecticut Valley, disappearing south at Fifteen Mile Falls; in Vt. it is only common in the extreme northeastern section; in Mass. it is occasional in the mountain region of Berkshire County, and pushes as far south as Amherst and Northampton, and in Conn. it is very rare, a few trees are in a pasture at Waterford, probably an escape.

The wood is light, soft, straight-grained, and a beautiful, clear pale buff yellow, comparable to satinwood; it is used for the interior finish of buildings, for sheathing and flooring, for general construction work, and for paper pulp.

Red Spruce
Picea rubra

A tree greatly prized for its strong timber, 50–80 and sometimes 100 feet high, with a trunk diameter of 2–3 feet. Bark ruddy brown becoming grayish with age, very rough, with small segments irregularly not perpendicularly set, the scales thin. The branchlets covered with rough, short, sepia brown hairs, the larger branches spreading horizontally near the center of the tree but the upper ones strongly ascending at an angle of about 45° with the stem. The little twigs on older trees droop characteristically from the branches.

The needles are short, curved, about ½ inch or more long, abruptly sharp-pointed, four-sided in section, and with extremely slight if any whitish bloom; the older needles dark dull green yellower at the tip, the new ones bright yellow green; they completely surround the tan-colored twigs.

The cones are ovoid 1¼-1½ inches long, light or ruddy brown, the scales with rounded edge, stiff, marginally thin, very slightly if at all eroded. They are clustered at the summit of the tree and drop in the late fall or remain in place for a year.

The Red Spruce is distributed from Newf. west to Pa. Minn. and northwestward; it extends south along the Alleghany Mts. to Ga. ascending to 4000 feet in the Adirondack, Green, and White Mts. and to 5000 feet in the mountains of W. Va. It is the most abundant conifer of the White Mts. where it holds almost exclusive possession of the wildernesses in Coos, Grafton, and Carroll Cos.

The wood is pale buff yellow, even-grained, light, and soft. The finest lumber is used for the sounding boards of pianos, the rougher for construction work, and the clearer for sheathing, clapboard, and flooring in house building, it is also converted into wood pulp.

The Red Spruce is so closely related to the Black, that until recently it has been considered a variety of the latter, but its botanical characters are distinct and without intermediate phases. It is a slow-growing tree, specimens with trunk diameters of 14-16 inches are often found to be 70 years old, while others with 24-inch trunks have been known to be more than 350 years old!

The danger of extermination to the Red Spruce forests of New Hampshire was finally averted on March 1, 1911, when President Taft signed the "Weeks Act" for the purchase of national forests at the headwaters of navigable streams, and the government in due course of time obtained control of approximately 100,000 acres in the White Mountain district.

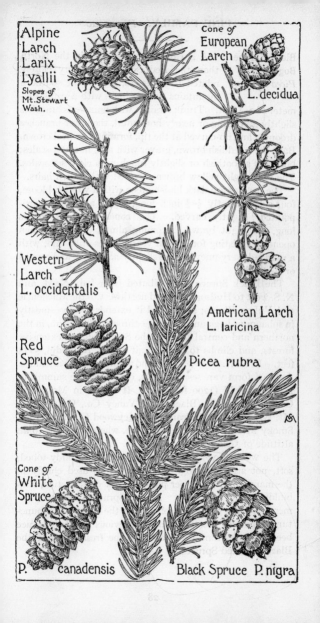

Alpine
Larch
Larix
Lyallii
Slopes of
Mt. Stewart
Wash.

Cone of
European
Larch

L. decidua

Western
Larch
L. occidentalis

American Larch
L. laricina

Red
Spruce

Picea rubra

Cone of
White
Spruce

P. canadensis

Black Spruce P. nigra

Black Spruce
Bog Spruce
Picea mariana

A smaller, slenderer tree in the North than the Red Spruce, but very closely related to it, 20–40, and in the southern mountains 90 feet high, with a trunk diameter of 2–4 feet. Trunk straight with numerous branches slightly ascending or nearly horizontal, the lower branches drooping and up-curved at the tip, forming a conical crown. Bark dark reddish brown, grayer with age, in small scales; branches smoothish or slightly rough with close-set scales. The twigs light yellow brown, covered with brown hairs.

The needles are dark bluish green with a whitish bloom, four-sided, mostly ½–¾ inch long, rigid, abruptly sharp-pointed, slightly curved. The cones are ¾–1¼ inches long, dull light brown, becoming almost spherical when opened, persisting for several years; scales stiff, thin, with a rounded, very uneven edge slightly narrowed, and ragged or toothed.

The Black Spruce is distributed from Lab. Newf. and N. S. west to Hudson Bay, and northwest to the Mackenzie and Yukon Rivers; southward it extends locally—mostly in sphagnum bogs and swamps—through Me. where, in the northern and central parts of the State it forms extensive forests, and climbs to the summit of Mt. Katahdin, 5215 feet. In N. H. and Vt. it is found at low and high altitudes. A dwarf form var. *semiprostrata*, occurs on the summit of Mt. Mansfield (4200 feet), Vt. It occurs in Mass. and Conn. and N. C. (Black Mts. Yancy Co., Grandfather Mt. Watauga Co., Balsam Mts. Heywood Co., and Great Smoky Mts. Swain Co.), and Tenn. where it climbs to an altitude of 5000 feet.

The wood is very light buff yellow, or is ruddy-toned, soft, not strong, straight-grained, and is used chiefly in the manufacture of paper pulp, and for construction, ship building, piles and posts. All the Spruces yield the commercial spruce gum; it is collected in the winter from punctures made on the trunk in the previous spring. Spruce beer is made from a decoction of the fresh twigs of the Black and Red Spruces.

A very large massive spruce of the far **Sitka Spruce**
Northwest, 160-180 feet high, with a *Picea*
trunk diameter of 10 feet. The big *sitchensis*
branches sometimes 20 feet long, drooping,
the branchlets pendulous. Bark madder purple, or brown,
scaly. Leaves flat, stiff, thick, sharp-pointed, bright olive
yellow green. Cones pendulous 2–4 inches long, thin-
scaled.

Range from Alaska to northern Cal. from sea level to
3000 feet elevation.

A very beautiful spruce of the coastal **Weeping**
mountains, common at elevations of **Spruce**
4000–8000 feet, growing 50–75 or rarely *Picea*
100 feet high. Branching to the ground, *Breweriana*
horizontally above, drooping below; the
tapering crown spirelike, the foliage conspicuously
pendulous.

The needles deep olive green, flat, not very sharp-pointed,
close set to the branchlets which are very numerous, and
stringlike, hanging down 4–8 feet in length with many
smaller lateral branchlets. Cones purplish, or plum-
color before opening, long and slender, russet brown after
shedding the seed.

Range through southwestern Ore. and northwestern
Cal. with a local distribution over steep northern slopes
of the Coastal Ranges. Reported on the northern and
eastern flanks of Mt. Shasta, but authentic records were
lacking as late as 1908.

A western spruce ranging in size from **Engelmann**
scrub form with almost prostrate stems, **Spruce**
to a large tree 150 feet high, with a trunk *Picea*
diameter of 4–5 feet; commonly with a *Engelmanni*
slender, symmetrical, pyramidal figure,
but the taller forest trees with narrow heads and pendulous
branches. Bark light cinnamon brown broken into large
thin scales; twigs slender, at first olive buff, at last tan red.

The needles are soft, flexible, and four-sided, $\frac{7}{8}$–$1\frac{1}{8}$
inches long, acute, slender, with the same catlike odor of

those of the White Spruce, and light blue green, whitish beneath, with a forward trend on the branchlets. The cone is long-ovoid, 1½–3 inches long, similar in color to those of the foregoing species, they fall in the autumn or early winter.

The Engelmann Spruce is a tree forming wide forests at high elevations, and is distributed from Alberta and B. C. among the mountains, south through Mont. Ida. Wash. Ore. to New Mex. and Ariz. It is the common spruce of the Selkirk Mts., Canada, and of the Yellowstone plateau of northwestern Wyo.

The wood is light, not strong, close-grained, and like the White Spruce in color except with an occasional ruddy tinge. It is largely manufactured into lumber.

Blue Spruce
Colorado Blue
Spruce
Silver Spruce
Picea
Menziesii

A beautiful, silvery, pale gray blue evergreen, the lightest colored of all the spruces, common in cultivation, 25–40 feet high, and in Colorado reaching a height of 100 feet, with a trunk diameter of 2–3 feet. The branches are horizontal, and the foliage is distinctly horizontal-layered. Bark gray brown, rough scaly, and on old trees deeply furrowed. Twigs light tan yellow to ruddy brown and smooth.

The needles are ¾–1⅛ inches long (shorter on the fruiting branches), light dull bluish sage green, with or without a silvery white bloom, stiff, sharp-pointed and curved, four-sided, emitting a disagreeable pungent odor when bruised similar to that of the White or Cat Spruce. Cones cylindrical, 2½–4 inches long, tan-colored, persisting on the tree all winter, the scales thin, flexible, longer than broad, and with jagged, blunt tips.

The Blue Spruce is distributed through the Rocky Mt. region of Colorado and eastern Utah, north to the Wind River Mts. of Wyo. It is frequently planted in parks and private grounds in the Eastern States, where the commonest specimens are a light sage green of a bluish tone, but not infrequently the tree is dull light green, and sometimes it has a rusty tinge. There are some beautiful but small specimens in the Arnold Arboretum, Jamaica Plain, Mass.

Colorado
Blue Spruce
Picea
Menziesii

Weeping
Spruce
Picea Breweriana

Sitka Spruce
Picea sitchensis
Nesqually River Vall.
Cal.

Engelmann Spruce
Picea Engelmanni

Siskiyou Mts. Cal.

a tall and handsome one on the lawn of Ellwanger and Barry's nurseries, Rochester, N. Y., and several in Roger Williams Park, Providence, R. I. The wood is soft, close-grained, not strong, and pale brown buff to white buff.

Norway Spruce
Picea Abies

A European tree commonly 40–50 and occasionally 100 feet high, with a trunk diameter of 2 feet, in common cultivation in many public parks and on private grounds throughout the Northern States. It is remarkable for its long, sweeping, pendulous branches and dark foliage. Bark ruddy brown, with rough, thick scales; on young trees smoother with thin flaky scales. Twigs brown, nearly smooth, or sometimes hairy, very pendulous.

The needles are a lustrous dark olive green, four-sided in section $\frac{5}{8}$–1 inch long, curved and sharp-pointed. The cones are cylindrical, pendent, very long, 4–6 inches, a beautiful pale buff tan color, or a light ruddy brown, slightly curved, and falling after the first winter; the scales, thin, stiff, broader than long, round-edged, or sometimes square-tipped and eroded.

This Spruce forms a conspicuous feature of the landscape in Norway. It has become established at several places in Conn. The wood is light, soft, close-grained, and a ruddy ochre or buff.

Picea Abies var. *pendula* is a form with extremely pendulous branchlets which is planted for ornament.

Balsam Fir
Balm of
Gilead Fir
Abies balsamea

The only native Fir of the northeastern States. Commonly 40–60 or rarely 80 feet high, with a trunk diameter of 1–2 feet. It climbs to the summits of high mountains where it becomes dwarfed or reduced to the size of a mere shrub, and the foliage (on the underside) appears more densely clothed with a blue white bloom. The little twigs do not droop from the branches as do those of the spruces. The bark is a warm gray, nearly smooth, entirely without scales, slightly horizontally ridged, more or less blistered with small excrescences or vescicles laden with the so-called Canada Balsam.

The needles are a lustrous deep blue green, $\frac{3}{4}$-1 inch long, blunt, flat, sometimes whitish in the central groove on the upper surface, and always broadly whitish either side of the midrib on the under surface, absolutely without the tiny stalk or stem which characterizes the needle of the Spruces, and borne flatly on either side of the pale brown (not tan-colored) branchlets. Sometimes the needles are strongly curved upward, but the general tendency of growth is lateral; the upward curve of the needle is accountable for the whitish appearance of the trees near or upon the summits of mountains in N. E. The needles are very aromatic when crushed and the soft fragrant twigs are used to stuff the so-called pine-pillow. The staminate flowers, about $\frac{1}{4}$ inch long, appear in May-June.

The cones are oblong-ovoid, 2–3$\frac{3}{4}$ inches long, maturing the first year, pale green, plum purple, or violet gray when young, excessively sticky with balsam at times, borne erect; the very thin scales are flat, rounded, and early deciduous—that is the mature cone disintegrates, shedding its scales and leaving only its core or axis on the tree through the winter; the scales are accompanied by obovate bracts tipped with an abrupt slender point.

The Balsam Fir is distributed from Newf. and Lab. west to Hudson Bay, Mich. and Minn., northwest to the Great Bear Lake region, and south to Pa. and along the high Alleghanies to Mt. Rogers, Grayson Co., Va. It is common in damp woods and mountain swamps throughout Me. climbs to an altitude of 4500 feet on Mt. Katahdin, to the same height, the timber line, on Mt. Moosilauke and nearly all other of the higher White mountains of N. H. It is also common in the swamps of the Contoocook and Miller Rivers more southerly in the State, and occurs frequently on the Green Mts. of Vt. and on Graylock in Mass. but is rare in Conn. at Middlebury, Goshen, Cornwall, and Salisbury.

The wood is light, soft, perishable, and pale buff streaked with brown; it is occasionally made into lumber, but is usually ground into wood pulp. Weight 25 lbs. to the cubic foot. The so-called Canada balsam or Venetian

Turpentine of this tree is commercially valuable both medicinally and in connection with painting.

Fraser Fir
Mountain
Balsam
Abies Fraseri

Exclusively a mountain Fir confined to the southern Alleghanies, commonly 20–40 or rarely 75 feet high, with a trunk diameter of 2 feet. Bark smooth, warm, light brownish gray. Twigs thickly beset with needles on the upper side.

The needles are $\frac{1}{2}$–$\frac{3}{4}$ inch long, olive green above, bluish white either side of the green midrib beneath, narrowly linear, and very blunt (commonly with a shallow notch at the tip), very persistent. Flowering in May.

Cone oblong-ovoid, 1–2 inches long; the scales bear conspicuously projecting, slender, sharp-pointed, rigid, erroded or lacerated bracts. The seed is produced at long intervals.

The Fraser Fir is distributed through the mountains of Va. N. C. and Tenn. on moist slopes, and climbs to an elevation of 5000–6000 feet often forming extensive forests. It is common on the highest summits, and does not occur below 4000 feet.[1] This is the Fir of the mountains about Asheville, N. C.

The wood is buff white, soft, not strong, light, and coarse-grained. It is not yet put to extensive use. The thin, clear sap furnishes the so-called Balsam used medicinally for healing purposes.

Alpine Fir
Abies
lasiocarpa

A mountain Fir of the Pacific slope (not infrequently a mere shrub on exposed summits), 60–80 and rarely 130 feet high, with a trunk diameter of 4 feet. The bark a light ashen gray, rather thin, broken into shallow ridges on old trees, smooth on medium-aged trees. Branches drooping, and on forest specimens 30–40 feet from the ground. Younger twigs rusty-haired.

The needles are dark blue green with a silver white bloom on the under side, flat, blunt, generally strongly curved upward. The cones plum purple, gray with age,

[1] *Vide* Gifford Pinchot in *Timber Trees of North Carolina,* p. 136.

Norway Spruce
Picea Abies

Balsam Fir
Abies balsamea
White Mts. N·H·

Black Mts. N·C·

Fraser Fir
Abies Fraseri

Alpine Fir
Abies lasiocarpa

Blue Mts
Wash.

---

growing in clusters: $2\frac{1}{4}$–4 inches long. Producing seed annually.

The Alpine Fir is distributed from southeastern Alaska south to B. C. western Alberta, Wash. Ore. Ida. western Mont. and Wyo. Ariz. and N. Mex.

Grand Fir
White Fir
Lowland Fir
Abies grandis

A very tall tree of lowlands or moist mountain slopes, 80–120 and occasionally 270 feet high, with a trunk diameter of 4 feet. The stem very straight, with branches spreading and drooping nearly to the ground both in the open forest and in isolation; the crown somewhat rounded. In close association the foliage extends from the apex one third or more of the length of the stem downward.

The needles are yellow green, flat, grooved, and notched at the tip, $1\frac{1}{4}$–2 inches long; on the upper branches crowded and curved upward.

The cones light yellow green, cylindrical, $2\frac{1}{2}$–$4\frac{1}{2}$ inches long, maturing in early autumn once in two or three years. The range is from southern B. C. (near the coast) to northern Ida. western Mont. Ore. and the northern coast of Cal.

White Fir
Abies concolor

A very large tree with characteristically whitish gray bark, 100–180 and occasionally 200 feet high, with a trunk diameter of 3–5 feet. The very rough, massive trunks scored with deep wide furrows, the bark pale ashen gray and immensely thick—often 6 inches. On young trees smooth and gray brown. The crown round, cone-shaped, with dense pale yellow green or pale bluish green foliage. The young trees sharply pyramidal.

The needles are very long, flat or curved, straight, blunt or pointed, twisted at the base; lower branch leaves $1\frac{1}{3}$–3 inches long. Very variable in form.

The cylindrical cone a very pale dull green or yellow green, or sometimes purplish, $3\frac{1}{2}$–$4\frac{1}{2}$ inches long. Maturing in early September.

The range is over mountain slopes from southern Ore. (Cascade Mts.), through Cal. into Lower Cal. and from Nev. Utah, and southern Col. to Ariz. and N. Mex.

An equally large fir with very whitish **Silver Fir**
gray bark 80-150 and in favorable situa- **Amabilis Fir**
tions fully 200 feet high, with a trunk *Abies amabilis*
diameter of 3-5 feet. Similar in contour
to the preceding species, the bark characteristically smooth,
unbroken, pale ashen gray, with whitish areas. Only
aged trees are seamed and then exclusively at the base.

The needles are $1\frac{1}{4}$ inches long, flat, sharply grooved
above, white-lined below, and commonly with a notch at
the tip, or sometimes blunt.

The deep plum-colored cones are $4-5\frac{1}{4}$ inches long,
and ovoid-cylindrical; they are ripe in September, and the
seeds fall in October, annually, but only prolifically every
2-3 years. The range is from southern Alaska through
the Coast and Cascade mountains of B. C. to Wash. and
Ore.

A very tall western fir 80-140 and in **Noble Fir**
exceptionally favorable environment 200 *Abies nobilis*
or more feet high, with a trunk diameter
of 5 feet; the crown a round-topped cone, the branches
short and mostly horizontal, the lower ones drooping, the
foliage remarkably dense, and massed on the upper surface
of the branchlets. Bark thin, divided into narrow, flat
ridges broken into scaly plates, ashen brown, ruddy
beneath.

The needles, lighter or deeper blue green, with the grayish tinge common to the firs, straight, or strongly curved
upward, thick-set on the upper side of the branchlet,
commonly with an abrupt sharp point, but those on the
lower branches notched at the tip, $1-1\frac{1}{4}$ inches long.

The cone is ovoid-cylindrical, $4\frac{1}{2}-7$ inches long, pale
tan-color when ripe, breaking up in October; the conspicuous, pointed bracts covering the scales and reflexed
closely upon them.

The range, as yet imperfectly known, is along the coastal
mountains of southwestern Wash. the Olympic Mts. on
Solduc River from Mt. Baker southward in the Cascade
Mts. Wash. and Bowlder Ridge (northernmost headwaters
of McKenzie River, Lane Co.), Ore.

The wood is heavy, firm, light brown, and easily worked, superior in quality to that of any of the firs.

Red Fir
Abies magnifica

Another tall, western fir, commonly 80-175 and occasionally 200 feet high, with a trunk diameter of 5 feet. The crown is narrow and round-topped in old trees, slender, and spirelike in young trees; the short lower branches droop nearly to the ground in most graceful curves. Bark smooth and a conspicuous ashen white on young trees and the upper parts of old trees. The trunks of older trees are scored by diagonal furrows, leaving hard, rough ridges with a vertical or diagonal trend. Foliage dark blue green with the usual grayish tinge.

The needles are $\frac{3}{4}$-$1\frac{1}{4}$ inches long, blunt, commonly wider at the tip than at the base, curved upward and crowded on the upper surface of the branchlets.

The cones are about 5-8 inches long, ovoid-cylindrical, and a deep plum purple or brownish purple when ripe; they break up, and drop the seed in September.

The range is along high mountain slopes and ridges in moist, cool situations, from southern Ore. (the Cascade Mts.), and northern Cal. (Mts. Shasta and Eddy and the Scott Mts.), and along the western slopes of the Sierra Nevada Mts. to a point 75 miles east of Lake Tulare, on Fish Creek (a tributary of the Kern River), and Poso (or Possey) Creek, a tributary of Lake Tulare, lat. 35° 40'.

The wood is a trifle heavier than that of *Abies nobilis*, soft, firm, and straight-grained; the color is ocher brown.

The Shasta Fir, *Abies magnifica* var. *shastensis*, is a form with conspicuous bracts on the cone-scales; the cones are also stouter.

Douglas Spruce
Douglas Fir
Pseudotsuga taxifolia

A very tall, Rocky Mountain species distinctly differing from both Picea and Abies, and yet superficially resembling the latter, but its buds are large and red brown, and its cones have persistent scales and lobed bracts. Under favorable conditions in its native habitat the tree grows 200 feet high, with a trunk diameter of 8-12 feet. The branches are horizontal, or

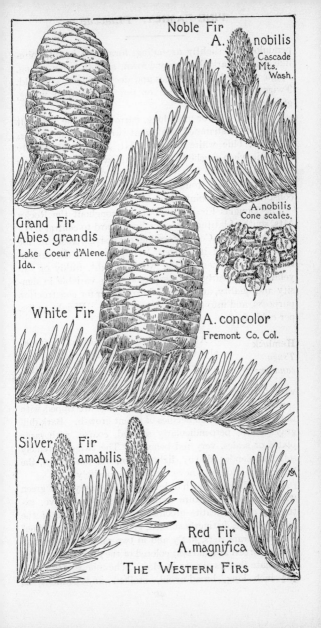

Noble Fir
A. nobilis
Cascade
Mts.
Wash.

A. nobilis
Cone scales.

Grand Fir
Abies grandis
Lake Coeur d'Alene.
Ida.

White Fir

A. concolor
Fremont Co. Col.

Silver Fir
A. amabilis

Red Fir
A. magnifica

THE WESTERN FIRS

pendulous, or slightly ascending, forming a broad, spire-like head. Bark dark gray brown, smooth when young, rough with red brown scales and deeply ridged when old. Twigs fine-hairy, yellowish or tan brown when young, grayer when old.

Needles ¾ inch or more long, narrowed at the base but not distinctly stemmed, somewhat two-ranked, as in *Abies balsamea*, blue white beneath, flat, blunt, and slightly aromatic when crushed. Cones narrow ovoid, 2–4 inches long, maturing the first year, pendent, short-stalked, with persisting scales, round-edged and accompanied with conspicuous long-pointed, laterally winged bracts.

The Douglas Fir is distributed throughout the Rocky Mts. south of latitude 55°, northwestward to central B. C. and the Pacific Coast, forming extensive forests in the northerly part of its range. It is planted in the eastern States for ornament. The wood is light, ruddy or tan yellow, with nearly white sapwood, very variable in density and quality, and is made into lumber for construction purposes, and into railroad ties and piles. Weight 32 lbs. per cubic foot.

Hemlock
Tsuga
canadensis

A large tree 50–80 and often in favorable situations 110 feet high, with a trunk diameter of 3–6 feet. The slender, spreading branches horizontal, drooping, with feathery foliage, graceful and plumelike. In late spring or early summer the younger twigs are tipped with the light yellow green needles of recent growth. Bark dull gray brown, perpendicularly seamed, coarse, with large plates or scales, very red beneath. The twigs extremely soft and slender, downy, light brown, not tan yellow, the branchlets seldom or never growing oppositely.

The needles are ½ inch or less long, lightest yellow green when new, when mature dark lustrous green above, extremely pale beneath—greenish white either side of the midrib, blunt, distinctly stalked, growing at an angle of 60° with the branchlets, flatly and in two ranks. The needle is the shortest and darkest colored of the evergreens. The staminate flowers appear in May. The cone is very small, ½–¾ inch long, broad-ovoid, stalked and pendent; it matures the first year, and persists on the branchlets through the winter.

The Hemlock is common in cold swamps, mountain slopes, ravines, and rocky woods; it is distributed from Lab. Newf. and N. S. west to Minn. (Carleton Co.), Wis. and Mich., and south to Del. and along the mountains to Ga. and Ala. It ascends to an altitude of 2000 feet in the White and Adirondack Mts.; abundant in the southern and central portions of Me. it becomes rare northward and almost disappears in Aroostook Co. and the northern Penobscot region; in N. H. it is scattered through the White Mountain woods, and disappears in northern Coos Co.; in Vt. Mass. and R. I. it is common in deep woods; in Conn. it is locally abundant. The wood is fairly light, tough-corky, coarse-grained, and difficult to work: it is subject to wind-shake, and readily splinters· it is durable under ground but not particularly so exposed to wind and weather; its color is a lusterless buffish white, faintly pink-tinged and often pale brown; it is manufactured only into rough boards, timbers, and joists. The inner ruddy bark of the Hemlock is rich in tannic acid, and is extensively used for curing leather. Oil of Hemlock is distilled from the young branchlets. The New York Indian name for this tree is "Oh-neh-tah"—Greens-on-the-stick.

The Carolina Hemlock grows exclusively in the Alleghanies. It is similar in most of its characters to the foregoing species, but a much smaller tree, commonly 35-50 and occasionally 70 feet high, with a trunk diameter of 2½ feet. The foliage is denser than that of the other species.

Carolina Hemlock Mountain Hemlock
Tsuga caroliniana

The needles are darker and longer, ½-¾ inch long, and are more thickly distributed over the branchlets. The drooping cones are also larger, ovoid, ¾-1⅓ inches long with oblong, widely spreading scales.

The Carolina Hemlock is found on dry, rocky hillsides, and is distributed locally through the mountains of southwestern Va. on the cliffs of New River (south fork), Ashe Co. and on the spurs of the Blue Ridge in N. C., in the gorge of the Doe River, Carter Co. Tenn. and in northern Ga. It usually grows singly or in small groves, never forming an exclusive forest.

Western Hemlock *Tsuga heterophylla*	The greatest of the hemlock trees, a western species, which often attains a height of 200 feet, with a trunk diameter of 8 or more feet. The branches short, slender, and pendulous.

The dark green needles ½ inch or more long. The cone also larger than that of *Tsuga canadensis*, ¾–1 inch long.

The Western Hemlock is distributed from southern Alaska south to B. C. Wash. Ore. and Cal. (Cape Mendocino and Marin Co.), and eastward to the Rocky Mts. of Mont. and the Cœur d'Alene and Bitter Root Mts. of Ida. It forms a considerable part of the western forests in which are the White Fir, Douglas Spruce, Mountain Pine, and Engelmann's Spruce.

Mountain Hemlock Black Hemlock *Tsuga Mertensiana*	A medium-sized western species, 30–70 and rarely 125 feet high, with a trunk diameter of 3 feet. The slender branches drooping, even to the narrow pyramidal crown, and sweeping gracefully down nearer the ground, the slender new twigs

pendulous. Bark dull madder brown, or lavender brown, deeply and narrowly furrowed, with rounded ridges.

The needles rounded and full, blunt, and distinctly stemmed, with a feathery, forward trend on the twigs, thickest on the upper surface, scarcely flat like those of *T. canadensis*. The cones are borne abundantly on or near the tips of the branchlets, in size variable, ¾–2 inches long (possibly longer), yellow green or plum purple when mature, different trees often bearing wholly different colored cones,[1] the open cones light brown, ripe in October.

The Mountain Hemlock is common on mountain slopes, and is distributed from the coast mountains of Alaska, southward through the Sierras of Cal., and eastward to Ida. and Mont. The wood is fine-grained, soft, pale

[1] *Vide* Sudworth in *Forest Trees of the Pacific Slope*

THE HEMLOCKS

Western Hemlock
T. heterophylla

Hemlock
Tsuga
canadensis

Douglas Fir
Pseudo-tsuga taxifolia
Portland. Ore.

Kootenai Co.
Ida.

Carolina
Hemlock
T. caroliniana

Mountain
Hemlock
T. Mertensiana

pinkish brown, and light. It has as yet no especial commercial value.

Bald Cypress
Taxodium
distichum

A stately deciduous tree common in the
southern swamps, which grows 50–80 and
in favorable situations 150 feet high. The
tree is often completely surrounded with
water from which its trunk rises perpendicularly 40 feet or
more with the line unbroken by a single living bough.
The branches are horizontal or else droop considerably.
Above the roots are frequently grouped a series of conical
so-called "knees" often a foot in diameter, which conspicuously rise from the roots several feet above the swampy
ground or the water, and also send downward strong,
deeply penetrating roots, the anchors by which the tree
is held staunchly in its soggy, muddy bed.[1] The bark is
thick, pale ruddy brown, divided perpendicularly into
broad, flat ridges with long, thin scales; the branchlets
slender, light olive green when young, terra cotta brown
when old.

The small needles are deciduous, $\frac{1}{2}$–$\frac{3}{4}$ inch long, linear,
flat, and light yellow green on both sides; some (those on
the flowering twigs) are awl-shaped and imbricated (overlapping on the branchlets). Cones tan brown, almost
spherical, commonly at the tips of the branchlets, with
thick, angular, somewhat shield-shaped scales; about 1
inch in diameter.

The Bald Cypress is common in swamps from southern
Del. (Sussex Co. southward along the coast), south to
Fla., and northwest to western Ky. southern Ind. (Knox
Co.), southern Ill. west Tenn. southeastern Mo. eastern
Ark. La. and Tex.

The wood is straight-grained, easily worked, heavier
than White Pine (29 lbs. to the cubic foot), and light brown,
but varied near the roots with areas of rich blackish brown,
similar in character to olive wood. It is commonly employed in general construction and for the manufacture
of fence posts, railway ties, and the exterior and interior
finish of buildings, doors, sashes, etc., in most of which

[1] *Vide* Lamborn in *Garden and Forest*, vol. iii, pg. 21.

uses it has rapidly taken the place of the now scarce White Pine. For the effective paneling of walls and doors it quite equals in beauty some of the more expensive imported hardwoods. The Cypress is a tree of slow growth; the aged trees of the swamps, about 200 years old, have a trunk diameter of only 20 inches.

California Big Tree
Sequoia gigantea. Sequoia washingtoniana.
Sudworth

The largest cone-bearing evergreen tree in the world, and the oldest. Commonly 250–280 feet high, but some exceptionally tall specimens measure over 300 feet, with trunk diameters of 17–24 feet at about 8 feet above the greatly swelled bases. Young trees with short, slender branches the full length of the stem, curving upward, forming a broad and sharp-pointed crown; after 300 years the lower limbs thin out, and the remaining ones carry a greater weight of dense foliage; older trees are usually clear of branches for 100 or more feet upward, their crowns are rounded, irregular, and open, the limbs large and crooked, and the foliage dense and drooping. Bark light cinnamon brown, the outer plates often a dull lavender gray, extremely thick and coarse.

The leaves are blue green, awllike, sharp-pointed and overlapping, the cone-bearing branchlets carrying shorter, more scalelike leaves; smaller twigs also carry shorter leaves. Flowers staminate and pistillate on the same tree. Cones dark blue green or olive green, mature at the end of the second season; dry, open cones dull ocher brown, the scales before opening resembling the wrinkled surface of a pineapple; 1–3 inches long.

The California Big Tree is scattered over restricted areas at an elevation of 5000–8500 feet on the western slopes of the Sierra Nevadas from southern Placer to Tulare Cos. The region covered includes approximately 50 square miles within which there are 26 groves; one of the largest of these called the Giant Forest contains 5000 trees; this is under Government and private ownership. Some groves contain very few trees—Deer Creek Grove but 30, and North Grove only 6.[1]

[1] *Vide* Sudworth in *Forest Trees of the Pacific Slope*, pg. 143.

Wood dull red brown, brighter when first cut, very light, brittle, and coarse-grained, commercially valuable; but larger trees yield only 30 per cent. of their bulk in lumber. Estimates place the age of these trees at 4000–5000 years; those with a diameter of 15 feet are probably 2500 years old.

Redwood
Sequoia
sempervirens

An extremely similar species 190–280 or rarely 300 feet high. Bark deep cinnamon brown, gray-tinged.

The leaves are deep yellow green, flat, sharp-pointed, stiff, $\frac{1}{3}$ – $\frac{3}{4}$ inch long, unequally distributed upon the branchlet, the main stems carrying short, scalelike forms, persistent on the branches for some years after the latter are cut, turning dull brown. Cones maturing in one season, ripe in September, similar to those of the preceding species.

The range is from southwestern Ore. south 10–30 miles inland through the Californian coast region to Salmon Creek Cañon, 12 miles south of Punta Gorda, Monterey Co. Generally within the fog belt and climbing on the western slopes of the Coastal ranges to an elevation of 2500 feet. It is not so long-lived as the other species: probably its age limit is 1400 years.

The wood is crimson brown, soft, brittle, straight-grained, and easily worked, the weight 24 lbs. to the cubic foot, heavier than that of the Big Tree (which is about 21 lbs.). It is of great commercial importance, and is manufactured into interior finish, doors, paneling, and furniture. The Sequoias are near relatives of the Bald Cypress which is territorially widely separated from them; they are the remains of an ancient genus which was at home in the Arctic Regions. They are now menaced more or less with destruction, and there is no rational excuse for any such vandalism; they are not safe outside of State or National ownership

Mr. George B. Sudworth has wisely said "the destruction, for whatever end, of all the great trees which it has taken thousands of years to produce could never be justified."[1] The question is not whether a great tree should

[1] Vide *Forest Trees of the Pacific Slope*, pg. 138.

Bald Cypress
Taxodium distichum
Jacksonville. Fla.

California Big Tree
Sequoia gigantea
Sierra Nevada Mts.

Redwood
Sequoia sempervirens
Santa Cruz Co. Cal.

be felled or allowed to stand, it is one which involves the proper cutting down of trees in general, and the right of the American people through experts to control and limit that cutting.

White Cedar
Coast White
Cedar
Chamæcyparis
thyoides

A slender evergreen of swamps, in the East 20–45 feet, and sometimes in the southern part of its range reaching a height of 90 feet, with a trunk diameter of 4½ feet. The branches are short, slender, ascending or nearly horizontal, the foliage delicate and feathery. The summit of the tree is spirelike or narrowly conical. Bark distinctly shredded and perpendicularly seamed, with a slight or pronounced spiral trend, on young trees detached in broad, thin, red brown strips, on old trees grayish brown, and less shredded.

The leaves are tiny, in close-pressed scales, opposite in four rows, $\frac{1}{10}$ inch long, light olive green, and aromatic strong-scented when crushed. The staminate catkins cylindrical. Cones tiny, spherical, $\frac{3}{16} - \frac{5}{16}$ inch in diameter, maturing the first year, opening toward the center, with about 3 rows of scales, which are thick and shield-shaped, with a slight protuberance in the center; seeds winged.

The White Cedar is common in swamps and marshy land, and is distributed (mostly on the coastal plain) from Cape Breton Island and Halifax, N. S. (where it is doubtfully indigenous), south to Fla. and Miss. (Pearl River). It is rare in Me. (reported from the southern part of York Co.); in N. H. it is only in coastal Rockingham Co.; in Vt. it is unknown; in Mass. common in the southeastern section; in R. I. common; and in Conn. occasional or frequent eastward.

The wood is light, soft, close-grained, but slightly fragrant, light brown tinged with red and pale buff, and very durable in contact with the soil. It is used for railroad ties, fence posts, shingles, and boat-building. Charcoal for gunpowder is made from the smaller trees.

It is a common tree of the Dismal Swamp (where it grows along with the Cypress), and of Gates, Tyrrell, and Dare Cos., bordering the Albemarle Sound. In many swamps it has furnished for years a large supply of sound, valuable timber, much of which in the shape of fallen trees has been excavated from the saturated peaty soil, or drawn up from various depths of water.

A northwestern species similar in some characters to the White Cedar, 75–100 feet high, with a trunk diameter of 3 feet. The narrow conical crown and drooping branches with pendulous, flat sprays quite unlike Red Cedar, almost "weeping" in habit. Bark ashen brown, cinnamon red within, with thin, diagonal ridges.

Yellow Cypress
Chamæcyparis nootkatensis

The foliage similar to that of the White or the Red Cedar, in close-pressed, prickly scales. Cones as in *C. thyoides*, small and spherical.

The range of Yellow Cypress, sometimes called Alaska Cedar, is along the coast and among the islands of southeastern Alaska and B. C. and on the coast and through the Cascade Mts. of Wash. and northern Ore., where it climbs to an elevation of nearly 7000 feet.

The wood is distinctly a *clear sulphur yellow*, and exceedingly fine-grained, weight 35 lbs. to the cubic foot, durable and easily worked; it is especially useful for interior finish and cabinet work. Trees with trunks 20 inches in diameter are about 275 years old.

A very beautiful, deep-toned evergreen tree 125–180 or more feet high, with a trunk diameter of about 4½ feet. The largest tree of the genus, with a dense pyramidal crown, the branches with an upward trend, but horizontal and drooping lower down. Bark narrowly and diagonally ridged, the color ashen brown.

Lawson Cypress Port Orford Cedar
Chamæcyparis Lawsoniana

The leaves in minute scales on peculiarly flat, feathery sprays, close-pressed, deep yellow green, and very soft to the touch, not prickly as in *C. nootkatensis*. Cones russet brown, small, almost berrylike.

The range is along the coast within the fog belt, from southwestern Ore. (Coos Bay), southward to Mad River (near Humboldt Bay), Humboldt Co. Cal. (within a few miles of the sea), 10–40 miles eastward to an elevation of 5000 feet on the western slopes of the Coast Range.

One of the most beautiful of the Cedars in common cultivation in this country and in Europe.

Arbor Vitæ
Thuja
occidentalis

An ornamental evergreen much cultivated for hedgerows and wind-breaks, commonly 20–40 and occasionally 60 feet high, with a trunk diameter of 2–4 feet. The trunk often buttressed at the base, and sometimes distorted and twisted; the branches short, the lower ones horizontal, the upper closely crowded with foliage and forming a dense conical head. Bark light brown or gray brown, shredded, separating into long narrow strips, seamed perpendicularly with a slight spiral trend, often with a strong spiral twist, twigs brown, smooth; small twigs flat, scaly, and tan brown. The foliage arranged in fan-shaped clusters, shining green.

The leaves are bright green, in overlapping scales, 4 rows on the two-edged branchlets or small twigs, the middle row flat, with a tiny slightly raised tubercle on each scale; with an aromatic odor when crushed. Cones small, when very young palest green, about ½ inch long, when old light reddish brown with 6–12 pointless, thin, oblong scales; they are persistent through the winter. The twigs of the Arbor Vitæ are larger and more flattened than those of the White Cedar, and its leafy clusters are more fan-shaped; the leaves are also larger and a purer, brighter green. The cones of the Arbor Vitæ are oblong with thin scales opening to the base of the cone; those of the White Cedar are spherical with thick, shield-shaped scales, and open toward the center.

The Arbor Vitæ grows in swamps and on cool rocky river and pond shores, from southern Lab. to N. S., west to Lake Winnipeg and Minn., and south to Pa. and along the mountains to N. C. and eastern Tenn. (Holston River). In N. C. it is reduced to a shrub or very small tree, and is confined to the mountains. In Me. it is common; in N. H. rare in Coos Co., not in the White Mt. district, and only occasional south of that point; in Mass. in the Berkshire Hills, and rare in Conn.

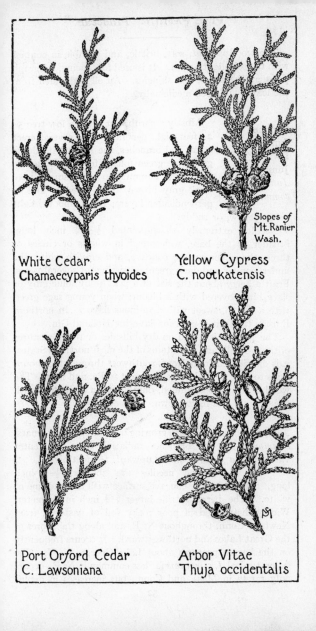

White Cedar
Chamaecyparis thyoides

Yellow Cypress
C. nootkatensis

Slopes of
Mt. Ranier
Wash.

Port Orford Cedar
C. Lawsoniana

Arbor Vitae
Thuja occidentalis

The wood is light, soft, brittle, and durable in contact with the soil; light brown. It is used for fencing, telegraph poles, railroad ties, and shingles. An oil is distilled from the leaves and used medicinally.

Common Juniper Dwarf Juniper *Juniperus communis* — Mostly a shrub, but often a low tree 5–24 feet high, generally with several erect stems and branches, the latter with dense gray blue green foliage forming a narrow plumelike summit to the small tree. Bark gray brown, thin, shreddy, and in perpendicular layers; twigs smooth, light ocher yellow, or ruddy.

Needles extremely sharp-pointed $\frac{1}{2} - 1\frac{3}{10}$ inch long, broader at the base, widespread in whorls or circles of three, the upper surface concave, and grayish white, the under, convex and dark green; persisting for several years. Fruit a berry about the size of a pea, fleshy, blue gray or slaty blue covered with a bloom; when young sage green with a bloom, sweet with a resinous flavor. In northern Europe the fruit is used for flavoring Holland Gin.

The Juniper is found on dry hillsides or rocky pastures of the cool hills and mountains of the most northern States; it is distributed from Newf. southwest through the mountains to N. C. and N. Mex. and west to Pa. and Man. The wood is hard, close-grained, durable when in contact with the ground, and light brown.

Juniperus communis var. *depressa* — A form growing in broad prostrate mats, the branches radiating from the center and curving upward, 1–3 feet high.

The needles are shorter, $\frac{1}{3} - \frac{1}{2}$ inch long, marked on the concave surface with a broad line of white. The berry a trifle larger $\frac{1}{4} - \frac{3}{8}$ inch in diameter. Widely distributed in poor rocky soil of pastures, from Newf. to Conn. throughout N. E. and along the shores of the Great Lakes and northwestward. It occurs frequently on the barren pastures about Lake George, N. Y. The taller, typical *J. communis* far less common in N. E., occurs only rarely in Mass. and Conn., but increases in extent southward. In southern Ill. (but in only a few counties) it attains its greatest height, about 24 feet.

A very prostrate and trailing form, with short, curved broader needles growing closer to the branchlets $\frac{1}{4}$–$\frac{3}{8}$ inch long, more abruptly pointed, and with a conspicuous white line on the concave surface. Exposed rocky barrens along the coast from Newf. to northern Mass. (where doubtful), also in the Rocky Mts. northwest to Alaska.

Juniperus communis var. *montana* *Juniperus nana*, **Willdenow**

A prostrate trailing shrub with scale-like, sharp-pointed, dark green leaves, growing mostly oppositely. Berry about the size of a pea $\frac{1}{4}$–$\frac{2}{5}$ inch in diameter, borne on a short, *backward-curved* stem or peduncle. This species is similar to the Savin of Europe, but the latter has obtuse leaves growing closer to the twig. It is found on barren, rocky, or sandy margins of swamps, from Newf. to N. Y., west to Minn., and northwestward.

Prostrate Savin *Juniperus horizontalis*

A rather small tree with a close, spire-like figure, 25–40 or sometimes in the south 90 feet high, with a trunk diameter of 4–5 feet; often ridged or buttressed at the base. The branches slender, ascending above, not quite horizontal below. It is one of the darkest colored of the evergreen trees. Bark light ruddy brown, shreddy, and separating into long, narrow strips, perpendicularly or decidedly spirally seamed. The twigs approximately four-sided, dark green when young, from the covering of the scaly leaves, red-brown when older.

Red Cedar Savin *Juniperus virginiana*

Leaves scale-shaped, $\frac{3}{32}$ inch long, very dark green or brown green, not flat nor fan-shaped as in Arbor Vitæ, but in 4 rows, rounded and overlapping, persisting for several seasons. On very young trees the leaf-form is Juniperlike, narrow, awl-shaped or needle-shaped, sharp-pointed, spreading, opposite-growing or in threes. Sometimes the two forms are associated on older trees. The inconspicuous flowers appear in April–May. Fruit about the size of a small pea, purplish or slate blue covered with a gray white bloom, borne on straight stems or peduncles.

The Red Cedar is one of the most widely distributed North American trees; it is common on dry, sterile hillsides or margins of lakes and streams, or in peaty swamps, and is found from N. S. and N. B., west to Georgian Bay, Ont. and to the Daks. central Neb. Kan. Okla. and eastern Tex., and south to northern Fla. The range along the coast is imperfectly known. In Me. it is somewhat rare and shrublike; in N. H. it is rare, only frequent in the southeastern section, and quite absent in the White Mt. district (except in Crawford Notch); it is frequent in the Champlain and lower Connecticut Valleys, and common in eastern Mass. Conn. R. I. and northern N. J. It reaches its finest development in the valley of the Red River, Tex.

The wood is light, soft, brittle, close-grained, easily-worked, fragrant, durable in contact with the soil, and its dual color is brownish lake red, with nearly white sapwood; it is generally used for posts, sills, railroad-ties, interior finish of buildings, pails, household woodenware, for closets and chests as a protection from the house-moth, and exclusively for lead pencils. It weighs 23 lbs. to the cubic foot. Oil of Red Cedar is distilled from the wood and leaves.

Juniperus barbadensis is a southern form not easily separable from the foregoing. The range is through the South Atlantic States and the Gulf coast region.

Rocky Mountain Red Cedar
Juniperus scopulorum

This is a very similar species the larger trees having drooping branchlets. Foliage both dark green and lighter gray green, with a whitish bloom. Mature berries, smooth, black covered with whitish bloom, appearing light gray blue, maturing the *second* season, containing usually but 2 seeds, rarely 1. The wood is similar to the foregoing. Range along the eastern foot-hills of the Rocky Mts. from Alberta to western Tex., and west to the coast of B. C. Wash. eastern Ore. Nev. and northern Ariz. generally above 5000 feet elevation, except near the coast. Probably in the Black Hills, S. Dak. and Okla. Range still imperfectly known.

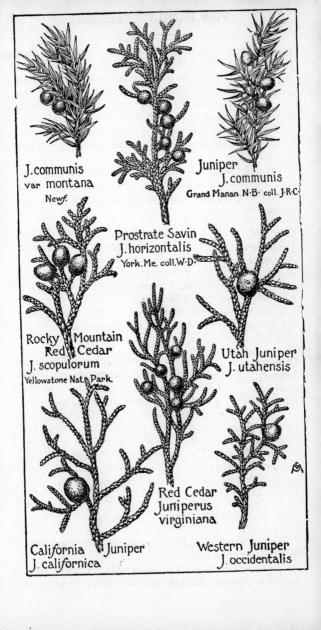

J. communis
var montana
Newf.

Juniper
J. communis
Grand Manan. N·B· coll. J·R·C·

Prostrate Savin
J. horizontalis
York. Me. coll. W·D·

Rocky Mountain
Red Cedar
J. scopulorum
Yellowstone Nat. Park.

Utah Juniper
J. utahensis

Red Cedar
Juniperus
virginiana

California Juniper
J. californica

Western Juniper
J. occidentalis

Western Juniper
Juniperus occidentalis

A similar species but rarely taller than the Red Cedar, when it reaches a height of 40-60 feet. Branches heavy, and often rising from the base and middle of the trunk, forming smaller trunks. Bark cinnamon brown, widely and shallowly furrowed. Foliage pale gray green. Berries $\frac{1}{4}$–$\frac{1}{3}$ inch in diameter, maturing the second season, similar to the foregoing. Wood also similar.

The range is from Ida. southeastern Wash. and eastern Ore. southward to southern Cal. (San Bernardino Mts.) on arid hills, dry plains, and at high elevations among the mountains.

Utah Juniper
Juniperus utahensis

A low-stemmed western tree 6-12 feet high, common throughout desert regions, at an altitude of 5000–8000 feet. Foliage pale yellow green. Berries commonly with but 1 (rarely 2) seed, covered with a white bloom, red brown beneath.

Range from southwestern Wyo. Utah, Nev. and western Col. to northwestern Ariz. and southeastern Cal. Wood light yellow brown, commercially of little value.

California Juniper
Juniperus californica

A species not easily separable from *J. occidentalis*, but distinctly different in the following characters. The bark of the straight trunk fluted and gray, the crown of the tree rounded or conical, bush and open. Foliage pale yellowish green, in short stringlike form, berries light red brown, $\frac{1}{4}$–$\frac{1}{2}$ inch in diameter, maturing the second season, covered with a white bloom, the skin thin and papery, the pulp sweet, fibrous, but not resinous as in the other species. The range is from central Cal. to Lower Cal.

YEW FAMILY. *Taxaceæ.*

Trees or shrubs, the American species with linear hemlocklike evergreen leaves.

The flowers commonly staminate and pistillate on separate plants, the staminate globular and scaly, the pistillate naked ovules finally surrounded by fleshy, berrylike pulp within which is the one bony seed.

A low shrub 2–3 or rarely 6 feet high, with a straggling habit, growing in clumps, with spreading branches.

**American Yew
Ground
Hemlock
*Taxus
canadensis***

The leaves hemlocklike, very dark green above, and an extremely beautiful, warm, *bright yellow green* beneath, short, about ⅝ inch or less long, linear, slightly curved, abruptly and sharply pointed, persistent on the brown twigs.

Flowers developing in April and May. Fruit a clear, translucent red (not scarlet) berry, cuplike, the top of the black seed within uncovered, resinous, ¼ inch long, extremely delicate in character and color. Ripe in August–September.

The American Yew is common in shady, rocky woodlands, especially in evergreen woods, and it ascends to an altitude of 2000 feet in the White, Green, and Adirondack Mts. It is distributed from Newf. west to Man., and southward to Va. Io. and Minn. It is frequent but local in Me. N. H. and Vt., locally common near Manchester, N. H., but only occasional among the trap hills of northern Conn.

The European Yew, *Taxus baccata*, is cultivated in this country with varying success; in Europe it grows to the proportions of a large forest tree; the leaves are darkest green and distinctly dull-pointed.

A small forest tree of the Pacific slope, 20–40 or very rarely 50–70 feet high, with a trunk diameter of 2 feet. The larger trees with an open conical crown, the slender branches horizontal or some-

**Pacific Yew
Oregon Yew
*Taxus
brevifolia***

what drooping, the twigs extremely pendulous, and branching alternately. Bark thin, in loose madder purple scales, the inner bark a magenta red.

The needles a warm deep yellow green, paler beneath, abruptly sharp-pointed, soft, and persistent. The fruit similar to that of *T. canadensis;* ripe in September.

The Pacific Yew is common on the coast and on mountain slopes, and is distributed from southern Alaska, B. C. (Queen Charlotte Island and Skeena River), east to the Selkirk Mts. Can. and the Rocky Mts. and Swan Lake, Mont., and south near the coast to Monterey Bay, and along the western slopes of the Sierra Nevada Mts. to Tulare Co., and also to the southern slopes of the Bitter Root Mts., Ida.

Savin
Florida Yew
Taxus
floridana

A very local southern species, a tree 10–18 feet high; the foliage aromatic when bruised, and firlike.

The leaves narrowly linear, $\frac{1}{2}$–$\frac{3}{4}$ inch long, deep green, abruptly sharp-pointed. Fruit red, as in *T. canadensis*.

The Florida Yew is found only in western Fla. along the east bank of the Apalachicola River, Gadsden Co., from Apalago to Bristol, Liberty Co.

GINKGO FAMILY. *Ginkgoaceæ.*

Oriental trees with alternately growing fan-shaped leaves, and staminate and pistillate flowers growing on separate trees. Fruit fleshy and plumlike, with a single, bony, nutlike seed.

Ginkgo
Maidenhair
Tree
Ginkgo biloba

An oriental tree cultivated for ornament in parks and gardens of this country, reaching a height of 45–60 and under exceptionally favorable conditions 80 feet.

In the neighborhood of the temples of Tokyo, Japan, it grows to a height of 100 feet, with a trunk diameter of 6 feet. The trunk and slender branches are mostly straight, the latter ascending, and set at an angle of approximately 45° with the stem forming a symmetrical ovoid figure. The bark is very dark brownish or blackish gray, on young trees smooth, on aged trees rough and perpendicularly seamed. The twigs stout, smooth, yellow brown, and shiny. The effect of the foliage and almost strict (upright) branches resembles that of the Lombardy Poplar.

The light dull green leaves grow in alternating clusters of 3–6, and are distinctly fan-shaped with a middle cleft,

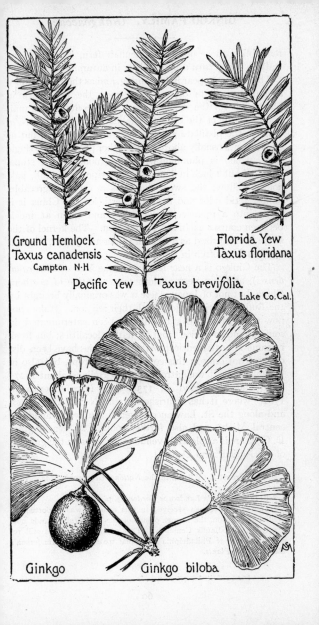

Ground Hemlock
Taxus canadensis
Campton N·H

Florida Yew
Taxus floridana

Pacific Yew   Taxus brevifolia
Lake Co.Cal.

Ginkgo   Ginkgo biloba

resembling those of the Maidenhair fern, but with long stalks. They turn a light yellow in autumn.

The flowers appear in late spring, and as they are staminate and pistillate on separate trees, the preference in planting is for the staminate tree on account of the malodorous fruit of the other. The staminate flowers are in catkins, the pistillate grow on long stalks in pairs, but as one flower is usually abortive, the other produces the single fruit, which is plumlike with an almond-shaped stone, ovoid, about 1 inch in diameter when ripe, and a dull, pale golden yellow; the sweet flesh has a very disagreeable, almost fetid odor and flavor; nevertheless, in China it is made into a preserve, or is baked and eaten at meals between courses as an aid to digestion. The kernel of the stone is also prized as a food in China and Japan, where it appears very often in the market-places.

The Ginkgo is a near relative of the Yew (*Taxus canadensis*), and is a very ancient tree, a native of northern China, but not of Japan where it was originally brought by the Buddhist priests along with their religion. It does not now exist in a wild state, having been exterminated in some unknown period from its native localities; but fossil remains almost identical with this species have been discovered not only in this country and Europe, but also in Greenland.[1] It was introduced into Holland about 1727–1737, into England in 1754, and into America in 1784,[2] where it has flourished in the North from Mass. and along the St. Lawrence River in southern Canada to central Mich., and also farther south. At Washington, D. C., there is a splendid avenue of the trees on the grounds of the Agricultural Dept.

[1] *Vide*, Ernest E. Wilson, in the *National Geographic Mag.*, Nov., 1911

[2] *Vide*, Downing's *Landscape Gardening*, p. 232.

"The first specimen received in this country was imported by William Hamilton, the former owner of the beautiful grounds now known as Woodlands Cemetery. This particular tree is still regarded as one of Philadelphia's arboreal treasures." Henderson's *Handbook of Plants*.

WILLOW FAMILY. *Salicaceæ.*

Trees or shrubs with alternate-growing leaves, attended with stipules (leaflets at the foot of the leaf-stems) persisting or deciduous, and with staminate and pistillate catkins borne on separate trees, expanding before or with the leaves. The fruit an ovoid or conic capsule containing numerous small seeds provided with silky hairs.

The bark of the Willows is practically similar in all the species, varying from gray brown to sepia brown, with a perpendicular trend on old trees. The leaves are commonly hairy beneath when young, but are described only in their fully mature condition.

The stipules are diagnostically important according to their absence or persistence, and their form.

Recorded similarities refer generally to character as well as form—either or both. Hybrids are not described though there are many.

A common Willow of the northeastern **Black Willow** States mostly a shrub, but often a tree *Salix nigra* 20-90 feet high with very rough, scaly, sepia brown bark.

Leaves attenuated lance-shaped, 2-4 inches long, rounded or acute at the base, often downy when young, smooth, deep green when older, with finely incurved teeth; the stem persistently downy and very short, about $\frac{1}{4}$ inch long. Stipules large, half heart-shaped, persistent.

Distributed along the banks of rivers and lake shores from N. B., west to Ont. eastern Dak. Neb. Kan. Okla. Cal. (from the Sierra Nevadas to Colusa Co. and the Sacramento River), and Ariz., and south to Fla. The one sizable native Willow in N. E. and the principal Willow of Md. and W. Va. It is abundant in N. C. on the Piedmont plateau.

Salix nigra var. *falcata.* A form with narrower, longer, scythe-shaped leaves, green on both sides. Common in the East from Mass. to Fla.

A more southern species resembling **Ward's Willow** the foregoing, but a much smaller tree *Salix Wardi* about 25-30 feet high. Found on gravelly shores. Leaves lance-shaped or slightly broader, exceedingly smooth, and prominently veined beneath; short stemmed. Stipules round kidney-shaped, persistent.

This Willow ranges along streams from Md. Va. (Potomac River), W. Va. through Ky. (Ohio River) and central Tenn. to Ill. (Horseshoe Lake near Venice), southern Mo. and Okla., and south to Fla. and Tex. Distribution imperfectly known.

Peach-leaved Willow
Almond-leaved Willow
Salix amygdaloides

A common Willow of the West, similar to the foregoing species, but sometimes 50–70 feet high.

Leaves broadly lance-shaped or ovate lance-shaped, long-pointed, extremely fine-toothed, about 17 teeth to an inch, deep green above, pale and smooth beneath, 4–5 inches long, the stems $\frac{1}{2}$–$1\frac{1}{8}$ inches long, slender. Stipules very small, vanishing by late spring.

This Willow is distributed from Que. (near Montreal) and N. Y. (Cayuga Co.) west to Alberta (upper Saskatchewan), south to W. Va. (Fayette Co.) O. and Mo. and west again over the plains to the Rocky Mts. where it ranges from southwestern Tex. to Ore. Wash. and B. C.

Bay-leaved Willow
Salix pentandra

A cultivated Willow introduced from Europe, often a shrub, mostly a small tree, with lustrous yellow green branchlets, rarely an escape to roadsides and margins of fields.

Leaves ovate or elliptical, sharp-pointed, rounded at the base, very finely glandular-toothed, about 18 teeth to the inch, lustrous green above, paler beneath, always smooth, $1\frac{1}{2}$–$3\frac{3}{4}$ inches long. Fertile catkins long, 1–$1\frac{3}{4}$ inches; mature in early June.

The range restricted to the northeastern States from eastern Mass. to Wash., D. C., and west to O.

Shining Willow
Salix lucida

A lustrous-leaved Willow, mostly a shrub, often a small tree 20 feet high, common on wet banks of streams. Bark light olive brown, twigs bright yellow green.

Leaves ovate lance-shaped, finely-toothed, 16 teeth to the inch, bright light green above, lighter beneath, fine-

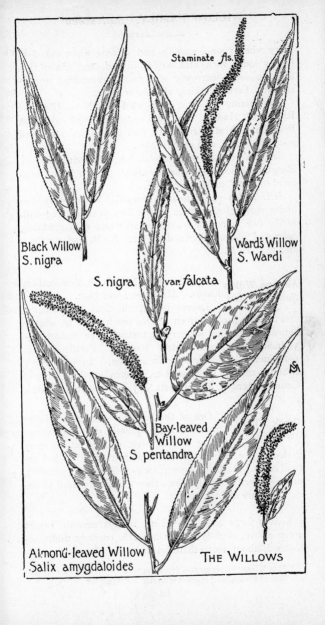

Staminate *fls.*

Black Willow
S. nigra

Ward's Willow
S. Wardi

S. nigra var. *falcata*

Bay-leaved
Willow
S pentandra

Almond-leaved Willow
Salix amygdaloides

THE WILLOWS

hairy when young, smooth and shining when old, 2–5½ inches long, with attenuated, curved, and sharp tips. Stipules small, narrowly semicircular, vanishing or persistent. Fertile catkins, 1¼–2 inches long.

The Shining Willow is distributed from Newf. (Exploits River) to Hudson Bay, and northwestward to Great Bear Lake, Mackenzie River, and the Rocky Mts., and south to Pa. Ill. and eastern Neb.

Salix lucida var. *angustifolia*. A form with smooth, elongated lance-shaped leaves about $\frac{9}{16}$ inch broad, confined to Newf. and eastern Que.

Salix lucida var. *intonsa*. Fernald. With leaves (the under surface) and twigs of the first year covered with ruddy fine hairs; the leaves broader and with gradually narrowed bases. Confined to Que. N. B. and northern and western N. E.

Autumn Willow
Salix serissima

A rather tall shrub with thin-leathery leaves. About 5–12 feet high.

Leaves broad, elliptical lance-shaped, short-pointed, olive green above, much paler or whitish beneath, somewhat leathery in texture when mature, 1¾–3 inches long, and finely toothed. Fertile catkins 1–1½ inches long, maturing in autumn. In cold mossy swamps, eastern Que., west to Alberta, south to western Conn. western N. Y. northern N. J. and the Great Lakes.

Crack Willow
Salix fragilis

One of the largest naturalized Willows from Europe, frequently 50–70 and sometimes 80 feet high, planted at an early period in the vicinity of Boston and other old New England cities. Bark dull brown; twigs yellow green, polished, and very brittle at the base; they are largely used in the manufacture of baskets.[1]

Leaves large 4–6 inches long, always smooth, bright green above, slightly lighter beneath, coarsely undulate-toothed, about 10 teeth to an inch. Stipules half heart-

[1] This Willow was imported from England before the Revolutionary War in the especial interest of basket manufacture.

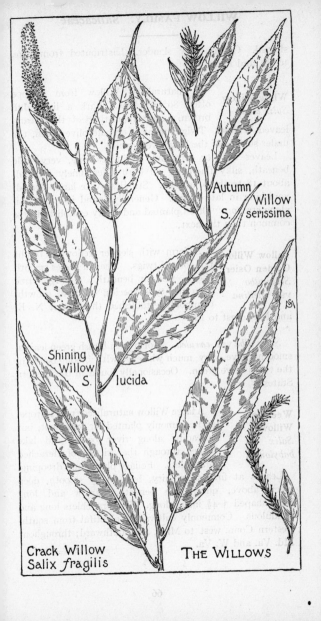

Autumn
S. Willow
serissima

Shining
Willow
S. lucida

Crack Willow
Salix *fragilis*

THE WILLOWS

shaped. Catkin very slender. Distributed from Que. to Pa. and Ky.

White Willow
Salix alba

A naturalized Willow from Europe often 80 feet high. Bark a light dull brown, darker than that of the Heart-leaved Willow. Twigs greenish, or pale olive green, the under surface of the leaves very white.

Leaves 2–4½ or commonly 3 inches long, very pale beneath, silky fine-hairy on both sides, finely toothed, about 18 teeth to an inch. Stipules ovate lance-shaped, vanishing in late spring. Generally found in moist soil along streams. Often planted and rarely established, less common than the next.

Yellow Willow
Golden Osier
Salix alba
var. *vitellina*

A form with slender yellow or bright tan-colored twigs. The old leaves smooth above, whitish beneath. A larger tree than the type species, of rapid growth, commonly established throughout N. E. and Md., west to Ida.

Salix alba var. *cærulea*. A form with bluish green leaves, smooth above, very much whitened with bloom beneath; the twigs olive green. Occasionally found in the Eastern States.

Weeping Willow
Salix babylonica

A large Willow naturalized from Europe, and commonly planted for ornament, but spreading along river banks and lake shores through the drifting of detached branchlets. Foliage plumy and drooping.

Leaves at first silky-hairy, but finally smooth, deep green above, quite pale beneath, narrow and long lance-shaped 3–4½ inches long. The branchlets long and pendulous. Commonly cultivated, plentiful from south-western Conn. west to Mich. and southward; throughout Md. Va. and W. Va.

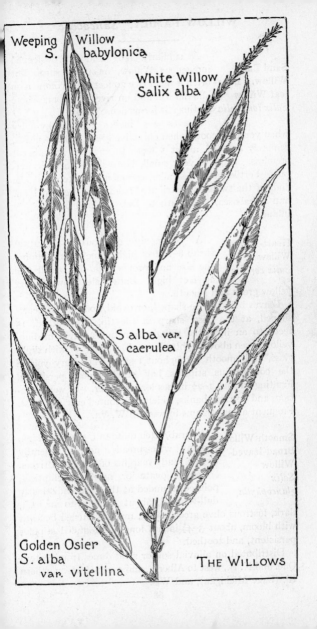

Weeping Willow
S. babylonica

White Willow
Salix alba

S alba var.
caerulea

Golden Osier
S. alba
var. vitellina

THE WILLOWS

WILLOW FAMILY. *Salicaceae*

Sand Bar Willow. Long-leaf Willow
Salix longifolia

A similarly long and narrow-leaved indigenous Willow, mostly a shrub but often a small tree 20 feet high, common on alluvial soil and on river sand-bars where at times it forms dense thickets.

Leaves 2–5 inches long, silky-hairy when young, smooth when old, olive green, paler beneath, remotely toothed, about 5 teeth to an inch, and almost stemless. Stipules very small, lance-shaped and deciduous. Fertile catkins slender, commonly clustered at the ends of the twigs. Distributed from Que., west to Man. and Athabasca, and south to Del. Va. and Tex. mostly inland.

Heart-leaved Willow
Salix cordata

A commonly distributed, beautiful shrub 8–12 feet high, sometimes attaining the size and proportions of a small tree 20 feet high. Bark pale brown, twigs yellow green and smooth.

Leaves broad lance-shaped, or ovoid, rounded or heart-shaped, at the base, sharp at the tip, fine-toothed, 15 teeth to an inch, the margin sometimes wavy, medium yellow green above, lighter beneath, without or with slight gloss, and smooth throughout except when very young; the conspicuous stipules half heart-shaped, persisting. Fruiting catkins 1–2¼ inches long, slender. In wet situations and on river banks, widely distributed east and west. Frequent along streams in western W. Va.

Smooth Willow Broad-leaved Willow
Salix glaucophylla

A shrub, often quite tall, 5–16 feet high, forming wide-spread thickets generally on the sandy margins of lakes and rivers. Leaves ovate or narrowly elliptical, pointed, rounded at the base, indistinctly dull-toothed, about 9 teeth to an inch, dark, lustrous olive green above, much whitened beneath with bloom, about 3–4½ inches long, the rounded stipules persistent, and toothed.

Distributed on alluvial soil or sand dunes from eastern Que. and N. B., west to Alberta, and south to Me. northern Ill. (Lake Michigan), and Wis.

Broad-leaved Willow
S. glaucophylla

Sand Bar Willow
S. longifolia

Heart-leaved Willow
Salix cordata

THE WILLOWS

WILLOW FAMILY. *Salicaceae*

Balsam Willow
Salix balsamifera
A shrub with many tall branches, or very rarely a small tree 5–25 feet high, the tree with a trunk diameter of about 6 inches—perhaps exclusively in Maine. Bark brown gray, smooth, twigs a shiny tan red, or olive.

Leaves elliptical, pointed, round or slightly heart-shaped at the base, distinctly or indistinctly dull-toothed, the teeth fine or coarse, irregular; deep olive green above, much paler beneath, smooth and prominently veined, about 2–3½ inches long, with a spicy, balsamic odor when crushed.

Distributed generally in swamps or lowland thickets, from Newf. and Lab. west to B. C., and south to Me. central N. H. (Holderness), northern Vt. (Elmore Mt. and Westmore, Willoughby Lake), northern N. Y. Mich. and Minn.

Salix syrticola
Fernald
A straggling irregular-growing shrub 3–7 feet high, with coarse twigs.

Leaves ovate, rounded at the base, short but sharp-pointed, finely-toothed, with about 18 teeth to an inch, dull olive green above, paler beneath, densely silky-hairy or hoary on both sides when young, the hairs shed when old. The conspicuous stipules heart-shaped, toothed, and persistent. The pistillate catkins finally very long (sometimes 4 inches), and crowded with flowers. Distributed from Lab. along rivers and the shores of the Great Lakes to Mich.

Bog Willow
Salix pedicellaris
A slender shrub 2–3 feet high, with erect light brown twigs, the leaves thickly clustered at the tips of the branchlets.

Leaves small 1–2½ inches long, narrowly obovate or elliptical, a trifle leathery in texture, the margin slightly rolled back, light, bright green above, pale and smooth beneath. Pistillate flowers in a thick cylindrical cluster. Commonly distributed over cold bogs and upland swamps, from eastern Que. (Table-topped Mt.) and N. B., west to B. C., and south through N. E. and N. Y. to N. J. to Isle Royale, Mich. and northern Io.

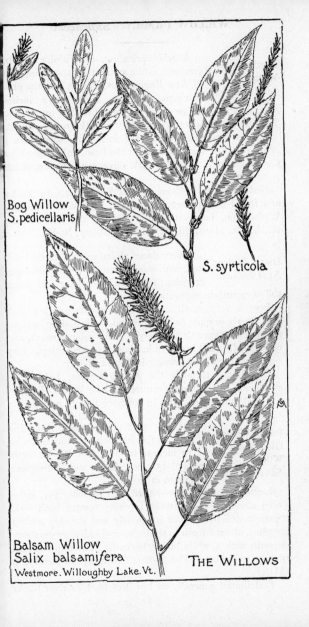

Bog Willow
S. pedicellaris

S. syrticola

Balsam Willow
Salix balsamifera
Westmore. Willoughby Lake. Vt.

THE WILLOWS

WILLOW FAMILY. *Salicaceae*

Bearberry Willow
Salix Uva-ursi

A wide-spreading, low, alpine shrub, confined to the summits of the mountains of New England and New York, the procumbent branches about 5–12 inches long, the dark foliage greatly crowded on the branchlets. The stout root penetrating deeply into the rocky ground.

Leaves very small about $\frac{1}{2}$–$\frac{5}{8}$ inch long (sometimes $\frac{3}{4}$ inch), obovate, tapering toward the base, dull-pointed (or Gothic-pointed), lustrous dark olive green above, much paler beneath.

Distributed throughout the north from Lab. to Alaska and found on the summits of Mt. Katahdin, Me., Mts. Washington, Lafayette, and other of the White Mts., N. H., Mt. Mansfield, Vt. and Mt. Marcy, N. Y.

Dwarf Willow
Salix herbacea

A very dwarf alpine species, matted and low, with stems scarcely 2–3 inches long, creeping; found in the mossy and damp soil of mountain summits.

Leaves very small and oval heart-shaped, $\frac{1}{2}$–1 inch long, nearly or quite as broad, round-toothed, deep lustrous green above, smooth and very slightly paler beneath, and net-veined. Catkins terminating the branchlets, very small and ovoid. Blooming in June and July.

Distributed through the Arctic regions, Lab. Que., and south to the alpine summits of the White Mts. and Mt. Katahdin, Me. Also in northern Europe and Asia.

Pussy Willow Glaucous Willow
Salix discolor

A shrub or small tree 10–12 and infrequently 25 feet high with a trunk diameter of 12 inches; in Md. and W. Va. commonly 15 feet high and infrequent. Common in N. E.

Leaves broadly lance-shaped or elliptical, 3–4 inches long, about $1\frac{1}{4}$ inches wide, tapering toward both ends, coarsely dull-toothed, or irregularly and sparsely scollop-toothed, about 6 teeth to the inch, bright olive green above, smooth with a white bloom beneath. The stipules commonly vanishing. The flowers blooming very early; in March.

Distributed generally on low, wet land, or river banks

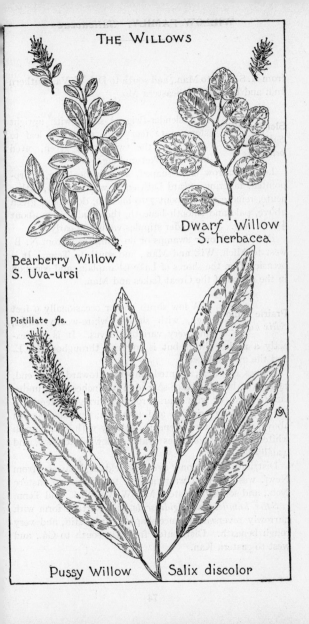

THE WILLOWS

Dwarf Willow
S. herbacea

Bearberry Willow
S. Uva-ursi

Pistillate fls.

Pussy Willow Salix discolor

from N. S. west to Man., and south to Del. W. Va. southern Ind. and Ill. and northeastern Mo.

Slender Willow
Salix petiolaris

A slender-twigged shrub with upright stems 4-12 feet high, similar in leaf to *S. sericea*, the twigs olive green, often used in basket-making.

Leaves narrow lance-shaped, 2½-4 inches long, sharp-pointed, tapering toward both ends, with shallow, rather acute, remote teeth, about 7 to an inch, deep olive green above, pale and smooth beneath, the slender stem about ½ inch long. The slender stipules vanishing early.

Distributed over swamps or on damp soil, from N. B. west to Mich. Wis. and Man., and south to Tenn. It is occasional on the shores of Lake Champlain, and common in the region of the Great Lakes and Man.

Prairie Willow
Salix humilis

A low shrub 3-5 or occasionally 9 feet high, with slender white-woolly twigs, and very variable leaves. It is not exactly a prairie shrub, but is common throughout N. E. and the middle West.

Leaves elliptical, pointed, tapering toward each end, reverse or broadly lance-shaped, 2-3½ inches long, undulate-toothed, or with coarse, rounded, irregular teeth, or the edge often crinkled and toothless; dull dark green above, very flocculent beneath, velvety with soft, grayish white hairs. The stipules ovate, somewhat toothed, and usually persistent.

Distributed commonly over dry fields and barrens, from Newf. west through western Ont. to Minn. and eastern Neb., and south to western Md. W. Va. N. C. and Tenn.

Salix humilis var. *rigidiuscula*, is a western form with narrowly reversed or lance-shaped leaves, stiff, and very rough beneath. Distributed from O., south to Ga., and west to eastern Kan.

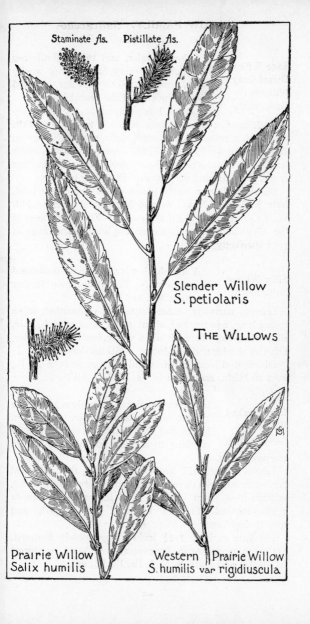

Staminate fls.   Pistillate fls.

Slender Willow
S. petiolaris

THE WILLOWS

Prairie Willow
Salix humilis

Western | Prairie Willow
S. humilis var rigidiuscula

WILLOW FAMILY. *Salicaceae*

**Sage Willow
Dwarf Gray
Willow**
Salix tristis

A low, slender, and tufted shrub 1–2 feet high, with very fine-hairy or woolly twigs, growing smooth with age, crowded toward the ends of the branchlets.

Leaves lance-shaped or reverse lance-shaped, small, 1–2 inches long, remotely toothed or tooth-less, with a rolled-back margin, dull grayish olive green above, white woolly beneath, the stem very short, $\frac{1}{12}$ inch long. The stipules tiny and early deciduous. The catkins dense, globular, and very small. Blooming in May.

Distributed over sandy plains or on dry rocky land, from N. H. and Mass., west to Minn., and south to Md. W. Va. Tenn. and along the coast to Fla., rarer west of the Alleghanies; the extreme eastern limit of the range as yet imperfectly known.

Silky Willow
Salix sericea

A tall shrub 5–12 feet high, occasional in northern N. E. but common farther south, in Md. and W. Va.

Leaves narrowly lance-shaped, sharp-pointed, $2\frac{1}{4}$–4 inches long, fine-toothed, about 15 teeth to an inch, pale, silky white-hairy beneath when young, less so when older. Stipules slender and deciduous. Catkins slender.

Distributed along streams and in swamps from N. B., west to Mich., and south to Va. W. Va. and N. C.

**Long-beaked
Willow**
Salix rostrata

A common shrub or rarely a small tree 15 feet high, with very dark olive green leaves and dark brown stems, sometimes climbing to an elevation of 2000 feet in the mountains.

Leaves coarse, stiff, leathery in texture, thin, elliptical lance-shaped, deep olive green and minutely downy above, whitish blue green beneath, 2–$3\frac{3}{4}$ inches long, coarsely scollop-toothed. Stipules toothed, heart-shaped, and mostly deciduous.

Pistillate catkins 1–$2\frac{1}{4}$ inches long, loosely flowered. On moist ground or in dry copses, from Newf. northwest to Alaska, and south to N. J. Pa. Ill. Ia., etc.

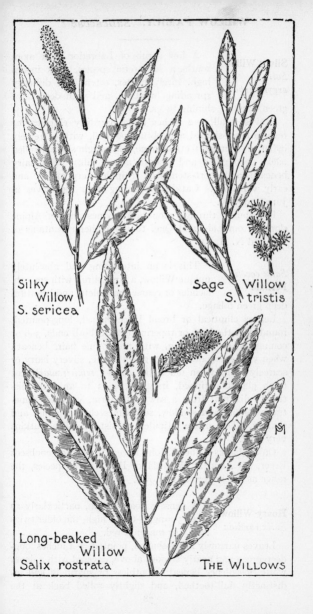

Silky
Willow
S. sericea

Sage Willow
S. tristis

Long-beaked
Willow
Salix rostrata

THE WILLOWS

WILLOW FAMILY. *Salicaceae*

Silver Willow
Salix argyrocarpa

A low shrub of Labrador or a more southern sub-arctic species, 6–15 inches high, rarely higher, often with diffusely spreading branches, and with deep olive green, smooth, shining twigs.

Leaves small, 1–2 inches long, narrowly elliptical or reverse lance-shaped and obtuse-pointed, with extremely indistinct rounded teeth or none, the margin slightly rolled back, deep green and smooth above, silky white-hairy beneath, and short-stemmed. Stipules very minute and early vanishing. Catkins appearing with the leaves in June and July.

Distributed through mountain ravines and on Alpine slopes, from Lab. and Que. to the higher mountains of Me. and N. H.

Salix coactilis
Fernald

This is an interesting and absolutely unique Willow, a large shrub with smooth, slender or coarse branchlets, and beautiful deep green foliage.

Leaves elliptical or broad lance-shaped, long-pointed, rounded at the base or tapering toward both ends, 3–6 or commonly 4 inches long, with ruddy fine hairs beneath when young, smooth, bright green above, silvery hairy or scarcely hairy when older, the coarse, *semicircularly* cut teeth glandular-tipped, irregular, 9–13 to an inch, distinctly different from a saw-tooth form, variable, sometimes remote and shallow, sometimes close together and shallow. The ovate stipules persistent. The catkins very long.

On the banks of the St. John River, N. B., the Penobscot River, Me., and at Wheatland, Ill. A new species, the range as yet imperfectly known.

Hoary Willow
Salix candida

A densely hoary shrub, particularly so when young, 2–6 feet high, the older twigs ruddy or magenta red.

Leaves narrowly lance-shaped, pointed, 3–4 inches long, deep green and nearly smooth above, covered with a dense white flocculence beneath, toothless or sparingly and indistinctly dull-toothed, and slightly rolled back at the

THE WILLOWS

Silver Willow
S. argyrocarpa
MT. Washington. N.H

S. candida

Salix coactilis
Wheatland Ill. and   near Bangor. Me. etc.

edge. Stipules lance-shaped and deciduous. Pistillate catkins nearly 2 inches long. Blooming in May.

Distributed, in cold bogs, from Newf. and Lab. to Athabasca, and southward to N. J. western N. Y. Pa. O. and Io.

Osier Willow
Salix viminalis

A small Willow introduced into this country from Europe, and occasionally an escape, 12–20 feet high, shrubby or treelike with long slender green twigs; cultivated for wicker-work.

Leaves narrowly lance-shaped, or linear, toothless, sharp-pointed, indistinctly irregular-edged, dark green and smooth above, silky white with fine hairs beneath, $3\frac{1}{2}$–$5\frac{1}{4}$ inches long. The narrow stipules deciduous. Pistillate catkins long (2–3 inches), and slender. Found in wet situations, locally established from Newf. to Pa.

Salix pellita

A tall shrub or small tree with tan-colored or olive twigs which ranges from the Gulf of St. Lawrence to Lake Winnipeg, and is found rarely in Me. and Vt., along river banks and in swamps.

Leaves similar in character to those of the preceding species, but much broader (sometimes reverse lance-shaped), white with velvety hairs beneath or nearly smooth, 2–4 inches long, with an irregular-scolloped or quite plain edge. The stipules deciduous. The pistillate catkins about $1\frac{1}{2}$ inches long.

Tea-leaved Willow
Salix phylicifolia

A shrub 2–10 feet high, with plum purple twigs sometimes covered by a whitish bloom, the slender branches widely spreading, commonly found on mountain slopes.

Leaves narrowly, or obovately elliptical, obtuse at either end, small, $1\frac{1}{4}$–$2\frac{1}{2}$ inches long, lustrous dark green above, pale with whitish bloom beneath, altogether smooth, leathery in texture like *S. rostrata*, irregularly and remotely or indistinctly scollop-toothed, or with no teeth. The stipules minute and soon vanishing. Pistillate catkins long and slender, flowering late; in June and July.

Distributed in wet situations from Lab. to Alaska, and

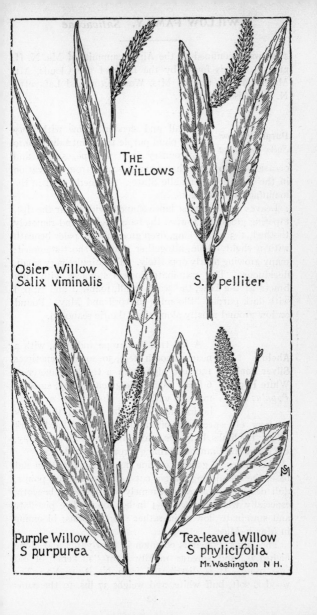

THE WILLOWS

Osier Willow
Salix viminalis

S. pelliter

Purple Willow
S purpurea

Tea-leaved Willow
S phylicifolia

Mr. Washington N H.

southward confined to the Alpine summits of Me. N. H.
and Vt. It is found by the Lake of the Clouds, Mt.
Mansfield, Vt., and on Mts. Washington and Lafayette,
N. H. Also in Europe.

Purple Willow
Salix purpurea

A tall and slender willow with very
supple plum purple twigs, introduced into
this country from Europe, 50–60 and
occasionally 80 feet high, sparingly escaped from cultivation
in the eastern and middle States. Formerly used in the
manufacture of baskets.

Leaves small, reverse lance-shaped (wider near the tip),
tapering gradually toward the base, slightly and remotely
toothed, 1–3 inches long, deep green above, paler beneath
with a slight bloom, altogether smooth, short-stemmed;
many growing nearly oppositely. The stipules very small,
deciduous. The staminate flowers stemless with tiny
bracts at the base, the scales small, rounded and tipped
with dark purple. Blooming in April and May. Found
on low ground mostly along the Atlantic seaboard.

Abele
Silver Poplar
White Poplar
Populus alba

A tall tree of Europe and Asia, with a
nearly smooth stem, 50–80 and sometimes
120 feet high, with a trunk diameter of
6 feet. Bark pale greenish gray, smooth,
marked with dark blotches of a rather
horizontal trend, the base of the trunk
on very old specimens often furrowed into hard, dark
ridges; the limbs, branches, and coarse twigs all light gray,
the spreading branches forming a round-topped head.

The leaves in general outline heart-shaped with a flat
base, the undulating margin cut into about 5 dull points,
dull deep green above, extremely white-woolly beneath,
especially when young, 2½–4 inches long. The pistillate
and staminate flowers in rather short catkins; blooming
in March–May.

The Silver Poplar is common in door-yards and along
highways, and spreads rapidly from "suckers" of old
tree roots. It is distributed from N. B. to Va. The
wood is soft, buff white, and weighs 37 lbs. to the cubic

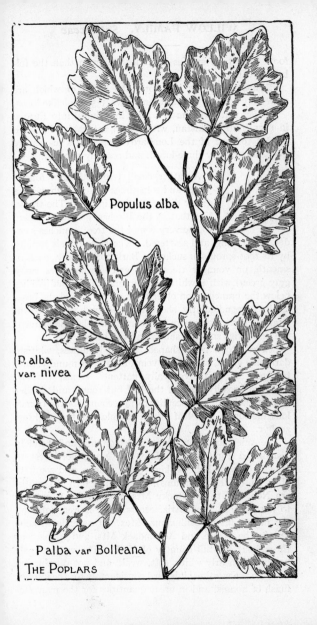

Populus alba

P. alba
var. nivea

P alba var Bolleana

THE POPLARS

WILLOW FAMILY. *Salicaceae*

foot. The type species is far less common than the following varieties:

P. alba var. *nivea* is a form the leaves of which are extremely cottony beneath, and have 3–5 maplelike lobes.

P. alba var. *Bolleana* is a form introduced into Europe in 1875 from Turkistan, with a compact habit of growth similar to that of the Lombardy Poplar; its leaves are maplelike, deeply three-lobed, and coarsely notched.

American Aspen. Poplar *Populus tremuloides*   A rather small tree with thin foliage 30–40 and sometimes 60 feet high, with a trunk diameter of 20 inches. The trunk, like that of the Birches, gradually tapers to the very top of the tree; branches slender, alternating, and scattered. The tree spreads rapidly by its root-sprouts or suckers. Bark horizontally marked, smooth, on younger trees gray green (sometimes rusty gray green) with a whitish bloom and dark sepia patches below the branches; on older trees rough toward the base, thick, perpendicularly short-furrowed and sepia brown. Branchlets slender, warm gray sometimes blackish stained; the new twigs smooth, shiny, and tan brown.

Leaves broad heart-shaped, a dull, lusterless, whitish, dark blue green, with white veins, bluntly or roundly, fine-toothed, and with vertically flattened stems, that is, flattened broadly nearest the leaf but round and slender nearest the twig; this peculiar form accounts for the tremulous motion of the leaf which waggles in the slightest zephyr.

The American Aspen grows on dry ground, and is widely distributed from southern Lab. and Newf. northwest to Hudson Bay and the Yukon River, Alaska, and south to N. J. Pa. (in the mountains), Ky. northeastern Mo. southern Neb. and to the Rocky Mts. along which it extends to northern N. Mex. Ariz. central Cal. Lower Cal. and the mountains of Chihuahua, Mex. It ascends to 3000 feet in the White and Adirondack Mts. and is frequent throughout the hill country of N. E. The wood is pale brown and nearly white, soft, weak, and not durable exposed to the weather; it is used considerably for the interior finish of houses, and in great quantities for the manufac-

American Aspen
Populus
   tremuloides

P. grandidentata
Pemigewasset Val.
   Campton. N·H

P. Fremontii
Reno Nev
pg. 92

THE POPLARS

ture of paper pulp and excelsior. The tree is colloquially named Popple.

Large-toothed Aspen
Populus grandidentata

A tree similar in character to the foregoing species, commonly reaching a height of 30-40 and sometimes 80 feet, with a trunk diameter of over 20 inches. The bark resembles that of the American Aspen but is commonly a trifle more buffish in tone; the younger twigs tan brown, the older greenish gray.

Leaves large, 3-5 inches long, roundish, not heart shaped, smooth on both sides though downy when young, with about 17 very coarse, dull-pointed teeth, dull whitish dark blue green, and with flattened stems similar to those of the American Aspen. There is a drooping-foliaged form of this tree in common cultivation, known as *P. grandidentata* var. *penduliformis*.

The Large-toothed Aspen is common on the borders of streams and on hillsides in rich or poor soil, and is distributed from N. B. and N. S. through southern Que. and Ont., west to Minn. and Io., and south to Pa. Del. and along the Alleghany Mts. to N. C. central Ky. central Tenn. southern Ind. and Ill. It is abundant in Me.; in N. H. it extends to the base of the Presidential range of the White Mts. through all the four great radiating valleys of the Ammonoosuc, Androscoggin, Saco, and Pemigewasset, and it is frequent in all the other N. E. States. The wood is used for purposes similar to those of the American Aspen.

Swamp Cottonwood
Downy Poplar
Populus heterophylla

A tree 30-75 or occasionally 90 feet high, with a trunk diameter of 3 feet. Bark dark gray brown, perpendicularly short-furrowed, the branches smooth, lighter colored, the twigs commonly coarse sometimes slender, and pale brown.

The leaves ovate, broad at the base, narrowed toward the blunt apex, sometimes quite heart-shaped, always shallowly so at the base, somewhat coarsely and shallowly round-toothed, olive green above, paler beneath and eventually smooth except on the veins, 3-5 inches long. Flowers in drooping catkins 3-4 inches long.

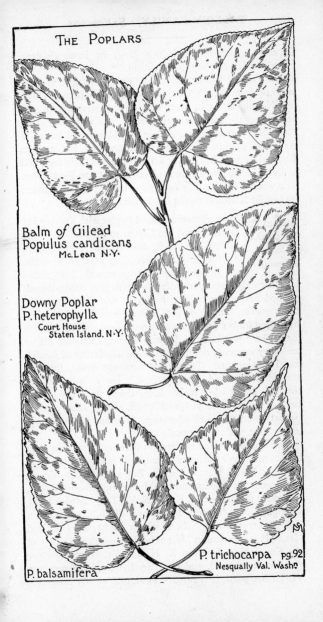

THE POPLARS

Balm of Gilead
Populus candicans
Mc.Lean N.Y.

Downy Poplar
P. heterophylla
Court House
Staten Island. N.Y.

P. balsamifera

P. trichocarpa pg.92
Nesqually Val. Wash?

Capsules ovoid, about ⅓ inch long, in loose clusters, crowded with cottony down within.

The Downy Poplar is common on the margins of river swamps from North Guilford (near New Haven) Conn. and Northport, L. I., south only on the coastal plain generally near the coast, to southern Ga. and westward along the Gulf to western La., and in the Mississippi basin, to Ark. southeastern Mo. southern Ill. and Ind. and western Ky. and Tenn. In N. C. it attains a height of 80 feet, and is found in the swamp lands of the lower Cape Fear River. The wood is light, soft, close-grained, and pale dull brown; its weight is 26 lbs. to the cubic foot.

Balsam Poplar
Tacamahac
Populus
balsamifera

A medium-sized Poplar with a somewhat narrowed head, from 20–50 and sometimes 90 feet high, the trunk perpendicular, the branches spreading at a wide angle. Bark on younger trees smooth, light umber brown, ruddy-tinged, on older trees dark gray ruddy-tinged, seamed perpendicularly with rough, rounded ridges; the twigs coarse, orange or tan brown, smooth and shining, becoming umber brown or gray with age, the spring buds larger, long-pointed, red brown, shining, resinous, sticky and very odorous, reminiscent of an admixture of sandalwood and onions! The leaves narrowly ovate, tapering toward either end, sharp-pointed, finely but obtusely toothed, about 2½–4 inches long, thick, firm, smooth on both sides, olive or yellowish green above, silvery white beneath, and with a slender stem. Flowers in long drooping catkins. May. Capsule ovoid.

The Balsam Poplar is common on alluvial soil, on river banks, and the borders of swamps; it is distributed from Newf. and N. S. west to Hudson Bay and Man. northwest to the coast of Alaska and the Mackenzie River (lat. 66°), and south to northern N. E. and N. Y. (Taughannock Falls, Cayuga Lake), central Mich. and Minn. Dak. (Black Hills), northwestern Neb. northern Mont. Io. Ore. and Nev. It is common in Me.; extends through the valley of the Connecticut between N. H. and Vt. becoming more plentiful northward, and it occurs frequently in northern Vt. farther south it is rare, or local, and mostly an escape from cultivation, although apparently native at Norfolk, Conn. The wood is light, soft, and pale brown or pale buffish white; it is used for boxes, pails, and household wooden-ware and for the manufacture of paper pulp, weight 24 lbs. to the cubic foot. The varieties in common cultivation are:

P. balsamifera var. *viminalis* (*P. laurifolia*. Sargent) with narrower ovate lance-shaped leaves.

P. balsamifera var. *latifolia* with broader heart-shaped leaves.

A species very similar to the foregoing, **Balm of Gilead** with broader, more or less heart-shaped *Populus* leaves, the stem and lower surface of *candicans* which are hairy, and with more wide-spreading branches forming a broader head and a more rounded figure, distinctly different from the other Poplars.

Probably a native of Asia, commonly cultivated in this country, and often an escape. Frequent along the Monongalia River in Marion Co., W. Va.

One of the largest of the Poplars, 70-90 **Carolina Pop-** and sometimes 160 feet high, with a trunk **lar. Cottonwood** diameter of 7 feet. Bark strongly seamed **Necklace** with conspicuously confluent ridges, light **Poplar** or dark brown when old, gray green when *Populus* young, and nearly smooth; the stem *deltoides* straight, the branches strongly ascending, the twigs ocher yellow.

The leaves scarcely deltoid (triangular), square or rarely slightly heart-shaped at the base, gothic-pointed and abruptly sharp-pointed, with remarkably conventional convex-concave coarse teeth (like the Greek curved key), olive green above, paler beneath and smooth, the long stems flattened. Flowers in long catkins. Capsules ovoid about $\frac{1}{4}$ inch long, in slender clusters.

The Carolina Poplar is common on bottom-lands from Que. (Lower St. Maurice River) and Vt. (shores of Lake Champlain), through western N. E., N. Y. and Pa. (west of the Alleghany Mts.), west to the Rocky Mts. from southern Alberta to northern N. Mex.; southward it extends through Maryland and the Atlantic Seaboard to western Fla. The wood is similar to that of *P. balsamifera,* and is used for the same purposes.

Black Poplar
Populus nigra

A tall tree 80–100 feet high, with a trunk diameter of 3–4 feet, commonly smaller. Bark rough, scraggy, with an indistinct perpendicular trend, gray brown like that of the Lombardy Poplar, the branches broadly ascending, twigs pale brown and slender.

The dull olive green leaves deltoid (triangular), almost square at the base, abruptly rounded laterally, tapering to an abrupt sharp point, broader than long, shallowly blunt-toothed, pale and smooth beneath, 2–3 inches wide. The staminate catkins 1–2 and the pistillate 2–5 inches long, the narrowly ovoid capsules obtuse at the tip, and very small. Blooming in April–May.

The Black Poplar is a European species which has become naturalized in this country; it has escaped from cultivation in the Hudson and Delaware River Valleys. The Lombardy Poplar, *P. nigra* var. *italica*, is the familiar spire-like tree of common cultivation, with almost vertical branches, and similar leaves. It is also a frequent escape from cultivation.

Lance-leaved Cottonwood Black Cottonwood
Populus acuminata

A slender western species, 40–60 feet high, with a trunk diameter of about 20 inches. Bark similar to that of the foregoing species, commonly grayish brown, the foliage smooth.

The leaves ovate, sharp-pointed, mostly rounded (sometimes narrowed) at the base, light green, paler beneath and smooth, 2–5 inches long, rather finely round-toothed, and with slender stems. Flowers in slender catkins, the staminate about 1½ the pistillate 3–4 inches long.

The range is as yet imperfectly known; it extends from Assiniboia, the Black Hills of S. Dak. and western Neb. through the Rocky Mts. in Mont. Wyo. and Col. to N. Mex.

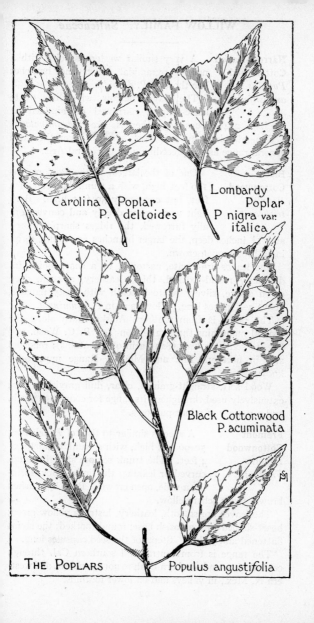

Carolina Poplar
P. deltoides

Lombardy
Poplar
P nigra var.
italica

Black Cottonwood
P. acuminata

THE POPLARS   Populus angustifolia

WILLOW FAMILY. *Salicaceae*

Narrow-leaved Cottonwood
Populus angustifolia

A very similar western species with a narrow pyramidal crown and branches like those of *P. deltoides*.

The leaves narrow, willowlike, ovate lance-shaped, narrowed or rounded at the base, 2–4½ inches long, otherwise like *P. acuminata*.

Generally in damp soil along streams, over the same general range as the preceding, and to central Ariz.

Black Cottonwood
Populus trichocarpa

One of the largest of the Poplars, 50–130 feet high, with a trunk diameter of 4 feet, but commonly 50 feet high. Bark light warm gray, deeply and conventionally furrowed, the ridges sharply scored and 1¼ inches deep, the larger branches ascending, forming a broad, open crown.

The leaves are ovate, narrowed to a sharp point, indistinctly round-toothed, thick, leathery, smooth, deep green above, silvery white beneath with rusty patches, about 3–4 inches long. Flowers as in *P. acuminata*.

The range is from southern Alaska south along the coastal mountains through Yukon Ter. B. C. Wash. and Ore. to southern Cal. (San Jacinto Mountains); reported also in northern Ida. and Mont. Range imperfectly known.

Wood soft, straight-grained, clear, dull grayish brown; extensively used throughout its range for cooperage stock, and a variety of minor purposes.

Fremont Cottonwood
Populus Fremontii

A species similar to that of *P. deltoides*, 50–90 feet high, with a trunk diameter of 4 feet. The trunk seldom straight, often curved or leaning, the limbs thick, forming a wide, open crown. Bark light ashen brown, twigs ocher yellow.

The leaves are smooth, leathery, lustrous yellow green, heart-shaped with a flatish base, round-toothed; the stems flattened and yellow. Stems of the seed capsules long.

The range is from central and southern Cal. through central Nev. and southern Utah to northern Ariz. and western N. Mex., in valleys and on lower foothills.

Wood pale brown, fine-grained, soft, brittle, heavier than the other Cottonwoods—about 35 lbs. to the cubic foot. It has no especial commercial value, and is commonly used for fuel.

SWEET GALE FAMILY. *Myricaceae.*

Shrubs with aromatic, sweet-scented, alternate-growing leaves, almost leathery in texture. The flowers in short, scaly catkins, staminate and pistillate on the same plant or on different plants.

A shrub with very dark brown, ascending stems 2–5 feet high, widely branched.

Sweet Gale
Dutch Myrtle
Myrica Gale

The leaves wedge-shaped, rounded and sparingly sharp-toothed at the apex, dark green and smooth above, pale and usually downy beneath (smooth when old), resinously aromatic when crushed, $1\frac{1}{2}$–$2\frac{1}{2}$ inches long. Staminate catkins in terminal clusters, the pistillate at the base of the leaves, scarcely $\frac{1}{3}$ inch long, each kind mostly on separate plants. Blooming in April–May.

Fruit resinously waxy, berrylike, dotted, attended by 2 ovate scales, crowded in a cluster of 2–6 nutlets.

Sweet Gale is common on the margins of ponds and streams, or in swamps, and is distributed from Lab. Newf. and N. E., west along the borders of the Great Lakes to Mich. and Minn., northwest to Alaska, and south in the Appalachian Chain to Va. It ascends to an altitude of 3000 feet in the mountains of N. E. and N. Y. It is common near Manchester, N. H., New Bedford, and Nantucket, Mass.

A small, slender, southern tree of sandy swamps on the coastal plain, 20–40 feet high, formerly confused with the northern shrubby species *M. carolinensis* of Miller. Bark warm brown gray, nearly smooth.

Wax Myrtle
Myrica cerifera

The small leaves 1–3 inches long, narrow lance-shaped, toothless or with few sharp teeth toward the apex, sharp-pointed, lustrous deep green above, paler and smooth beneath, very resinously fragrant when crushed, almost evergreen. Flowers as in the foregoing, the staminate catkins oblong, scattered. Blooming in March–April. The berrylike fruit scattered, very small, about $\frac{1}{10}$ inch in diameter, hard, lavender or gray white, coated with resinous wax, in microscopic, rounded particles.

The Wax Myrtle grows in sandy marshes or in wet woods, and is distributed from southern Md. along the coastal plain to Fla., west through the Gulf States to Rockport, Arkansas Bay, Tex., and northward west of the Mississippi River, to the Washita River, Ark.

Bayberry
Myrica
carolinensis

A compact shrub 2–7 feet high, with smooth light brown gray stems; the twigs smooth, or often downy—at least so when young.

The leaves similar to those of *M. cerifera*, but larger, the few (if any) teeth near the apex, rounded, sharp-tipped, the texture softer and thinner, and the apex blunt; 2–4 inches long, fragrant. Blooming in April–May. The similar fruit a berry $\frac{1}{8}$ inch in diameter, in crowded clusters, gray white, resinously waxy. It was commonly used by the early settlers of the eastern States in the manufacture of candles, and is still used for making the aromatic bayberry candle sold in New England in the holiday season. The method of collecting the wax is simple, the berries are steeped in boiling water, which after cooling is skimmed; one pound of the fruit yields about four ounces of wax.

The Bayberry is common in sandy or dry stony soil near the coast, from Prince Edward's Id. and N. B., south to Fla. and Ala. It is also occasional in the bogs of northern N. J. and Pa., and on the shores of Lake Erie.

Sweet Fern
Myrica
asplenifolia

The Sweet Fern which, of course, is not a fern but a fernlike shrub, grows 1–2 feet high, with commonly a dull red or dark brown, scragged, woody stem.

The leaves are very narrowly elliptical or linear, dark green and shining above, much paler and smooth beneath, with a rolled-back edge and many small, rounded, oblique lobes; 3–5 inches long, fragrant when crushed. The

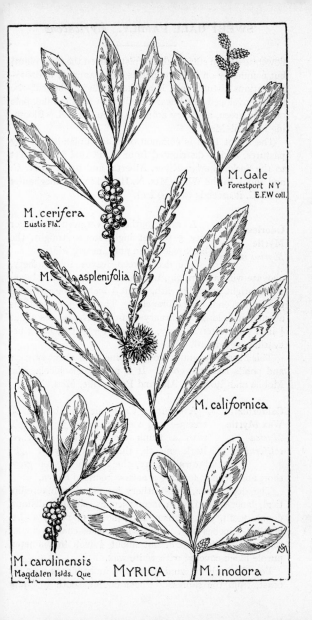

M. Gale
Forestport N Y
E.F.W coll.

M. cerifera
Eustis Fla.

M. asplenifolia

M. californica

M. carolinensis
Magdalen Islds. Que

MYRICA

M. inodora

flowers are often staminate and pistillate on the same plant, but commonly on separate plants, the staminate in drooping catkins about ⅛ inch long, the pistillate spherical, the nutlet enveloped in 8 linear bractlets, in fruit burlike, pale or rusty green, and very aromatic when crushed. Blooming in April–May.

The Sweet Fern is common on stony uplands and dry pastures, and is distributed from N. B. and N. S., west to the Saskatchewan River, Alberta, and south to N. C. and Ind. In the White Mts. N. H. and in the Alleghanies of N. C. it ascends to 2000 feet.

Odorless Myrtle *Myrica inodora* — A rare southern evergreen shrub or tree 5–18 feet high; stems straight, the bark pale ashen gray, nearly white.

The deep green leaves thin-leathery, obovate with a blunt tip, toothless, the edge turned backward, bright green beneath, about 3 inches long, crowded toward the ends of the branches. The pale green catkins about 1 inch long. February–March. The berries about ¼ inch long, often solitary, gray white—that is, black beneath, covered with white wax.

This Myrtle generally grows on pine lands about swamps and ponds near the coast. It is near Apalachicola, Fla. Mobile and Stockton, Ala. and Poplarville, Miss.

California Wax Myrtle *Myrica californica* — A beautiful Californian shrub or small tree 3–8 and occasionally 25–35 feet high, with a trunk diameter of 14 inches. Bark smooth, thin, dark gray or light brownish gray, the branches ashen gray, short and slender, forming a narrow rounded crown.

The deep green, thin-leathery leaves willowlike, elliptical, lance-shaped, with inconspicuous, shallow, distant, double teeth, yellow green, and smooth or nearly so beneath, 3–6 inches long. Berries in crowded clusters similar to those of *M. cerifera*, but about ⅛ inch in diameter, purple black covered with white wax.

Found mostly on sand dunes and moist slopes near the coast, from the shores of Puget Sound, south to Santa

Monica, Cal. It attains its greatest size and most beautiful form on the shores of the Bay of San Francisco.

CORKWOOD FAMILY. *Leitneriaceae.*

Shrubs or small trees with toothless, alternate-growing leaves, and staminate and pistillate flowers borne on separate plants.

A stout southern shrub or tree 3–9 or sometimes 22 feet high, with a trunk diameter of 5 inches. Bark warm brown gray, smooth; the young twigs densely downy.

Corkwood
Leitneria floridana

The bright green leaves narrowly or broadly elliptical or slightly obovate, pointed at either end, sharply at the tip, toothless, pale green and very finely downy at least on the veins beneath, 3–6 inches long. The staminate and pistillate flowers in short catkins, the staminate about 1½ inches long, the pistillate shorter; preceding the leaves. Blooming in March. The nutlike, obovoid fruit is leathery, brown, roughly net-veined, ¾ inch long, ⅓ inch thick.

The Corkwood is found in swamps from southern Mo. (Butler and Dunklin Cos.), and southeastern Ark. (Varner, Lincoln Co.), to western Fla. (near Apalachicola). It is extremely local, and the range is as yet imperfectly known. The wood is very porous, and is one of the lightest of all woods, weighing but 12½ lbs. per cubic foot; the weight of water is 62½ lbs. per cubic foot.

WALNUT FAMILY. *Juglandaceae.*

Trees with compound, alternate-growing leaves, and staminate and pistillate flowers occurring on the same tree.

A broad-spreading, medium-sized tree 30–45 and sometimes 90 feet high, with a trunk diameter of 1–4 feet. The heavy lower branches frequently extending almost horizontally. It lacks symmetry, the rough limbs are scraggy and the foliage sparse. Bark light brown gray, very rough, seamed with rather short

**Butternut
Oilnut
White Walnut**
Juglans cinerea

perpendicular, flat-topped ridges on the older trees, but on younger trees comparatively smooth and gray, inner bark bright green; twigs very light brown, newer ones hairy and green, rather coarse.

Leaves compound, with 7-17, commonly 11, bluntly lance-shaped leaflets, yellow green above, lighter and especially downy beneath, very shallow-toothed, the stems and branchlets sticky with downy hairs. The long petioled leaves waggle with the passing breeze; they are very tender and are quickly destroyed by spring and autumn frosts. Flowers staminate and pistillate on the same tree, the staminate in pendulous catkins. Fruit ellipsoid, 1¾-3 inches long, the husk green throughout the summer, with yellow sap, covered with sticky hairs, brown after the time of frost; the shell with exceedingly sharp and rough ridges, pointed at the tip end; the meat two-lobed at the base, sweet and very oily.

The Butternut is common in pastures, rich woods, and on moist hillsides; it is distributed from southern N. B. west through Que. eastern Ont. Minn. Dak. southeastern Neb. southern Mo. and northeastern Ark., and south to Del. and along the mountains to Ga. and Ala. (head-waters of the Black Warrior River, Winston Co.). It is abundant in Me. and N. H. frequent in Vt. Mass. and Conn., and fairly common in R. I. The wood is light brown, a trifle hard, very beautiful but coarse in grain, and weighs 29 lbs. to the cubic foot. It is occasionally used for the interior finish of houses and for furniture, but has no especial economic value. The tree is sometimes tapped in the spring along with the maple for its sweet sap, and the green husks of the fruit are used for making a yellow dye. In spring the budding tree is green yellow, and in autumn, before a hard frost deprives it of its foliage, it is bright yellow.

Black Walnut
Juglans nigra

A tall, handsome tree 50-75 and sometimes 150 feet high, with a trunk diameter of 3-4 feet, and not infrequently 8 feet in the Ohio Valley; the trunk straight with stout branches nearly horizontal below, and at a sharp angle with the

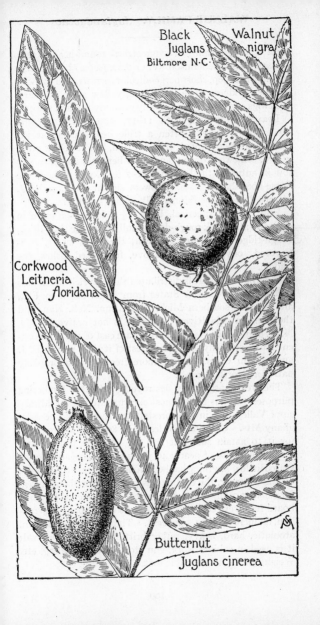

Black
Juglans
Biltmore N·C·

Walnut
nigra

Corkwood
Leitneria
floridana

Butternut
Juglans cinerea

stem above, forming a symmetrical round-headed tree.

Bark warm medium brown, or dark (sepia) brown, very rough, with deep, short perpendicular furrows, and rounded confluent ridges. The inner bark yellow after exposure; the twigs stout, very gray-downy or ruddy tan and smooth.

Leaves compound, with 11–17, sometimes 23 ovate lance-shaped leaflets, often a trifle heart-shaped at the base, and taper-pointed; they are thin, bright yellow green above, somewhat downy and paler beneath, and turn yellow in autumn; the long stem 1–2 feet long, without the horse-hoof-shaped base. Flowers similar to those of *J. cineria*, the catkins thinner. Blooming in May.

Fruit almost spherical, large, 1⅓–3 inches or more in diameter; the husk rough-dotted dull green, the shell thick, rough-ridged, dark sepia brown; the meat sweet, rich-flavored, oily, two-lobed above, four-lobed below the middle.

The Black Walnut is distributed through rich woodlands in the eastern United States from Mass. south to Fla., and west to southern Mich. Wis. Minn. Neb. Kan. and the San Antonio River, Tex. It is not native in Me. N. H. and Vt.; in Mass. it is very rare east of the Connecticut River and only occasional west of it; it is rare in R. I. and also in Conn., though more frequent and probably native at North Canaan.

The tree is practically destroyed for further lumbering purposes. It has been almost exterminated in the Mississippi Valley and in the forests directly west of the Alleghany Mts. Certainly not less than 80 years are required for it to attain sufficient size for valuable timber, and during the lapse of nearly 40 years since it began to grow scarce little if anything has been done to increase the supply; on the contrary, the cutting has proceeded without regard for existing conditions. In the year 1899, over 38½ million board feet were cut, and seven years later about 48⅜ million, an increase of 24.5 per cent. The wood is deep brown, aromatic, hard, heavy, rather brittle and coarse-grained; it is used in cabinet work, gun stocks, boat building, etc. Weight 38 lbs. to the cubic foot.

WALNUT FAMILY. *Juglandaceae*

A western Walnut of medium size, or often a shrub 6–12 or occasionally 50 feet high, with a trunk diameter of 3 feet, the grayish branches ascending forming a narrow head. Bark scaly, deeply furrowed, light brown.

Mexican Walnut
Juglans rupestris

The compound, deep yellow green leaves with 9–23 lance-shaped leaflets, coarsely toothed, 2½–4 inches long, generally fine-hairy beneath. The slender catkins appear in April–May. The fruit is small, ¾–1½ inches in diameter; the nut with a sweet kernel.

The range is from central Tex. in the valleys of the Colorado, Llano, and Guadalupe Rivers, west through N. Mex. and Ariz., and south.

A Californian tree or sometimes a shrub 6–15 or occasionally 40–60 feet high, with a trunk diameter of 2 feet, with heavy limbs and pendulous branches, forming a round-topped head.

California Walnut
Juglans californica

The compound leaves of 11–17 leaflets 6–8 inches long, are similar to the foregoing, but broader, a trifle curved, and coarsely round-toothed. Catkins similar to the last 2–3 inches long. Fruit also similar, the thin husk covered with some downy hairiness.

The range is over the Californian coast region on bottom-lands about 30 miles from the sea, from the valleys of the Sacramento and San Joaquin Rivers, south to the San Bernardino Mts.

A tall, slender nut-tree of the Mississippi Basin, commonly 70–80 and occasionally 170 feet high, with a trunk diameter of 6 feet. Bark rough pale buffish gray strongly but brokenly perpendicular-seamed. The largest of the Hickory trees and widely planted in the South and in California (selected varieties) for its nuts.

Pecan
Carya illinoensis

The leaves compound, with 9–15 asymmetrical, narrow, long-ovate leaflets, fine-toothed, sharp-pointed, often curved, warm deep yellow green, the young leaves minutely downy, the older ones comparatively smooth. The staminate catkins or tassels pendulous and about 5 inches long, in clusters of three. Flowering in April–May. The fruit 1½ or more inches long, the husk thin, ocher-haired, four-angled, parting in four sections when ripe, often persisting on the branch through the winter after discharging the nut which is olive-shaped, lustrous tan brown, and thin-shelled, the kernel delicately flavored and sweet. Ripe in September–October.

The Pecan is common in rich, moist soil of the bottom-lands, and is distributed from eastern Io. (Sabula), south through Mo. southern Ill. and Ind. to western Ky. Tenn. central Ala. Miss. Ark. Okla. and central Tex. (Concho River). Its range has been considerably extended by cultivation. Wood, lightest brown, hard, brittle, and not economically valuable. Weight 46 lbs. to the cubic foot.

Shellbark or Shagbark Hickory
Carya ovata

A large and beautiful tree with wide-spreading boughs, 60–90 and occasionally 140 feet high, with a trunk diameter of 4 feet, especially valued for its delicately flavored nuts. Bark pale brown gray, remarkably shredded and shaggy, loosely attached, hanging in strips commonly a foot long and several inches wide, the tips outcurved from the trunk. The foliage a handsome deep green, the branches rather pendulous, the general contour irregularly ovoid, with a narrow head.

The large leaves compound, with 5–7 leaflets (commonly 5), the 3 upper ones obovate, tapering toward the base and abruptly pointed at the tip, 4–6 inches long, very finely and shallowly toothed, dark yellowish green, scarcely paler beneath and smooth. Staminate catkins green, in clusters of three. Blooming in May. The fruit nearly globular, flattened, the thick husk separating into 4 sections, the nut, thin-shelled, buff white, compressed laterally, the kernel very sweet. The principal Hickory nut of the market, ripe in October.

The Shagbark Hickory is common in rich uplands and is distributed from the valley of the St. Lawrence River, and southern Me., south, especially along the Appalachian Mt. chain to western Fla. central Ala. and Miss., and west

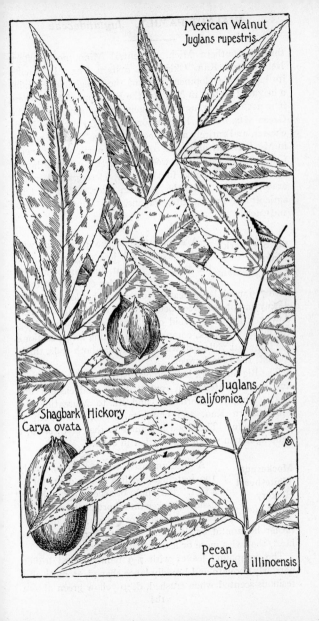

Mexican Walnut
Juglans rupestris.

Juglans
californica

Shagbark Hickory
Carya ovata

Pecan
Carya illinoensis

through southern Mich. to central Minn. northeastern Neb. central Kan. Okla. and eastern Tex. It reaches its highest development west of the Alleghanies, attains a height of 80 feet in N. C. on the Piedmont plateau where it is not common, and is frequent in Vt. only west of the Green Mts. In N. H. it is common as far north as Manchester, and entirely absent north of Lake Winnepesaukee; in Me. it is only along the coast as far north as Harpswell, Cumberland Co. The wood is extremely hard, heavy (52 lbs. to the cubic foot), tough, close-grained, measurably flexible, and pale brown in color. It is used for agricultural implements, wagons, tool handles, baskets, and fuel.

Big Shellbark
Kingnut
Carya laciniosa

A similar tree to the preceding, with coarse-flaked much less shaggy bark, but the twigs very stout, buff, or even deep tan color. The similar compound leaves with 7–9 much larger leaflets (often 8 inches long), slightly downy and bronze green beneath, the young leaflets densely downy. The fruit ovoid or ellipsoid, 2–2½ inches long, the husk very thick, completely separating into 4 sections, the large nut yellowish white, pointed at both ends, thick-shelled; the kernel sweet.

The Big Shellbark is found exclusively on river bottoms, and is distributed from central N. Y. and eastern Pa., west through southern Ind. and Ill. to Muscatine, Io. Mo. eastern Kan. and Onachita, Okla., and south to central Tenn. The wood is similar to that of *C. ovata*, a trifle lighter in weight and darker in color.

Mockernut
White-heart
Hickory
Carya alba

A medium-sized tree 60–70 or rarely 100 feet high, with a trunk diameter of 4 feet. Bark light or ashen brown, deeply fissured, broken into short, confluent ridges, corky-surfaced, not shaggy; the branches rather horizontal or drooping, forming a narrow-topped head, the twigs more or less persistently fine-downy.

The compound leaves with 7–9 blunt-toothed leaflets narrowly obovate and broadly lance-shaped, aromatically, resinous-scented when crushed, deep yellow green above paler and nearly smooth beneath when old, and very fine. downy especially when young. The large fruit obovate, ovoid or globular, $1\frac{1}{2}$–$2\frac{1}{4}$ inches long, the husk splitting some distance below the middle; the nut light brown, globular, or narrowly ovoid, the kernel small with indifferent flavor, though sweet. Ripe in October–November.

The Mockernut is common on rich hillsides or bottom-lands from eastern Mass. through Ont., west to the north shore of Lake Erie, Ont. Mo. eastern Neb. Kan. and the Brazos River, Tex., and south to Cape Canaveral and Tampa Bay, Fla. It is abundant on the Piedmont plateau, N. C., frequent in eastern Mass., and common in R. I. The wood is heavy, hard, and strong. It is not commercially distinguished from Shagbark Hickory.

Small-fruited Hickory
Carya microcarpa

A species very similar to *C. alba*, the bark very rough and scaly but not shaggy, the twigs often tan red, the foliage smooth and similar to that of *C. glabra*.

The compound leaves with commonly 5 smooth leaflets, otherwise as in *C. glabra*. The fruit very small flattened-globular or obovoid, the husk thick (fully $\frac{1}{8}$ inch) splitting nearly to the base, the nut buff brown, pointed at the tip, thin-shelled, about $\frac{3}{4}$ inch long. Distributed through the Mississippi Valley generally eastward; from Que. eastern Mass. central N. Y. eastern Pa. Md. (Montgomery Co.), to central Mich. southern Ind. and Ill. and Mo., mostly on uplands.

Water Hickory Bitter Pecan
Carya aquatica

A slender tree of wet land or swamps, 40–60 or occasionally 100 feet high, with a trunk diameter of 3 feet. Bark thin, light ashen gray, on old trees extremely shaggy, curling away in thin scales (like *C. ovata*), the branches slender, irregular, and short, the twigs gray or sepia black.

The compound leaves with 9–15 comparatively narrow, lance-shaped leaflets, often curved, sharp-pointed and slightly or indistinctly sharp-toothed, deep yellow green above, nearly smooth and slightly paler beneath. The fruit ovoid or pear-shaped, 1–2 inches long, the thin husk splitting to the base, the nut very at and variably angled, soft-shelled; the kernel extremely bitter.

The Water Hickory is distributed on the coastal plain from Va. (Mobjack Bay), south to Cape Malabar and Caloosa Rive , Fla., the Gulf region to the Brazos River, Tex., extending northward through western La. to northeastern Ark. eastern Miss. and southern Ill. (Equality, Gallatin Co.). In N. C. it is confined to swamps of the coastal plain where it grows to a height of 50 feet. It reaches its greatest development in the Mississippi and Yazoo River Valleys. The wood is soft, strong, and brittle, the weight 46 lbs. to the cubic foot. It is inferior in quality to that of other hickories, and is mostly used for fences and fuel.

Pignut Hickory
Carya glabra

A medium-sized tree 50–60 and occasionally 120 feet high, with a trunk diameter of 5 feet. Bark thick, deep gray brown, shaggy, not deeply scored, the confluent ridges flattened, the smooth branches slender. the lower ones drooping, forming a narrow long-ovoid head, the twigs slender.

The compound leaves with 5–7 (rarely 9) smooth, deep yellow green, ovate lance-shaped and broadly obovate, sharp-toothed leaflets; rarely they are sparsely fine-hairy beneath on the ribs. The fruit 1 inch long, pear-shaped or prolate-spherical, the husk thin, splitting about halfway down; the nut dull light brown, with a thick, hard shell, the kernel at first sweet, finally bitter. Both the husk and its enclosed nut often fall unseparated to the ground. Ripe in October-November.

The Pignut Hickory is common in dry woods, and is distributed from southern Me., west to southern Ont. southern Mich. Minn. eastern Neb. eastern Kan. and Okla., and south to Indian River and Peace Creek, Fla. and the Nueces River, Tex. It is fairly abundant in N. C. on the Piedmont plateau where it grows to a height of about 75 feet, locally frequent in York Co., Me. and along the coast region and the Merrimac River as far north as Manchester, N. H., and local in Vt. (W. Castleton, Pownal, and Marsh Hill, Ferrisburgh). The var. *villosa.* Robinson,

Mockernut
C. alba

Water
Carya

Hickory
aquatica

Leaves
of
C. laciniosa
and
C. alba
practically
alike

Big Shellbark
C. laciniosa

Fruit of
C. microcarpa

Fruit
of
C. glabra

Fruit
of
C. aquatica

is a form with long soft woolly hairs on the leaf stems and catkin stems, the under surface of the relatively small leaflets are also covered more numerously with large scalelike glands (viewed under the glass). Distributed from Va. and N. C. to Mo., and south. The wood is not essentially different from that of *C. ovata*. It weighs 51 lbs. to the cubic foot.

Bitternut Swamp Hickory *Carya cordiformis*
A tall tree of swamps 50–75 and sometimes 100 feet high, with a trunk diameter of 4 feet, the branches slender, ascending, drooping below, forming a narrow-topped head. Bark thin, light brown or warm brown gray, shallowly and finely fissured, the ridges strongly confluent, separating into somewhat thin flakes. The twigs buff.

The compound leaves with 7–11 (commonly 9) broadly lance-shaped, fine-toothed leaflets deep yellow green above, slightly paler beneath and a trifle downy. The fruit 1 inch long, rarely longer, ovoid or obovoid, the husk thin, splitting about half-way down, the nut buff or gray, pointed at the tip, thin-shelled, the kernel at first sweet finally very bitter.

The Bitternut is common in rich woodlands or in various soils, and is distributed from western Que. and southern Me., west to the north shore of Lake Huron, and to Minn. eastern Neb. Kan. Okla. and Tex., and south to Fla. It is rare in southern Me. and absent in central N. H., though it extends up the Valley of the Connecticut to Wells River; it is occasional in Vt., west of the Green Mts., and common in southern N. E. In N. C. it grows to a height of 80 feet, and is abundant only in the mountains. The wood is inferior to that of the other hickories.

Nutmeg Hickory *Carya myristicaeformis*
A tall western Hickory 70–80 and sometimes 100 feet high, with a trunk diameter of 2 feet, the stout, nearly horizontal branches forming a somewhat narrow head. Bark a deep brown gray often ruddy tinged, broken into small scales or confluent, short, shaggy ridges; twigs a dull buffish gray.

The compound leaves composed of 5–11 (commonly 9) narrowly ovate, pointed leaflets, dark green above, finely white-hairy and shiny or nearly smooth beneath.

The fruit about 1¼ inches long, ellipsoid, the thin husk splitting nearly to the base; nut conspicuously brown-striped, pointed at either end, very hard-shelled. The kernel not edible.

The Nutmeg Hickory is usually found on alluvial soil, and is distributed from Pine Bluff, Arkansas City, and Red River above Fulton, Ark. to central Ala. between the Tombigbee and Alabama Rivers, from Demopolis to Gallion and Mhoons Valley, Miss. It is also at Goose Creek, Cooper River, S. C. Often cultivated in the middle Atlantic States. The wood is light brown, hard and strong, the weight 50 lbs. to the cubic foot.

BIRCH FAMILY. *Betulaceae*.

Trees or shrubs with alternate-growing leaves, and staminate and pistillate flowers borne on the same tree, or very rarely on different trees, the staminate in nearly erect or drooping, the pistillate in pendulous catkins.

A shrub 3–8 feet high, with many deep brown, strongly ascending stems, common in hedge-rows and thickets, the russet twigs until old, bristly and glandular.

**Hazelnut
Filbert**
*Corylus
americana*

Leaves narrowly heart-shaped or ovate, abruptly pointed, the edge a trifle irregular with subsidiary points, and fine-toothed, dull dark green and rough above, paler with downy hairs beneath, 3–5 inches long, with short stems, the base mostly overlapping the branchlet. The staminate catkins mostly solitary, 3–4 inches long, blooming in April. Fruit an almost globular, chestnut brown nut enclosed within a pair of broad leafy, cut-toothed bracts covered with down or with glandular bristles at the base, very sweet, furnishing the principal Hazelnut of the market. Ripe in September–August.

The Hazelnut is common in thickets and hedge-rows from Me., west to the valley of the Saskatchewan River, Alberta, and Kan., and south to northern Fla. Less frequent in the mountain districts than the next species.

Beaked Hazelnut
Corylus rostrata

A northern shrub 3–8 feet high, with several or many upright, thickly clustered stems, common in roadside thickets and hedge-rows. Bark light ocher yellow or brown ocher dotted with buff, the young twigs ocher yellow with an almost imperceptible fine hairiness (under the glass).

Leaves very broadly ovate, abruptly pointed, scallop-lobed at the base, the lobes mostly overlapping the stem, the margin with 6–8 subsidiary, lateral points at the termination of the ribs, double-toothed, dull dark green, hairy and deeply seamed above, lighter green, densely velvety hairy and prominently ribbed beneath, the stems about ½ inch long. Fruit an ovoid nut, edible and sweet, inclosed within a densely bristly cup or leafy covering terminating in a long tubular beak.

The Beaked Hazelnut is common in thickets throughout the North, extending from Que. west across the continent to the Pacific Slope, and south to Del. O. Mich. and Mo., and along the mountains to Ga.

Ironwood
American Hop
Hornbeam
Leverwood
Ostrya virginiana

A small tree 25–40, and in the Southwest 50 feet high, with a trunk diameter of 2 feet. Bark gray brown (ocherish beneath), scaly, scored perpendicularly into long, flat narrow strips about 4 inches long, out-curling at the tips; the slender branches irregular, nearly horizontal, often drooping, forming an ovoid crown.

The leaves about 3½ inches or more long, narrowly ovate, sharp-pointed, rounded at the base, very sharply double-toothed, dull light green above, paler and downy beneath, with many strongly defined veins. Staminate flowers in usually three drooping catkins, the pistillate erect. The fruit hoplike, formed of several veined, papery-leafy, fine-hairy sacs each containing a hard nutlet, the cluster approximately 2¼ inches long.

The Hop Hornbeam is found in dry open woods, and is distributed from N. S. and N. B. (Bay of Chaleur) along the St. Lawrence and Lower Ottawa Rivers, and the northern shores of Lake Huron, to western Ont. northern

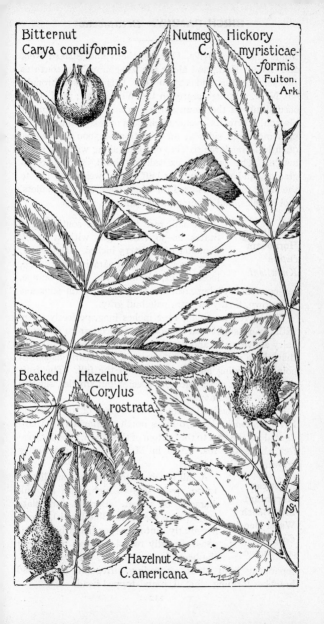

Bitternut
Carya cordiformis

Nutmeg Hickory
C. myristicae-
-formis
Fulton.
Ark.

Beaked Hazelnut
Corylus
rostrata

Hazelnut
C. americana

Minn. the Black Hills, Dak. northern and eastern Neb. and eastern Kan., and along the Alleghany Mts. south to Jacksonville, Fla. and eastern Tex. It is common throughout N. E. although scarce in the White Mts.; in N. C. it occurs only in the mountain region and on the Piedmont plateau, where its average height is only 25 feet, and on high mountain sides at an elevation of 5000 feet it frequently forms large patches of forest along with the sugar maple. The wood is exceedingly hard, strong, close-grained, and pale brown or buff white; weight 51 lbs. to the cubic foot. It is used for wheel cogs, wedges, mallets tool handles, and farming implements.

Knowlton's Hornbeam *Ostrya Knowltoni* A small, rare tree of the southwestern States 20–30 feet high, with a trunk diameter of about 15 inches. Bark scaly, light brown gray, separating into long, loose strips, showing the bright orange, tan-colored bark beneath, the twigs at first (in summer) red brown, finally smooth, pale buff gray.

The leaves are small, 1½–2 inches long, perfectly ovate with a very slight heart-shaped base, deep green and soft-hairy above, paler and downy beneath, the teeth less sharp than those in *O. virginiana*, the apex not nearly as sharp-pointed; turning an ocher yellow in the fall. The fruit similar to that of the previous species, but smaller, slightly magenta-stained at the base.

The range confined to the southern slope of the Colorado River Cañon in Ariz. 70 miles north of Flagstaff. Abundant along the trail to the bottom of the cañon, at 6000–7000 feet above the sea. Also in Mex. Range imperfectly known.

American Hornbeam Blue Beech Water Beech *Carpinus caroliniana* A tall shrub or sometimes a small tree 12–20 rarely 50 feet high, with a trunk diameter of 3 feet. Bark a dark slate gray (hence the name Blue Beech), scored irregularly into perpendicularly corrugated, broadly rounded ridges resembling the beech in smoothness; the trunk short, separating into stout, spreading, irregular limbs and branches forming a broad, round-topped head.

BIRCH FAMILY. *Betulaceae*

The leaves are long, ovate, almost suddenly sharp-pointed, rounded at the base, very sharply double-toothed, often asymmetrical, 2-4 inches long, deep green above, paler and slightly fine-hairy on the straight ribs beneath which continue to the prominent teeth, the stems very slender. The staminate catkins 1¼ inches long; bracts (leafy formations) at the base of the pistillate flowers three-lobed, in clusters, developing conspicuously above the base of the ovate nutlets which mature in September.

The Blue Beech is found in wet woods or along streams, and is distributed from N. S. and Que. west to the north shores of Georgian Bay, Lake Huron, northern Minn. eastern Neb. and Kan. Okla. and Trinity River, Tex., and south to Cape Malabar and Tampa Bay, Fla. In N. C. it grows commonly along all water-courses to a maximum height of 25 feet, in N. E. it is generally common, less frequent toward the coast, and absent in the White Mts. It attains its best development on the western slopes of the southern Alleghany Mts., southern Ark., and eastern Tex. The wood is hard, light brown, close-grained, and not commercially valuable. Weight 45 lbs. to the cubic foot.

A medium-sized tree 45-50 and in favorable situations 80 feet high, ovate in contour, the dark brown trunk fairly straight, with a diameter of 5 feet, the upper branches ascending, the lower ones **Black Birch** **Cherry Birch** **Sweet Birch** *Betula lenta*
nearly horizontal, slender and often drooping. Bark dark slate gray, brown on younger trees and their slender branches, smooth, not peeling, strongly marked with long, horizontal lines resembling the bark of the Cherry Tree, on old trees broken into irregular gray brown plates. The twigs slender, smooth, glossy, red brown with elongated dots; strongly wintergreen-flavored. Beer is made from the fermented sweet sap of this tree, and oil of wintergreen is distilled from its inner bark and twigs.

The leaves grow alternately in pairs, they are pointed-ovate, bright green above, lighter beneath and smooth except on the veins, more or less heart-shaped at the base, finely double-toothed, and sharp-pointed. The pistillate catkins, cylindrical, stout, erect, and stemless, 1-1¼ inches

long, with smooth, not downy scales, produced only once
in 3-4 years; staminate catkins 2½-3 inches long, in
clusters.

The Black Birch is found in rich woods and on moist
fertile ground or river banks, from Newf. west to Ont.
and the islands of Lake Huron, and south to Del. Ind. and
central Ia. and along the Alleghany Mts. to central Ky.
Tenn. and western Fla. It occurs frequently in Me. and
follows the watercourses to the highlands of central N. H.
and as far north as Windsor in the valley of the Connecticut; it is frequent in western Vt. Mass. R. I. and Conn.
excepting near the coast. In Md. and N. C. it is common
in the mountain regions, and rare or absent in other parts
of these States. The wood is heavy, strong, hard, close-
grained, and deep ruddy brown with yellow sapwood; it
is frequently used in the manufacture of furniture, and
boat-building, and very often for ship-building in N. S. and
N. B. Much of it is cut in N. C. for lumber; it makes an
excellent fuel. Weight 47 lbs. to the cubic foot.

Yellow Birch
Silver Birch
Betula lutea

A tall tree 50-65 and not infrequently
95 feet high, with an irregular perpendicular trunk 2-4 feet in diameter, characterized by its ragged, ocher yellow bark and
rugged, spreading branches. Bark a lustrous, silvery, pale
yellow gray, peeling horizontally into very thin ribbonlike
layers, which give the stem of the tree a very lacerated
appearance, the horizontal markings mostly elongated;
on old trees where the silvery, outer bark is shed, the under,
red brown bark becomes rough, fissured, and broken into
irregular scales. On very young saplings the yellowish
bark has a sheen like that of satin.

The leaves are deep, dull green above, downy beneath
on the veins, ovate with a slight point, rather coarsely
double-toothed, and have a contracted, heart-shaped base.
The flowers appear in early spring before the leaves; the
staminate catkins long, pendent; the pistillate erect,
stemless, oblong or ovoid, 1-1½ inches long, with downy
scales nearly ½ inch long; produced every 2-3 years.

The Yellow Birch is common in rich, moist woodlands,
and on damp, shady mountain slopes, from Newf. west
along the northern shores of the Gulf of St. Lawrence, to

Hop Hornbeam
Ostrya virginiana
Milton. Mass. J·R·C· coll.

Knowlton's
Hornbeam
O. Knowltoni

Hornbeam
Carpinus
caroliniana
Williamstown. Mass
E·F·W· coll.

Black Birch   Betula lenta

Abittibi Lake, Ont. (near the border of Que.), southern Man. Rainy Lake River, and the western shores of Lake Superior, Minn., and south to Del. Ill. and along the mountains to eastern Tenn. and N. C. The tree is called "Merisier Rouge" in Quebec. It is more or less common throughout N. E., and climbs to an elevation of 3000 or more feet in the mountains. In N. C. it is confined to the high mountains; in Md. it is common in swamps and glades and along mountain streams. The wood is heavy, strong, hard, close-grained, and light brown with pale sapwood: it is used in the manufacture of flooring, furniture, wheel hubs, spools, and woodenware and it makes a most excellent fuel. Weight about 42 lbs. to the cubic foot.

Red Birch
River Birch
Betula nigra

The Red Birch is a southern species, a graceful, medium-sized tree, 30–50 and occasionally 80 feet high, with a trunk 3 feet thick, commonly, but not invariably, divided into strong ascending limbs at a point 6–8 feet above the ground. In maturity it attains a rather symmetrical ovoid figure. Bark thin, lustrous reddish brown, peeling easily into more or less translucent, curling, papery, tan buff layers; on old trees dark red brown, deeply furrowed perpendicularly, and broken into platelike scales, the upper branches shaggy with loose, tan-colored layers; the twigs are slender, cinnamon or brown red, mostly smooth (always downy when young), and not aromatic.

The bright green leaves are angularly ovate, rather wedge-shaped at the base, unevenly double-toothed, pointed at the tip, and whitish downy beneath (including the stems), particularly so when young. Flowering in April–May. Pistillate catkins short-stemmed, soft, downy, cylindrical, stout, erect, 1–2 inches long, ripening in late spring or early summer.

The Red Birch is distributed beside rivers and ponds, or in low marshy woodlands, from Beaver Brook, Pelham, southern N. H.[1] Nashua River near Fitchburg, Merrimac River near Lawrence and Lowell, Spicket, and Shawsheen Rivers, Mass. and Wading River, Long Island, N. Y.,

[1] *Vide* Fredk. W. Bachelder's Preliminary Plant List, Manchester Inst, Arts and Sciences.

southward east of the Alleghany Mts. on the coastal plain
to western Fla., thence west to Trinity River, Tex., north
through Miss. to Okla. eastern Kan. eastern Neb. (Missouri River), central Minn. southern Wis. (near Madison),
and O. It is not reported from Me. Vt. R. I. or Conn. It
is common throughout Md. and is found from the coast to
the mountains along streams and in swamps in N. C. The
wood is light, rather close-grained, strong, and light brown
with buff sapwood; it is used in the manufacture of furniture, woodenware, and in turned articles. Weight 36 lbs.
to the cubic foot.

A small tree with a slender stem, 20–30
and sometimes 35 feet high, with a trunk
diameter of 6–10 inches, commonly growing in groups, the stem usually with two
slight, opposed curves; the branches very
slender, thin-foliaged, somewhat drooping
toward the base but rigidly ascending

White Birch
Gray Birch
Oldfield Birch
Poplar Birch
Betula
populifolia

toward the apex of the tree. Bark, dull white, horizontally
lined, close, not easily separable into layers, with triangular sepia brown patches below the base of each bough;
branchlets brown and terra-cotta red roughly dotted with
gray white, or with age becoming dull white.

The leaves are about 2½ inches long, a lively, bright,
shining green, thin, translucent, lighter on the under side,
triangular, abruptly sharp-pointed, fine-toothed over a
five-notched margin, smooth throughout; the stems 1 inch
(more or less) long, pale yellow, and slender, causing the
leaves to tremble in every passing breeze. Pistillate
catkins light green, cylindrical, slender-stemmed, ¾–1⅛
inches long, crowded with tiny, four-angled bracted seed
resembling the outline of a bird in flight, the attached,
tiny scales tan brown; staminate catkins commonly solitary, 2–3 inches long.

The Gray Birch is most common on waste land, and
rocky slopes or swampy depressions of hillside pastures; it
is distributed from Prince Edward's Id. N. B. and the
lower St. Lawrence River, west through N. E. and N. Y.
to the southern shores of Lake Ontario, and south, mostly
along the coast, to Newcastle Co., Del. It is common

through N. E. and northern N. Y., but not very common in W. Va. It rapidly takes possession of neglected, burnt-over, and deforested land, and is difficult to eradicate as it readily sprouts from the stump. Its vivid green foliage is remarkably brilliant in strong sunlight especially in the late spring, and its pale green and yellow coloring is scarcely less attractive under the autumn sun. The wood is somewhat soft, close-grained, but not strong or durable, and pale brown with nearly white sapwood. It is only useful for the manufacture of spools, shoe pegs, wood pulp, and barrel hoops, and for fuel. Weight 36 lbs. to the cubic foot.

White Birch
Canoe Birch
Betula pendula

A medium-sized tree 40–50 feet high or more, with a trunk diameter of 10–18 inches and with slender, flexible, often drooping branches, the branchlets and leaves absolutely smooth in youth as well as age, but the former usually covered with small resinous excrescences.

The bark buffish white, chalky, separating into papery layers, the inner ones from pale buff to light bronze, aromatic, conspicuously marked with horizontal darker lines; the white trunk marked by sepia brown patches extending laterally from either side of a branch, but the triangular figure common on the trunk of the Gray Birch less noticeable or quite absent.

The leaves deep green, a trifle sticky when young, asymmetrical, triangular, or regularly and broadly ovate, more or less angular or nearly straight across (rarely slightly heart-shaped) at the base, the point sharply prolonged, the stem slender, the margin double-toothed; about 3 inches or less long. The pistillate catkin slender, pendent, produced each year, similar to that of the Gray Birch, the brownish or straw yellow ascending scales smooth, about $\frac{3}{16}$ inch long—longer than those of the Gray Birch, staminate catkins mostly in groups of 2–3.

The White Birch is common in rocky woods or on wooded hillsides, and is distributed from Que. northwest to Man. the region of the Saskatchewan, and Alaska, and locally south to Me. Vt. N. H. and Ill. It is a northern species with varying forms, and a native of Europe and

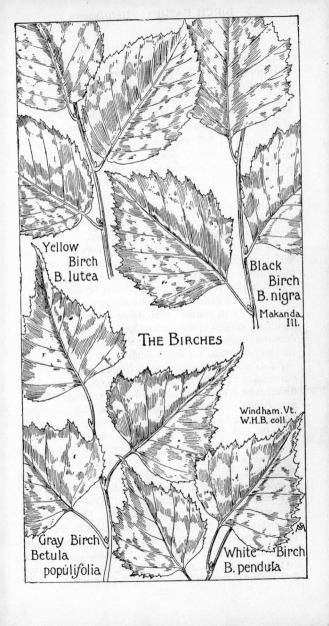

Yellow
Birch
B. lutea

Black
Birch
B. nigra

Makanda,
Ill.

THE BIRCHES

Windham. Vt.
W.H.B. coll.

Gray Birch
Betula
populifolia

White Birch
B. pendula

Asia. The N. E. form of this species with blue-green foliage, locally common in Vt. (Windham and Stratton), and probably elsewhere in northern N. E., has been named by Mr. W. H. Blanchard, *Betula caerulea*—Blue Birch. It is a tree of usually high altitudes (1500–2000 feet) whose bluish foliage is easily distinguished from that of other birches even at a considerable distance.

Canoe Birch	A medium-sized tree common in the
White Birch	north, found in upland woods or on hill-
Paper Birch	sides, also a native of Europe and Asia.
Betula alba	It grows to a height of 40–50 feet, and
	is frequently reduced to the dimensions of

a shrub. The branchlets and twigs in the type species and its varieties, are fine-hairy, with branches ascending, never drooping (except in varieties in cultivation).

The leaves are ovate, sharp-pointed, rounded or wedge-shaped at the base, about 2½–3 inches long at maturity, olive green and smooth above, much paler, glandular dotted, and a trifle hairy on the veins beneath, sharply toothed over a generally six-notched margin, more grace-fully curved in contour than those of *Betula pendula*. Pistillate catkins ¾–1½ inches long, about ½ inch in diameter, inclined or drooping on slender stems, staminate catkins pendulous, 1–2 inches long.

Betula alba is distributed from Newf. west through the Great Lake region to B. C., and south to N. E. The local distribution is as yet undefined. Its less common varieties are: *Betula alba* var. *glutinosa*. A tree with pendulous branches, the leaves 1¼–2 inches long, woolly on the veins beneath, and the spreading catkins on straight stems. Confined to the Wassataquoik Valley, Me. *Betula alba* var. *cordifolia*. A small tree, or on alpine slopes a mere shrub, with small, broad-ovate leaves, heart-shaped at the base, and woolly on the veins beneath; confined to cool mountain woods and exposed slopes. Distributed from Lab. and Newf. south to the White Mts., N. H. and Mt. Katahdin, Me.[1] *Betula alba* var. *minor*. A dwarf alpine shrub, with rather stout stems, the small leaves ovate, rounded, and broad at the base, glutinous and smooth,

[1] *Vide* Fernald in *Am. Jour. Science*, Sept., 1902, pg. 178. " The Relationships of Some American and Old World Birches."

$\frac{5}{8}$–$1\frac{1}{2}$ inches long. Fruit a mostly erect cylindrical catkin $\frac{1}{2}$–$1\frac{1}{8}$ inches long. This dwarf species is confined to alpine regions and cold bogs, and is distributed from Lab. west to Alberta (the Saskatchewan River), and south to northern N. E. (Mts. Washington and Katahdin), and Minn. Common also in Greenland.[1]

There are many horticultural varieties of *Betula alba*. A weeping form and another with fine, drooping branchlets are most commonly seen in parks and on lawns. The bark on the lower part of the trunk is often rent with dark, short, perpendicular fissures, and the leaves are slashed into deep, narrow, sharp-pointed lobes.

A large handsome tree 50–70 and often 100 feet high, with a trunk diameter of 2–3 feet, developing a somewhat irregular figure with a chalky white trunk, the stout branches also white and ascending; branchlets brown, white-dotted, the young twigs buff and woolly. Bark white, chalky, separating into aromatic papery layers from creamy buff to light tan, the

Paper Birch
Canoe Birch
White Birch
Betula alba var.
papyrifera
Betula papy-rifera,
Marshall

color deepening inward with each successive layer, all conspicuously marked with longer or shorter horizontal lines, blackish on the white, terra-cotta brown on the buff layers; *never copper-colored except in high altitudes*. The outer white bark scarred by sepia black patches extending laterally either side of a branch, but not triangle-shaped as on the Gray Birch.

The leaves are deep green, generally with a pointed-oval figure, sometimes slightly heart-shaped at the base, coarsely toothed over a shallowly six-notched margin, woolly above and beneath, especially over the ribs and stem when young, smooth and rather rigid when old, $2\frac{1}{4}$–$3\frac{1}{2}$ inches long. Flowers in April–May. Pistillate catkins short-stemmed, cylindrical, hard, $\frac{3}{4}$–$1\frac{3}{4}$ inches long, spreading or drooping.

The Paper Birch is the most common and beautiful birch of northern N. E. and N. Y. It is found in rich woods

[1] *Vide* Fernald in *Am. Jour. Science*, Sept., 1902, pg. 178. "The Relationships of Some American and Old World Birches."

and rocky uplands, and is distributed from Newf. west to the southern shores of Hudson Bay, northwestward to Great Bear Lake, the Yukon River, and the coast of Alaska, and south to Long Island, N. Y. northern Pa. central Mich. and Minn. northern Neb. Dak. (the Black Hills), northern Mont. and northwestern Wash. In Me. it is abundant, in N. H. it climbs in the White Mts. to a high altitude, in Vt. and Mass. it is more or less common, and in Conn. it is occasional northward and rare near the coast. The wood is hard, very close-grained, and pale brown with thick, nearly white sapwood; it is used for spools, shoe pegs, shoe lasts, wood pulp, and fuel. Weight 37 lbs. to the cubic foot. The tough, extremely resinous, durable, water-proof bark is used by the Indians for their canoes, and for baskets, boxes, and souvenir articles.

Western Birch
Betula alba
forma *occidentalis*[1]

A tree of the Pacific slope 70–90 or occasionally 100 feet high, with a trunk diameter of 3 feet. Bark smooth shining orange brown or a copper red, often with a plum-colored bloom, the spreading, slender branches forming a narrow, round-topped head, the slender red brown branchlets drooping.

The leaves similar to those of *B. alba* var. *papyrifera*. This tree is a form, not a distinct species nor even a variety. The copper-colored bark is a character or phase of *B. alba* var. *papyrifera*, which may be seen on the slopes of the higher White Mts. of N. H.—Mts. Washington, Lafayette, and Moosilauke, at an elevation of 4000 or more feet.

The Western Birch is distributed from northwestern Wash. and southwestern B. C. to Ida. and Mont., but its range is at present little known as it has not been satisfactorily separated from *B. alba* var. *papyrifera*.

Swamp Birch
Low Birch
Betula pumila

A shrub with dark brown, scarcely papery bark, the stems 1½–9 feet high, generally erect; the young twigs and under surface of the young leaves thickly covered with soft hairs.

[1] *Vide* Fernald in *Am. Jour. Science*, vol. xvi., Sept., 1902, pg. 173 "The Relationships of Some American and Old World Birches."

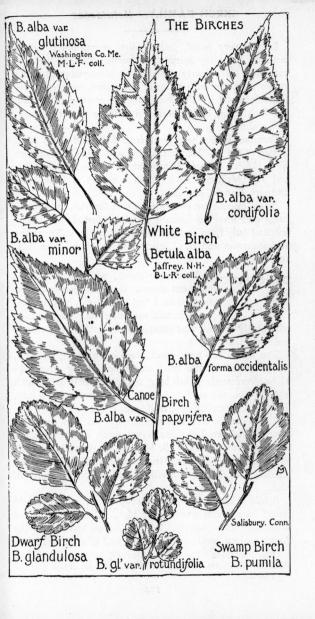

THE BIRCHES

B. alba var. glutinosa
Washington Co. Me.
M·L·F· coll.

B. alba var. cordifolia

White Birch
Betula alba
Jaffrey. N·H·
B·L·R· coll.

B. alba var. minor

B. alba forma occidentalis

Canoe Birch
B. alba var. papyrifera

Dwarf Birch
B. glandulosa

B. gl' var. rotundifolia

Salisbury. Conn.

Swamp Birch
B. pumila

Leaves very small, yellow olive green, much lighter beneath, fine silky-hairy when young, obovate (broader near the tip), nearly circular or kidney-shaped, $\frac{3}{8}$–$1\frac{1}{4}$ inches long, the surface finely net-veined, not resinously glandular-dotted. Pistillate catkins, erect, hard, small, $\frac{3}{8}$–1 inch long, light green. Staminate catkins longer, soft, inclined.

Common in northern bogs, from Lab. and Newf. west through Que. to Ont. and Minn., and south to northern N. J. (Morris Co.), O. (Champaign Co.), Ind. (Lake Co.), and Ill. (McHenry Co.). Also a native of Greenland, northern Europe, and Asia.[1]

Betula pumila var. *grandulifera*.[2] A form with the young twigs and leaves resinously glandular-dotted. It is distributed only from western Ont. west to the valley of the Saskatchewan and B. C., and south to Mich. Minn. Ida. and Ore.

Dwarf Birch
Betula glandulosa

An Alpine shrub, with erect or procumbent stems, 1–3, but generally not more than 2 feet high, or quite prostrate on mountain summits; the brown branchlets mostly smooth and conspicuously dotted with raised, resinous glands.

The leaves are very small, deep olive green, obovate, wedge-shaped at the base, sometimes nearly round, $\frac{1}{3}$–$1\frac{1}{8}$ but commonly $\frac{3}{4}$ inch long, smooth on both sides, with about 18 coarse, scolloped teeth. Flowers in June–July. The pistillate catkins $\frac{1}{3}$–$\frac{7}{8}$ inch long.

The Dwarf Birch is common in the Arctic regions, and is distributed from Lab. and Newf. south over the higher mountain summits of N. B. Me. and N. H., and along the shores of Lake Superior, Minn. west to Kamtschatka and Alaska, and south to northern Cal. Utah, Col. and S. Dak.

Betula glandulosa var. *rotundifolia* is an extremely dwarf form about 7–10 inches high, with very round or sometimes kidney-shaped leaves. Range throughout the Arctic regions, westward to Alaska and Siberia, and south

[1] *Vide* Fernald in "The Relationships of Some American and Old World Birches," *Am. Jour. Science*, Sept., 1902, pg. 187.

[2] The same.

on the alpine summits of mountains in Me. N. H. and Vt
It is common on Mt. Katahdin, Me., Mts. Washington,
Lafayette, and Moosilauke, in the White Mts., N. H., and
on Mt. Mansfield, Vt.

A northern, mountain shrub 2–8 feet high. The young branchlets slightly downy or smooth, the older branchlets smooth, dark ruddy brown.

Green Alder
Mountain Alder
Alnus crispa[1]

The leaves broadly ovate, rounded at the base, dark olive green above, smooth and glutinous, slightly fine-hairy on the prominent rusty veins beneath, very irregularly fine, sharp-toothed, the edge often a trifle ruffled, $1\frac{1}{4}$–$2\frac{1}{4}$ inches long. The staminate flowers in green yellow catkins about $1\frac{1}{2}$ inches long; the pistillate about $\frac{1}{2}$ inch long, ovoid and finally conelike, persisting through the winter. Blooming in April.

In moist soil on mountains, or on the margins of cool ponds, from Lab. to N. B. and on Mt. Katahdin, Me., Mts. Washington and Lafayette, N. H., Mt. Mansfield, Vt., Mt. Whiteface, N. Y. and the higher Alleghanies to N. C.

A similar shrub or small tree at most 15 feet high. The light brown branchlets covered with fine down (under the glass), or when dried with a grayish skin.

Downy Green Alder
Alnus crispa
var. *mollis*[2]

The large leaves similar to the last, but 2–4 inches long, permanently fine-hairy or downy beneath, and rusty on the veins. The pistillate cones $\frac{5}{8}$–$\frac{3}{4}$ inch long similarly persistent.

In moist thickets and rocky banks from southern Newf. west through Que. to Lake Winnipeg, and south to southern Me. and N. H. western Mass. N. Y. and Lake Superior.

This is the common Alder of the northeastern and northern States; a shrub or small tree 8–12 and occasionally 30 feet high, with a single smooth trunk 6 inches

Speckled Alder
Hoary Alder
Alnus incana

[1] *Vide* Britton and Brown's Ill. Flora of the Eastern U. S. under A. Alnobetula.

[2] *Vide* Gray's *Manual of Botany*, 7th ed. under *A. mollis*; in 6th d. *A. viridis* in part.

in diameter, or more frequently a group of several stout stems. Bark gray brown with lighter horizontal markings.

The leaves broadly elliptical or ovate, sometimes slightly asymmetrical, sharply and irregularly double-toothed, frequently notched, dark dull green above, with deeply impressed ribs, very rusty downy mostly on the veins beneath, or sometimes simply with a bloom. The purple and yellow staminate catkins about 3 inches long. Fruit round-winged seeds (samaras) in a small, ovoid cone persisting through the winter. Common in swamps and moist thickets, and on the margins of streams from Newf. west to the Saskatchewan, and south to Pa. northern Ia. and Neb.; also in Europe–Asia.

Smooth Alder
Hazel Alder
Alnus rugosa

A shrub or small tree 6–20 feet high, rarely 40 feet high, with smooth bark, the young shoots a trifle downy. The common Alder southward.

The broad leaves obovate, narrowed toward the base to a wedge-shape, blunt at the tip, more regularly cut with very fine teeth than the other Alders, glandular-tipped, dark green above, little lighter and a trifle downy or smooth beneath, the veins rusty and scarcely impressed, the stem short. The purple and yellow catkins as in the last, appearing before the leaves (in the north). March–April. Fruit ovate samaras in an ovoid cone about $\frac{2}{3}$ inch long which persists through the winter. Distributed mostly on the coastal plain from Me. to Fla. and Tex. but southward farther inland and on the Piedmont plateau, very rare west to Minn. On the northern limit of its range many individuals seem to be intermediately related to *A. maritima*.

European
Black Alder
Alnus vulgaris

A medium-sized tree introduced from Europe 50–70 feet high, in general cultivation and an occasional escape. Bark smooth, gray brown with pale gray horizontal markings.

The leaves broadly ovate or obovate, dark green above, slightly paler and downy on the veins beneath, glutinous, and coarsely toothed, the teeth glandular-tipped. Stami-

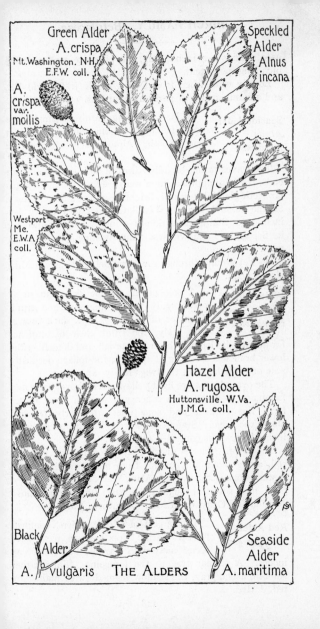

Green Alder
A. crispa
Mt. Washington. N.H.
E.F.W. coll.

Speckled
Alder
Alnus
incana

A.
crispa
var.
mollis

Westport
Me.
E.W.A.
coll.

Hazel Alder
A. rugosa
Huttonsville. W.Va.
J.M.G. coll.

Black
Alder
A. vulgāris   THE ALDERS

Seaside
Alder
A. maritima

nate catkins 3–4 inches long, the pistillate cone about ¾ inch long; persistent.

Locally established from Newf. to N. J. Pa. and Ill., and a common tree of parks and gardens.

Seaside Alder
Alnus
maritima

A late flowering shrub or small tree 10–30 feet high, the branchlets light brown and smooth. Almost exclusively on the coast.

The leaves rather broadly elliptical and pointed at both ends, the base approaching a wedge shape, the more regular teeth glandular-tipped, bright deep green above, rusty on the veins beneath. Pistillate cones very bulky ¾–1 inch long. Staminate catkins 1–2 inches long. Flowering in September, the wingless fruit ripening the following year.

On wet ground through southern Del. and eastern Md.; also in Okla.

White Alder
Alnus
rhombifolia

A tree of the Pacific slope, 30–50 or occasionally 70 feet high, with a trunk diameter of 2 feet. Bark dark brown, thin, scaly, the trunk clear of branches for about ½ its length, the crown broad and domelike, the lower branches drooping at the tips, the foliage decidedly pale or whitish green, the twigs ruddy tan.

The ovate leaves are light yellow green above, paler and fine-hairy beneath with ocher yellow ribs, 2½–4 inches long, fine-toothed, and sometimes irregularly notched along the edge. Staminate flowers in catkins about 5 inches long. The cones ½–⅞ inch long.

The White Alder is distributed generally over gravelly soil, along mountain streams from northern Ida. to the eastern slope of the Cascade Mts., Wash. and southeastern Ore., and south through the Coast ranges, the Sierra Nevada and Cuayamaca Mts. to southern Cal.

Red Alder
Alnus oregona

The largest of all the Alders, confined to the Pacific slope, 40–90 feet high, occasionally with a trunk diameter of 25 inches. A similar tree to the foregoing. Bark rather smooth, ashen gray, the shallow seamed twigs mahogany red, dotted.

the leaves similar to the last, larger, 3–5 inches long, ovate, coarsely toothed and pointed along the edge, rusty-haired especially on the veins beneath. Flowers similar to the last, but the cones longer $\frac{2}{3}$–1 inch long.

The Red Alder occurs on the borders of streams and on moist ground from Alaska through the Coast ranges of B. C. western Wash. Ore. and Cal. to the Santa Inez Mts. near Santa Barbara, southern Cal. The wood is light ruddy brown, cherrylike, brittle, and a trifle hard, often used in cabinet work; weight about 28 lbs. to the cubic foot.

A shrub or small tree of the Pacific slope 6–15 or occasionally 25 feet high, with a trunk diameter of 6 inches. Bark smooth, thin, and dark grayish brown, slightly seamed and thin-scaled, the smooth twigs grayish magenta.

Mountain Alder
Alnus tenuifolia

The ovate leaves 2½–4 inches long, dark green and smooth above, paler green, smooth or minutely hairy beneath, the midribs and stems ocher yellow, coarsely and sharply toothed over the many-notched edge. Flowering in March; the staminate catkins 2–3 inches long. Cones $\frac{1}{2}$–$\frac{5}{8}$ inch long.

The Mountain Alder follows the courses of mountain streams, and flourishes on cool springy hillsides from Alaska, and B. C. south through the Rocky Mts. to N. Mex. and southern Cal.; westward it extends to eastern Wash. and Ore. and climbs to an altitude of 6000–7000 feet on the western slopes of the Sierra Nevadas.

BEECH FAMILY. *Fagaceae.*

Trees or shrubs with alternate-growing leaves, and staminate and pistillate flowers which occur upon the same tree, the staminate in long, slender, tassellike, erect or drooping catkins, the pistillate tiny, scaly, and urn-shaped, finally developing the bur and the acorn.

A wide-spreading tree 45–50 and occasionally 100 feet high, with a trunk diameter of 2–4 feet, the continuous stem and almost horizontal, slender branches

Beech
Fagus grandifolia

forming a symmetrical, round-topped figure; the leafage conspicuously horizontal in manner of growth. Bark very smooth, light warm gray with patches of darker gray, buff, and whitish gray, often the colors of lichen-growth. Hence the tree has been called the "Painted Beech." Twigs very slender, zigzagged, light gray brown or brown ocher, lustrous and smooth.

Leaves papery thin, sharp-pointed, ovate, narrowed at the base, remarkably finely straight-veined, the veins distinctly terminating at the rather coarse sharp teeth; about 5 inches long, light green above, but slightly lighter beneath, altogether smooth except a slight downiness underneath on the midrib, very short-stemmed, changing to a light gold yellow in the fall. The leafy sprays are remarkably and conventionally flat; the pale buff leaves persist on the branches through the greater part of the winter. The staminate flowers on long, silky, drooping stems appear in May along with the leaves. Fruit a tiny bur with soft, spreading, recurved prickles; opening in four sections; it remains upon the branch after the nuts have fallen. The nuts (two in each bur) are brown, shining, three-sided, sweet, and edible, ripe in September–October. Borne in rhythmic abundance every 3–4 years.

The American Beech is common on rich uplands and on moist rocky ground from N. S. west to the north shores of Lake Huron, northern Wis. Mich. and Minn., and south through N. C. to Fla. It is more or less plentiful in the hilly parts of N. E. but rare near the coast. It reaches its greatest development on the bluffs of the lower Mississippi basin. The wood is close-grained, hard, and a pale brown or buff. It makes excellent fuel, and is occasionally used in the manufacture of woodenware, chairs, shoe-lasts, etc. The weight is 43 lbs. to the cubic foot.

Carolina Beech A similar tree to the type species, con-
Fagus fined to the coastal plain of the south, and
grandifolia var. the western and southwestern lowlands.
caroliniana[1] The leaves are smaller, proportionally broader, often slightly heart-shaped at the

[1] The determination by Fernald and Render.

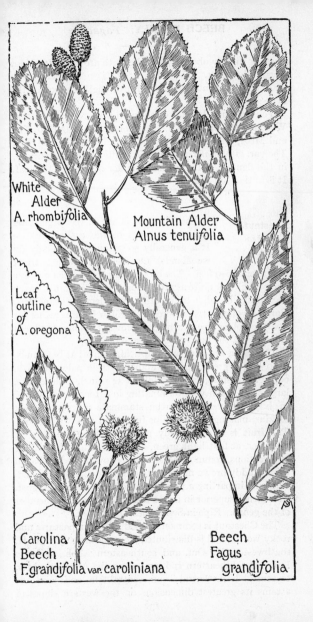

White
Alder
A. rhombifolia

Mountain Alder
Alnus tenuifolia

Leaf
outline
of
A. oregona

Carolina
Beech
F. grandifolia var. caroliniana

Beech
Fagus
grandifolia

base, or slightly obovate, and the teeth are very often (not invariably) finer. The foliage color is a distinctly dull, deep bluish green compared with the lighter green of the type species.

The Carolina Beech is distributed from N. J. Del. (near Wilmington), and W. Va. (Pocahontas Co.), south to Fla. and Miss., and southwest from O. to Tenn. Mo. and Tex. The var. *caroliniana*, forma *mollis*, differs from the variety, in the densely, soft, fine-hairy under surface of the leaf. It is in the Gulf States.

Chestnut
Castanea dentata

The Chestnut is one of the largest and commonest trees of the eastern States. It is generally 50–70 and occasionally (in woodlands) 120 feet high, with a trunk diameter of 6–9 feet. The brown gray trunk often massive and straight, or quite as often short and divided into heavy ascending boughs terminating in slender branchlets. Bark on younger trees scored by shallow fissures rather far apart, on older trees warm gray brown, the long, confluent ridges light, the furrows darker ard deeper.

The leaves are narrowly elliptical, pointed at both ends, deep bright green, smooth above, a trifle paler beneath, corrugated, straight-veined (about 34 veins), with remote, large teeth, each vein terminating in a tooth. Flowering in July; the yellowish green staminate flowers in erect catkins, making the tree-tops fuzzy and pale with bloom. The fruit is a sharp-spiny globular bur, 2–3 inches in diameter, at first light green, finally light brown, opening in 4 sections, commonly containing 3 ovate wedge-shaped bright ruddy brown nuts, white-downy at the pointed end. The burs imparting a paler tinge to the foliage in August. The kernel superior in flavor to that of any other member of the genus. Ripe in September–October.

The Chestnut is common in good soil, or in pastures and rocky woods, and is distributed from southern Me. N. H. southwestern Vt. Ont. and southeastern Mich., south to Del. and southeastern Ind. and along the Alleghany Mts. to central Ken. central Tenn. central Ala. and Miss. It attains its greatest dimensions on the western slopes of the southern Alleghanies. It is scarcely indigenous north of latitude 43° in N. E., but it is frequent in the Merrimac valley south of Concord, in Me. south of Portland, and in the Connecticut valley south of Windsor. There are also a few trees at Rutland and Burlington, Vt. It is unfortunately liable to a bark disease caused by a fungus parasite known as *Diaporthe parasitica*, and as a consequence great numbers of the tree have been destroyed especially in northern N. J., and in the immediate vicinity of New York and Philadelphia.[1] The trunk is also attacked, not infrequently, by the chestnut borer, *Ariopalus fulminans.*

The wood is light, soft, durable, coarse-grained, pale brown, and not strong; it is used for furniture, picture frames, railroad ties, fence posts, and piling. It weighs 28 lbs. per cubic foot. Large quantities of the nuts are sold at retail in the eastern cities in the fall, at the approximate rate of seven dollars per bushel! At the age of 5 years the Chestnut bears fruit, and in 15 years it is valuable for its timber. It is indeed a most extraordinary and rapid-growing tree.

Generally a shrub, 8–15 feet high, with characters similar to those of the Chestnut, but in the South a small tree sometimes 40 feet high, with a trunk diameter of 2 feet. Bark smooth, except on old trunks brown gray, the young shoots downy.

Chinquapin
Castanea pumila

The leaves deep green and smooth above, densely white downy beneath, long ovate or rather more bluntly elliptical than those of the Chestnut, yet acute-pointed and sharply, almost spinily toothed, 3–5 inches long. Flowering in June. The bur 1–1½ inches in diameter, the nut solitary and ovoid, not flattened except when rarely there are 2 in a bur. Ripe in September.

The Chinquapin is found in dry upland thickets and woods, and is distributed from N. J. and southern Penn. (Franklin, Cumberland, and York Cos.), west to Ind., and south to northern Fla. and eastern Tex. (Neches River). The wood is coarse-grained, durable, strong,

[1] *Vide* Haven Metcalf and J. Franklin Collins in Bull. 467, U.S. Dept. Agriculture, "The Control of the Chestnut Bark Disease."

deeper brown. Weight 38 lbs. to the cubic foot; not economically valuable.

**Western
Chinquapin
Golden-leaved
Chestnut**
*Castanea
chrysophylla*

A tree of the Pacific slope closely allied to *Castanea pumila*, commonly 30–50 and rarely 80–100 feet high, with a trunk diameter of 4 feet. Bark on older trees deeply furrowed, with flattened ridges composed of wide ruddy brown plates, bright mahogany red within, on younger trees thin, smooth, dark gray brown, the large ascending limbs forming a dome-shaped crown. On higher mountain slopes reduced to an almost prostrate shrub; the foliage evergreen.

The leaves are elliptical, or narrowly so, pointed at either end, with a toothless, slightly rolled-back edge, short-stemmed, lustrous deep yellow green above, covered with minute golden yellow scales beneath, leathery in texture, persisting for about 3 years on the branchlets, 3–6 inches long. Flowers in flexible terminal spikes, yellow green—June. Fruit a spiny bur 1–1¾ inches broad, opening in 4 divisions containing a (generally) single chestnut-colored nut, sweet and edible.

The Western Chinquapin is common on mountain slopes, in sheltered ravines or valleys, generally in dry gravelly soil, and is distributed from southwestern Wash. south through the Cascade Mts. the Sierra Nevadas, and the Coast Ranges, to the San Jacinto Mts. southern Cal. Wood soft, brittle, fine-grained, and pale ruddy brown. Weight about 38 lbs. to the cubic foot. Trees with trunks from 18–25 inches in diameter are 150–190 years old.

White Oak
Quercus alba

A large oak of great economic value, 50–70 and sometimes in favorable situations 150 feet high, with a trunk diameter of 6–8 feet. The trunk short, the branches heavy and wide-spreading, the figure, in the open, sometimes broader than high. Bark whitish gray, or lightest buffish brown, firm, furrowed into deep, perpendicular ridges, with narrow, long, flat scales; the twigs greenish or gray, smooth, sometimes with a slight bloom.

Chestnut
Castanea
dentata

Shrub
with blunt
Southern
form
leaf
Cal.

Chinquapin
C. pumila

Western

Chinquapin
C. chrysophylla

The leaves are bright olive green above, much paler and smooth beneath (fine-hairy when very young), and are deeply divided into 7-9 blunt, *rounded* lobes, wedge-shaped at the base, about 4-7 inches long, obovate in outline. Staminate flowers in long, slender, threadlike catkins, appearing in May-June.

The light brown acorn commonly in pairs, with an ovoid nut and hemispherical cup, the scales of which are knobby but become small and thin at the rim; the meat sweet, edible. Maturing the first year.

The White Oak usually occurs in dry, upland woods, or on sandy plains and gravelly ridges, and is distributed from southern Me. west through southwestern Que. and central and southern Ont. to southern Mich. and Minn. southeastern Neb. and eastern Kan., and south to northern Fla. (St. John's River and Tampa Bay), and the Brazos River, Tex. It is not indigenous in northern and central N. H. but it extends (scattered) up the valley of the Connecticut as far as the mouth of the Passumpsic River in Vt. It is common only west of the Green Mts., and in southern N. E. It reaches its best development on the slopes of the Alleghany Mts., and in the valley of the Ohio River. In N. C. it attains an average height of 75 feet, and is most plentiful on the Piedmont plateau—which comprises nearly the western half of the State.[1] The wood is strong, heavy (50 lbs. to the cubic foot), hard, tough, and close-grained, very durable in contact with the soil, and pale brown with lighter sapwood. It is used in ship-building, for construction, cooperage, agricultural implements, etc., also for interior house finish, baskets, fencing, clapboards, and fuel. The bark is also used for tanning. Commercially it is one of the most important and valuable timber trees of the United States.

Post Oak
Iron Oak
Quercus stellata

A rough-appearing but useful oak, very variable in habit, reaching a height of only 9-35 feet at the northern limit of its range, but often 50-100 feet high in the South, and on the coast of Florida reduced

---

[1] *Vide* Gifford Pinchot in *Timber Trees of North Carolina*, pg. 90.

to a low shrub. The stem usually straight, the branches mostly horizontal, and the bark a dull, light brown, and rougher than that of the White Oak, with shorter ridges and scales. The twigs light terra-cotta brown when young, sepia brown when old, covered with rough down (under the glass).

The leaves are dull dark green, leathery, rough above, gray-downy beneath, cut irregularly into 5–7 rounded, spreading lobes, the upper lobes often much the larger. Flowering in May–June. The grayish brown acorn similar to that of the White Oak, small, with a deeper hemispherical cup covering about $\frac{1}{3}$ of the nut, much less knobby, rather smooth-scaled. The meat sweet. Maturing the first year.

The Post Oak is common in sandy, or poor soil, and is distributed from southern Mass. (Falmouth to Brewster, Cape Cod, and the islands of Naushon, Nantucket, and Martha's Vineyard), North Kingston and Wickford, R. I. and Long Island, N. Y., south over the coastal plain (and the Piedmont plateau) to northern Fla. southern Ala. and Miss., and westward from Long Island to Mo. eastern Kan. and Okla., thence to the coast—La. and Tex. (San Antonio River), and west to meridian 100°. On Nantucket Island, eastern shore, near Wauwinet, there are a few trees less than 10 feet high; there is one in Tom Never's Swamp, another at Saul's Hills, and a group of 4 trees one mile northwest of Siasconset.[1]

In Conn. it is local, usually on rocky ground near the coast at Lyme, Branford, New Haven, and westward. It grows to a height of 50 feet in N. C. and attains its best development on the Piedmont plateau. The wood is very heavy, hard, close-grained, tough, and durable in contact with the soil; but it cracks badly in drying. It is used for shipbuilding, fence posts, railroad ties, cooperage, and construction, also for fuel. Weight per cubic foot 52 lbs.

[1] *Vide* E. P. Bicknell in Bulletin Torrey Bot. Club, vol. **xxxvi.** pg. 25.

BEECH FAMILY. *Fagaceae*

Overcup Oak
Swamp Post
Oak
Quercus lyrata

A large tree common in swampy lands of the coastal plain, 50–70 and very rarely 100 feet high, with a trunk diameter of 3 feet. The bark a dull gray brown, rough and thin-scaly, the branches much smoother, slender, generally horizontal, often drooping, forming (in the open) a round-topped symmetrical figure.

The large leaves are 5–8 inches long, bright olive green above, densely white-woolly beneath (in age more smooth), the 3–4 spreading lobes on either side a trifle acute or blunt, the general outline elliptical; they grow in crowded order at the summit of the branches, and turn a deep cardinal red in autumn. The large acorn, broader than it is deep, about 1 inch in diameter, *nearly covered* by the rough-scaly, thin, fringed cup. Maturing the first year; ripe in Oct.

The Overcup Oak is found on coastal flats or in alluvial swamps of rivers, and is distributed from N. J. and Md. (Potomac River near D. C., and Patuxent River, 3 miles below Laurel) south along the coast through N. C. (as far inland as Anson, Orange, and Nash Cos.), to western Fla., and west through Ala. Miss. and La. to Tex. (valley of the Trinity River), and through Ark. and southeastern Mo. (near Allenton) to central Tenn. southern Ind. and Ill. (Rafes Mill, Embarras River in southeastern Jasper Co.). It attains its greatest development in the valley of the Red River, La. Ark. and Tex. It is not so common on the Atlantic seaboard. The wood is heavy, hard, strong, close-grained, durable, and a warm deep brown. It is used for purposes similar to those for which White Oak is employed; the weight is 52 lbs. to the cubic foot.

Bur Oak
Mossy-cup
Oak
Quercus
macrocarpa

A similar but larger northern Oak, having the same ashen gray or gray brown, thin-scaly bark, 40–80 and occasionally 160 or more feet high, with a trunk diameter of 6 feet. It is one of the tallest oaks of the eastern United States. The younger branchlets conspicuously corky-ridged, but this is not an altogether dependable character.

The large leaves are 5–8 inches long, lustrous deep olive

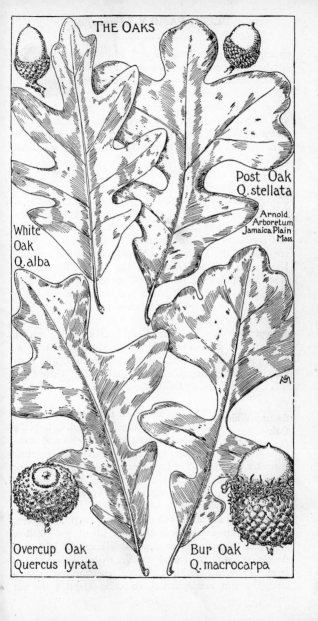

THE OAKS

White
Oak
Q. alba

Post Oak
Q. stellata

Arnold.
Arboretum
Jamaica Plain
Mass.

Overcup Oak
Quercus lyrata

Bur Oak
Q. macrocarpa

green, much paler beneath and white-woolly, with 3–4 notched and rounded lobes on either side; obovate in general outline. They turn a dull rusty or maroon red in autumn. Flowering in May–June. Acorn very large 1¾ inches across the hemispherical cup, which with its frayed and ragged edge (the coarse upper scales are long-awned) resembles a miniature bird's nest, and covers about ½ the nut. The acorns are extremely variable in size, and mature the first year.

The Bur Oak is found in the rich soil of bottom-lands, and is distributed from N. B. and N. S. west through the St. Lawrence River Valley to Ont. and Man. (south of Lake Winnipeg), and from the Penobscot River, Me. (Orono), shores of Lake Champlain Vt. Ware River, Mass. and Lancaster Co. Penn. west and southwest to the eastern base of the Rocky Mts. Mont. western Neb. central Kan. central Tenn. Okla. and the Nueces River, Tex. It is a rare Oak in N. E. with no known station in N. H. or R. I. and, excepting Vt., with few stations in the other States. It is reported from Canaan and Salisbury, Conn. It attains its greatest development in the Ohio and Mississippi Valleys. The var. *olivaeformis* is a form with a slender leaf the lobes of which are deeply cut and narrow. The wood is deep brown, tough, close-grained, and commercially not distinguished from that of the White Oak; it is a trifle lighter, 47 lbs. to the cubic foot.

Swamp White Oak
Quercus bicolor

A large tree with flaky bark similar to that of the foregoing species, but the ridges somewhat longer, 50–60 and occasionally 110 feet high, with a trunk diameter of 8 feet. The branches very scragged, the bark often shredded, making the appearance of the tree extremely rough; younger trees with not very coarse seams; bark a warm light brown.

The leaves are large, 6–8 inches long, deep olive green, densely white-woolly beneath, with about 5–6 shallow scolloped lobes on either side, sometimes the lobes cut deeper, obovate in general outline, wedge-shaped at the base. Flowering in May. Acorn, chestnut-red, 1 inch long, the cup hemispherical, enclosing about ½ the nut or less, often fringe-edged, the upper scales being awn-pointed; frequently in clusters of 2–3 on a long stalk. Maturing the first year, generally in October.

The Swamp White Oak is common on the borders of swamps and streams, and is distributed generally over the lowlands from southern Me. (York Co.), Vt. (the Champlain Valley), and southwestern Que. west through Ont. and southern Mich. to southeastern Io. and western Mo., and south to the Potomac River, D. C. northern Ky. and Ark. and along the Alleghany Mts. to northern Ga. It is rare in northern N. E., found only in southern N. H. (Rockingham Co.) and the borders of Lake Champlain, Vt. where it is frequent, and is more or less common in Mass. R. I. and Conn. The wood is similar to that of the White Oak and is not commercially distinguished from it; it is used for the same purposes. The weight is about 48 lbs. to the cubic foot.

A large southern oak economically valuable, 70–90 and occasionally, in favorable situations, 120 feet high, with a trunk diameter of 7 feet. The bark gray, scaly, and rough, the trunk comparatively massive, the branches stout.

Basket Oak
Cow Oak
Swamp
Chestnut Oak
Quercus
Michauxii

The leaves are bright deep green above, much lighter or grayish beneath and downy, set with about 10–11 regular, scolloped teeth on either side, elliptical or obovate in outline, 4–8 inches long and rather rigid. The staminate flowers appear in April–May. The large acorn about $1\frac{1}{8}$ inches long and $\frac{7}{8}$ inch broad, with an ovoid nut, and a not very deep hemispherical cup the scales of which are appressed, hard, and acute; the meat sweet, edible. Maturing the first year, ripe in October.

The Basket Oak is found on river banks and in swamps, and is distributed from Del. (near Wilmington), south along the coastal plain and the Piedmont plateau (particularly Bladen Co. N. C.), to northern Fla., thence through the Gulf States to the Trinity River Valley, Tex., thence north along water courses to Ark. southeastern Mo. central Tenn. and Ky. and to the valley of the lower Wabash River. It reaches its highest development on the rich bottom-lands of southeastern Ark. and La. The wood is light brown, heavy (50 lbs to the cubic foot), hard, strong, durable, and close-grained. It is used in basket-making, and for the same general purposes as those of the Post Oak its qualities being similar.

Chinquapin Oak
Yellow Chestnut Oak
Quercus Muhlenbergii

A tall, handsome, light-colored oak, 40–80, and occasionally 160 feet high, with a trunk diameter of 7 feet. The thin bark a dull silvery gray; in age the surface thin-scaly.

The leaves are bright yellow green above, silvery gray (fine woolly) beneath, with about 11 rather sharp-pointed, scolloped teeth on either side, narrowly sharp-elliptical in outline, slender-stemmed, about 4–7½ inches long. Flowering in May-June. The small acorn almost round, about ¾ inch long, the hemispherical cup thin, the scales small, not very rough. The nut edible, maturing the first year.

The Yellow Chestnut Oak is common in dry hillside soil, rich river bottoms, and on limestone ridges, and is distributed from Gardiner Island, at the mouth of Little Otter Creek, Ferrisburgh, Lake Champlain, Vt. and the Hudson River Valley north of Newburg, N. Y. west through southern Ont. to southern Minn. eastern Neb. Kan. and Okla. and to Ark. northern La. central Miss. central Ala. and Tex. (Nueces River and cañons of the Guadalupe Mts. westerly); east of the Alleghanies the limit is the upper Potomac River, D. C. It is rare in N. E. and beside the station on Lake Champlain, is reported only from Canaan, Salisbury, Kent, and New Milford, in Conn. The wood is hard, strong, close-grained, durable, brownish, and heavy (54 lbs. to the cubic foot), and serves for many purposes similar to those for which Post Oak is employed.

Scrub Chestnut Oak. Dwarf Chinquapin Oak
Quercus prinoides

A shrub Oak 3–9 or rarely 12 feet high growing in clumps generally on rocky hillside pastures, the stems about 1–2 inches in diameter. Bark light warm gray, the branchlets and twigs dull tan-color, generally smooth; the bark checked and scaly when old.

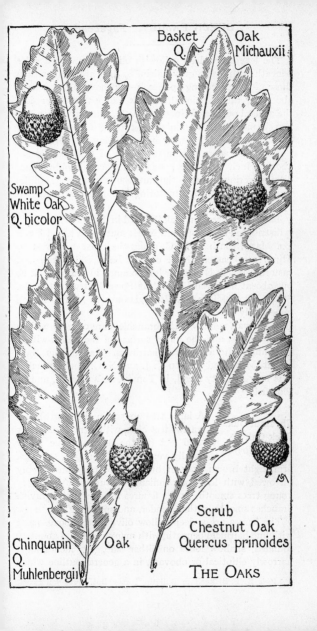

Basket Oak
Q. Michauxii

Swamp
White Oak
Q. bicolor

Chinquapin Oak
Q. Muhlenbergii

Scrub
Chestnut Oak
Quercus prinoides

THE OAKS

The leaves are deep yellowish olive green, much paler beneath with a fine gray hairiness, they are smaller than those of the preceding species, 4–6 inches long, and have about 6–7 rather pointed, shallow scollops on either side, the general outline distinctly obovate, acute at the tip, the margin more or less undulating; turning a beautiful rusty red in autumn. Flowering in April–May. The lustrous chestnut red acorn is similar to that of *Q. Muhlenbergii*, about ¾ inch long, the hemispherical cup knobby, thin, deep, covering about ½ the nut, the kernel sweet, edible; produced abundantly, maturing the first year, ripe in October.

The Scrub Chestnut Oak is found in dry, sandy soil, and is distributed from southern N. H. southern Vt. and Essex Co. Mass., south to N. C. along the coast, and west to Minn. southeastern Neb. central Kan. Okla. Ala. and eastern Tex. It is more or less common in southern N. E. but absent northward except at Pownal, Bennington Co. Snaky Mt. Addison Co. Vt. and southern N. H. Range imperfectly known.

In the var. *rufescens*, the branchlets are covered with a fine hairiness, and the under surface of the leaves with a very fine white and tawny hairiness. Range from Nantucket, Mass. and L. I. to N. J. and N. C. In Nantucket it is near Sankaty Head, in Tom Never's Swamp, and at Plainfield.[1]

Chestnut Oak
Rock Oak
Quercus Prinus

A large tree 40–50 (in the North) and often 100 feet high, with a trunk diameter of 4–6 feet (in the South). The trunk generally very tall and straight, the bark firm, light brown gray or blackish, coarsely and deeply furrowed with long perpendicular fissures, but on very young trees smooth, or the fissures far apart; the grayish branches smooth, rather slender, and spreading.

The leaves are a deep yellow olive green above, paler with fine hairiness beneath, with many veins and about 10 rounded, shallow lobes on either side, 5–7 inches long, narrowly elliptical or obovate, in a general outline which

[1] *Vide* E. P. Bicknell in Bulletin Torrey Bot. Club, vol. **xxxvi.**, pg. 26.

is similar to that of the chestnut leaf. Flowering in May.
The acorn is a particularly lustrous chestnut red, long-
ovoid, slender, about $1-1\frac{1}{3}$ inches long, the thick cup
hemispherical, rough with hard knobby scales covering
nearly $\frac{1}{2}$ the nut; the meat not sweet, scarcely edible.
Maturing the first year, in late October.

The Chestnut Oak is found on dry hillsides and in rocky
woods, and is distributed from southern Me. (Saco River
Valley), west to Vt. (Charlotte, through Addison, Rutland,
and Bennington Cos., to Pownal), and the Genesee Valley
N. Y. to Lake Erie, (from Niagara River to Amherstburg),
and eastern Mass. (the Blue Hills near Readville), and
south to the Potomac River D. C. central Ky. and Tenn.
and through the Alleghany Mts. to northern Ga. and Ala.
It reaches its best development in the mountains west of
Franklin and Montgomery Cos. N. C., particularly on the
lower slopes at 2000–4000 feet elevation, where with other
oaks and the chestnut it forms a large part of the forest.
Above 4000 feet it grows on the driest and rockiest ridges.
On the Piedmont plateau it is smaller, seldom reaching a
diameter of 12 inches.[1] It is not a common oak of N. E.,
though it is not infrequent in eastern and southern N. H.
and is found along the western section of Vt. It is frequent
in eastern Mass. R. I. and Conn. In N. Y. in the lower
Hudson River Valley it is locally common. The wood is
heavy, durable, hard, tough, close-grained, and deep
brown. It is commonly used for railroad ties, fencing, and
fuel. The bark is rich in tannin, and is used in large
quantities for tanning leather. The weight is 47 lbs. per
cubic foot.

A large, spreading, evergreen, southern
Oak 40–50 and sometimes 60 feet high,
with a trunk diameter of 7 feet. The bark
very dark brown, rough, deeply furrowed,

Live Oak
Quercus
virginiana

the ridges and branches a grayer brown. In the open the
tree forms a symmetrical broad-topped figure with wide
spreading limbs, and drooping, hoary gray branchlets.

The small, leathery, evergreen leaf is without lobes, or
teeth, and has a perceptibly undulating edge, or it is

[1] *Vide* Gifford Pinchot in *Timber Trees of North Carolina*, pg. 94.

bristle-tipped at the scarcely toothlike, dull, terminal points. Length 2–4 inches, smooth, very dark olive green above, pale green and hoary with finest hairs beneath, oblong or elliptical in general outline. Flowering in March –April. The small, very dark brown acorn, about ⅔ inch long, long-stemmed (¼ inch), the cup top-shaped, covering ⅓ of the nut, the scales close-pressed, small; kernel not edible. Maturing the first year; ripe in September– October.

The Live Oak is commonly found in dry soil, from Mobjack Bay, Va., and on islands near the coast, south to Biscayne Bay, Fla., and along the Gulf coast (from Cape Romano) to the mouth of the Rio Grande, and inland to the Red River, and Apache and Guadalupe Mts. Tex. It also extends to Central America and Cuba. It reaches its greatest development in the South Atlantic States, but in the interior of Texas it is often reduced to a shrub. In N. C. it occurs near the coast on sandy soil along with the Water and Willow Oaks. North of Cape Hatteras it is rare, but from Cape Lookout to Cape Fear it is plentiful, and at the mouth of Cape Fear River, on Smith's Island, it forms a considerable part of the maritime forest, and is associated with the Palmetto. The wood is extremely hard, heavy, and close-grained; it is difficult to work and turns the edges of tools with discouraging frequency, but it takes a superb polish, and makes a beautiful interior finish for buildings and ships; the color is light golden brown. It is used for shipbuilding, and the bark is occasionally used for tanning. The weight is fully 60 lbs. to the cubic foot; it is the heaviest wood of all the oaks.

Red Oak
Quercus rubra

The tallest of the northern oaks 50–80 and in rich woods occasionally 140 feet high, with a trunk diameter of 2–6 feet, the trunk branching often at quite a distance from the ground (in the woods), the many rather heavy branches irregular and ascending, or in the open, nearly horizontal. Bark on very young trees nearly smooth grayish brown, on old trees dark brown, or dark gray brown, the perpendicular furrows shallow, the ridges flat-topped, coarse, rather long and somewhat regularly set—distinctly differ-

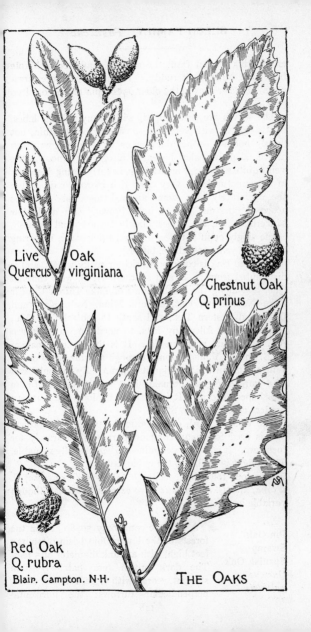

Live Oak
Quercus virginiana

Chestnut Oak
Q. prinus

Red Oak
Q. rubra
Blair. Campton. N·H·

THE OAKS

ent in this respect from the shaggy character of Maple bark; the inner bark ruddy. The new twigs are terra-cotta, or ocher brown, the older ones sepia brown, or often gray.

The leaves are wavy-edged, with many-pointed lobes, bristle-tipped, with very few subsidiary points, thin, not deeply notched, either dark green or deep yellow green above, slightly paler beneath, altogether smooth, the veins quite white; 4–7 inches long, in early spring deep red, in autumn turning a very dark rich maroon red. Often the moderately long stems are red-tinged above. The acorn is chestnut red or light brown, with a shallow saucerlike cup, the scales closely lapped and smooth, borne singly or in pairs on a short, thick stalk, maturing the *second* year; not edible, bitter.

The Red Oak is common in rich or rocky woods, and is distributed from N. S. and southern N. B. west through Que. and along the north shores of Lake Huron to near Lake Namekagon Ont. eastern Minn. Neb. Kan. and Okla. and western Tex., and south to central Tenn. Va., and along the Alleghany Mts. to northern Ga. southern Ala. Miss., and northern Fla. It is the common oak of N. E. and N. Y. and extends through and far north of the White Mts., in which region it is practically the only oak. The var. *ambigua*, Fernald, has deeper-cupped (more top-shaped) acorns. It is distributed along the northern borders of the Eastern States.

The wood is hard, coarse-grained, strong, light brown, and is used for many common purposes, but rarely for furniture. It is too coarse-grained to be especially valuable. The weight is 41 lbs. to the cubic foot.

The four following species *Q. palustris*, *Q. coccinea*, *Q. texana*, and *Q. elipsoidalis* have extremely similar though variable leaves.

Pin Oak
Swamp
Spanish Oak
Quercus
palustris

A tall tree commonly 50–80 and in the forests of the lower Ohio basin often 110 feet high, with a trunk diameter of 5 feet. The dark brown (gray-patched) stem straight, scored with close, shallow, short, perpendicular furrows; the horizontal limbs slender and somewhat drooping, all more or less set with tiny branchlets which occasion the name Pin Oak.

The leaves are bright deep olive green above, paler below with a tufted fine-hairiness at the angles of the ribs, very deeply cut, with 2–3 narrow lobes on either side, the sharp points bristle-tipped; length 3–5 inches, the general outline broad-ovate; they turn a rich cardinal red in autumn. Flowering in May. The small acorn nearly globular, with a shallow saucerlike cup about ½ inch broad, the scales thin and flat; maturing the second year, ripe in October, not edible, bitter.

The Pin Oak is common in moist ground, and is distributed from central Mass. (Amherst), west to southeastern Mo. Kan. northern Ark. eastern Okla. and central Ky., and south to the Potomac River, Va. It reaches its finest development in the rich bottom-lands of the Ohio River Valley. In N. E. it is confined to the Connecticut River Valley and one or two stations in southern R. I. The wood is hard, strong, light brown, coarse-grained, and weighs 34 lbs. to the cubic foot. Commercially it is not valuable. It is used mostly in construction.

A medium-sized tree in the North, 40–50 or in advantageous circumstances 170 feet high, with a trunk diameter of 4 feet. The dark brown bark with very irregular, shallow furrows, thick and rough, internally reddish, the trunk rather massive, often with grayish patches, the limbs heavy, quite horizontal below, ascending to a round-topped head above. **Scarlet Oak** *Quercus coccinea*

The leaves thin, bright olive green above, paler and dull below with tufts of tan-colored hairs at the rib-angles; like those of the foregoing species they are very deeply cut into about 7 narrow lobes of 3–5 or more points bristle-tipped; length about 4–6 inches, the general figure broadly ovate, often nearly square-cut at the base. They turn a bright cardinal red in autumn (in the sunlight), more brilliant than the usual red coloring of the oaks, but never actually scarlet nor anything approaching that uncompromising hue! The small acorn has a thin, saucer-shaped or top-shaped cup, about ½ inch broad, the nut is nearly globular, the scales of the cup close-pressed; maturing the second year, ripe in September and October, not edible, slightly bitter.

The Scarlet Oak is found in dry, sandy or gravelly soil, and is distributed from western Me. and southern N. H. south to N. C. and Ill., and west through central N. Y. to southern Ont. central Mich. southern Minn. and south-eastern Neb. It reaches its highest development in the lower Ohio basin. In N. C. it is abundant on the Piedmont plateau where it attains a height of 80 feet. In the mountains it is common at elevations of 2500–3500 feet. In southern N. E. it is fairly common, but in northern N. H. and Vt. it is quite absent. The wood is like that of the Red Oak, coarse, and commercially of no considerable value; it makes good fuel. The weight is 42 lbs. per cubic foot.

Texan Red Oak
Quercus texana

One of the largest of the American Oaks 50–70, and in the bottom-lands of the lower Mississippi River 180 feet high, with a trunk diameter of 7 feet. The bark brownish gray (on older trees darker ruddy brown) with darker stripes and spots, the ridges broad, broken into irregular plates, the furrows shallow; the branches smooth and grayish brown.

The leaves thin, bright olive green above, lighter beneath and with tufts of light hairs at the angles of the veins; like those of *Q. palustris* deeply cut into 5–9 commonly 7 narrow, generally three-pointed, bristle-tipped lobes; length about 3–6 inches. The general figure broadly ovate, nearly square at the base. Turning brown red in autumn. Flowering in April. The acorn oblong, rather variable in size, $\frac{3}{4}$–$1\frac{1}{2}$ inches long, the top-shaped cup covering $\frac{1}{3}$ of the nut, the brown or gray scales with a permanently woolly surface. Maturing the second year, ripe in September.

The Texan Red Oak is found in the rich soil of river swamps or on moist limestone hillsides, and is distributed from Ind. west to northeastern Io. (Waterloo), and south through western Ky. Tenn. and N. C. to Fla. (the Apalachicola River), and through southern Mo. Ark. and La.

Pin Oak
Q. palustris

Scarlet Oak
Q. coccinea

Texan Red Oak
Quercus texana

THE OAKS

Yellow Oak
Q. ellipsoidalis

to western Tex. (Limpio Mts.). The range imperfectly known. In N. C. it grows to a height of 50–70 feet, and is scarce, and entirely local from Lincoln Co. eastward to Person Co. In western Texas it is reduced to a shrub or small tree. The wood is coarse-grained, strong and ruddy brown. It is heavier than most of the oaks, and weighs 57 lbs. to the cubic foot.

Yellow Oak
Quercus
ellipsoidalis [1]

A medium-sized western tree resembling *Q. palustris;* a new species imperfectly known. The bark gray with shallow furrows, internally yellow.

The leaves resemble those of *Q. palustris,* and have 5–7 lobes; they turn ocher yellow or brown buff in autumn. The acorn also resembles that of *Q. texana* in its characters, but is very much smaller, about $\frac{3}{4}$ inch long.

The Yellow Oak is found in clay or gravelly soil, and is distributed from southern Mich. to Io. and Man. Range not fully known.

Black Oak
Quercitron
Quercus
velutina

One of the finest and largest eastern oaks, commonly 50–70 and in favorable situations 160 feet high, with a trunk diameter of 6 feet. Bark deep warm gray, or sometimes nearly sepia (internally orange yellow), thick, very rough, broken into short, thick ridges, more or less rounded. The branches light gray brown, stout and spreading, smooth, forming in the open a symmetrical figure.

The leaves are deep lustrous green above, dull whitish olive green beneath, the veins covered with a fine hairiness; they are more or less deeply cut into about 3 lobes on either side, each terminating in 3 or more bristle-tipped points; length 4–6 inches. They turn a russet brown or dull red in autumn. Flowering in May. The acorn is light brown, about 1 inch long, the top-shaped cup covering about $\frac{1}{2}$ the nut, the scales coarse, long, and rather loose; the kernel yellow and bitter, maturing the second year, ripe in October, not edible.

The Black Oak is common on dry, gravelly uplands, and

---

[1] Gray's *Manual of Botany*, 7th ed., pg. 342.

is distributed from southern Me. (York Co.), and western Vt. west to western Ont. and central Minn., and south to northern Fla., southwest it extends to eastern Kan. Okla. and eastern Tex. In N. E. it is not common, but occurs frequently in the lower Merrimac Valley, N. H., in the Connecticut Valley, southern Vt., in eastern Mass., in R. I., and in Conn. In N. C. it attains an average height of 85 feet, and is abundantly distributed over the mountain region and that of the Piedmont plateau. The var. *missouriensis* has leaves with persisting rusty down beneath, and the scales of the acorn-cup are also downy. The wood is heavy, hard, strong, coarse-grained, and light ruddy brown. It is used for construction and cooperage; weight 44 lbs. to the cubic foot. The bark is rich in tannin, and a yellow dye is extracted from it, commercially known as Quercitron.

Spanish Oak
Quercus falcata
A medium-sized or large Oak 50–80 and in the forest often 100 feet high, with a trunk diameter of 5 feet. The bark sepia brown, often blackish, very roughly and deeply seamed, the somewhat smooth branches grayer. Often a tree with a wide-spreading top and broad figure.

The leaves variable, dull dark green above, paler and very downy beneath, divided into about 3–5 slender, slightly curved lobes, each terminating in 1–3 bristle-tipped points, the bases conspicuously rounded, the general figure broadly obovate; about 4–7 inches long. Flowering in April–May. The acorn globular, small, about $\frac{2}{3}$ inch long, with a saucer-shaped cup, top-shaped at the base, covering about $\frac{1}{2}$ the nut; the kernel bitter, not edible; maturing the second year, ripe in October.

The Spanish Oak is found in dry upland or sandy lowland soil, and is distributed from southern N. J. (reported from Bucks Co. Pa.), south through the seaboard States to central Fla., and through the Gulf States to eastern Tex. (Brazos River), and northward to Ark. southwestern Mo. central Tenn. and Ky. and southern Ill. and Ind. In N. C. it is widely distributed over the State and is very common on the Piedmont plateau where it attains a height of 70–80 feet. It is rather sensitive to late frosts. The wood is heavy, hard, strong, coarse-grained, but not durable, weight 43 lbs. to the cubic foot. The bark yields a large amount of tannin.

Bear Oak
Black Scrub
Oak
Quercus
ilicifolia

Commonly a shrub 3–10 feet high, though occasionally it attains the dimensions of a small tree 20–24 feet high, with a trunk diameter of 6–10 inches. It often forms dense thickets on mountain sides in the South, the figure straggling, the stems crooked, and the branches spreading. Bark dark grayish brown, generally smooth, but roughly seamed on older trunks.

The small leaves 3–4 inches long, dark yellow green above, grayish white and downy beneath, with 2 broad, shallowly cut lobes on either side each terminating commonly in a single, blunt, bristle-tipped point, or rarely with 7 lobes, the general outline obovate, turning rusty yellow or russet brown in autumn. Flowering in early May. The light brown acorn barely ½ inch long, with a top-shaped cup covering about ½ the nut which is pointed at the apex; the scales closely overlapped. Maturing the second year, ripe in October–November.

The Bear Oak is common on sandy barrens or rocky soil, and is distributed from Me. (Mount Desert Island), through eastern and southern N. E. and N. Y. (Lake George and Hudson River Valley), to N. J. (pine barrens), and eastern Pa. and along the Alleghany Mts. (east in Md. to Montgomery Co.), to northwestern N. C. (King and Crowders Mts.), and Ky. It is common in southern N. E. (Mass, R. I. and Conn.), Mount Desert, Me. (and eastward), but local at Conway N. H., and Bellows Falls, Vt.

Water Oak
Quercus nigra

A small tree 28–40 but in favorable situations 80 feet high, with a trunk diameter of 4 feet. The bark smoothish above, but in rough ridges with shallow fissures below. light warm gray, or brownish. A tree commonly with a broad irregularly spreading top, mostly confined to the coastal plain, with many varietal forms, not fully studied.

The thick leaves often evergreen but generally deciduous, a rich, deep olive green above, lighter beneath, but smooth

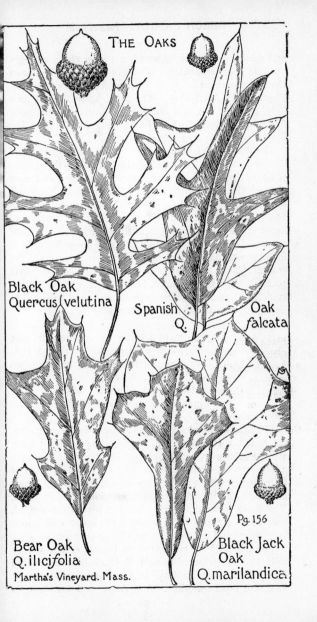

THE OAKS

Black Oak
Quercus velutina

Spanish
Q.

Oak
falcata

Bear Oak
Q. ilicifolia
Martha's Vineyard. Mass.

Pg. 156

Black Jack
Oak
Q. marilandica

and shining on both sides, small, 2–4 inches long, strongly obovate in general outline, with 3 blunt, rounded lobes at the tip, or without lobes, the lobes with or without bristles. Flowering in April–May. The small acorn about ½ inch long, globular, set in a saucer-shaped, shallow cup, with fine, close scales; the kernel very bitter. Maturing the second year, ripe in October.

The Water Oak is common on wet flats, and swamps, and is distributed south from southern Del. along the coastal plain to Cape Malabar and Tampa Bay, Fla., and west through the Gulf States to the Colorado River, Tex., and northward through Ark. eastern Okla. to southeastern Mo. (Black River), central Tenn. and Ky. It reaches its finest development on the maritime borders of the Gulf States. In N. C. it grows to a height of 40–50 feet, and is found mostly on the borders of swamps and streams of the coastal plain, and southern portions of the Piedmont plateau. The wood is hard, heavy (weight 46 lbs. to the cubic foot), strong, coarse-grained, and light brown. It has no especial value, and is used mostly for fuel.

Black Jack Oak
Barren Oak
Quercus marilandica

A small tree 25–40 or rarely 60 feet high, with a trunk diameter of 2 feet. The very rough bark sepia brown, often nearly black, heavily scored with deep furrows and broken ridges. The branches irregular, spreading, and generally drooping.

The broad, thick leaves dark lustrous olive green above, paler and rusty-hairy beneath, about 4–6 inches long, strongly obovate or wedge-shaped in general outline, with 3 lobes at the extremely broad tip, each bristle-tipped; not infrequently with 5 moderately deep lobes; turning brown or yellow russet brown in autumn. Flowering in April. The acorn is small, nearly globular, with a top-shaped, coarse-scaled cup covering about ½ the nut, about ¾ inch long; maturing the second year, ripe in October.

The Black Jack Oak occurs on barren, sandy, or clay soils, and is distributed from N. Y. (Forbell's Landing and Pine Island, Jamaica Bay, L. I.), through northern O. Ind. and southern Mich. (Ann Arbor and Lansing), to

Minn. southeastern Neb. central Kan. and Okla., and south to Fla. (Matanzas Inlet and Tampa Bay), and Tex. (Nueces River). It reaches its finest development in southern Ark. and eastern Tex., and occurs in all sections of N. C. though rare in the mountains. The wood is heavy, hard, strong, and dark brown; it is used principally for fuel, and has little commercial value. Weight 46 lbs. per cubic foot.

An Oak 40–60 and not infrequently 90 feet high, with a trunk diameter of 3 feet. Bark deep dull brown, rather smooth above, rougher below with small scales, the furrows without a marked perpendicu- **Laurel Oak** / **Shingle Oak** / *Quercus* / *imbricaria*
lar trend, the limbs a lighter gray, forming an irregular, spreading top. Commonly a forest tree, confined to mountain districts, and in the west, to rich, alluvial, wooded lowlands.

The leaves thick, smooth, lustrous dark olive green above, grayish with downy hairs beneath, shaped like the laurel leaf, elongated elliptical, pointed, bristle-tipped, 3–6 inches long, the margin often slightly ruffled. They are finally a pale leather brown, in late autumn. Flowering in April–May. The acorn nearly globular, set shallowly in a saucerlike (slightly top-shaped) cup, with close-pressed scales. Maturing the second year, ripe in October.

The Laurel Oak is found in rich woods, and is distributed from eastern Pa. (Lehigh Co.), west through southern Mich. (Washtenaw and Kalamazoo Cos.), and Wis. to eastern Neb. northeastern Kan. Mo. and northern Ark., and south to D. C. and through the Alleghany Mts. to central Tenn. northern Ga. and Ala. It reaches its best development in the Ohio basin, and grows to a height of 40–50 feet in the Alleghany region of N. C. It occurs locally in eastern Mass. The wood is heavy, hard, coarse-grained, and pale brown; it is occasionally used for con-struction and shingles, and it makes an excellent fuel. The weight is 48 lbs. per cubic foot.

Willow Oak
Quercus phellos

An Oak 40–60 and in favorable situations 80 feet high, with a trunk diameter of 4 feet. Bark deep ruddy brown, shallowly seamed, the branches smooth, spreading. A tree often cultivated in the southern cities for its beauty and its shade.

The leaves nearly evergreen, bright light olive green above, paler beneath (or downy when young), smooth on both sides, lance-shaped like the willow leaf, $1\frac{3}{4}$–4 inches long, terminating with a bristle point. Flowering in April. The small acorn $\frac{1}{2}$ inch long, the nut globular, set in a shallow saucerlike cup, with close-pressed small scales. Maturing the second year, ripe in October.

The Willow Oak is common on low rich ground near the coast, or on sandy uplands, and is distributed from western Long Island (Suffolk Co.), and Tottenville (S. I.) N. Y. to northeastern Fla., and through the Gulf States to the Sabine River, Tex., and northward through Ark. to southeastern Mo. central Tenn. and southern Ky. It reaches its finest development in the Gulf States; in N. C. it occupies the coastal plain, and is scattered in wet locations, over the greater part of the Piedmont plateau. It is entirely local on Staten Island and Long Island, N. Y., and is found near the road between South Amboy and Monmouth, and at Long Branch, N. J.

The var. *laurifolia*, has larger, longer leaves, 2–6 inches long, elliptical, with blunt tips, and the base of the acorn cup is more rounded. It occurs from N. J. to Fla. and La. The wood is strong, softer than that of other oaks, close-grained, light ruddy brown, and weighs 46 lbs. to the cubic foot. It is used for wheel hubs and general construction, but is not commercially of great value.

NETTLE FAMILY. *Urticaceae.*

A mostly tropical Family including several tribes of trees with alternate-growing leaves, and staminate and pistillate flowers on the same or on different trees, in the Elms mostly polygamous, rarely perfect; the fruit winged seed, or berrylike.

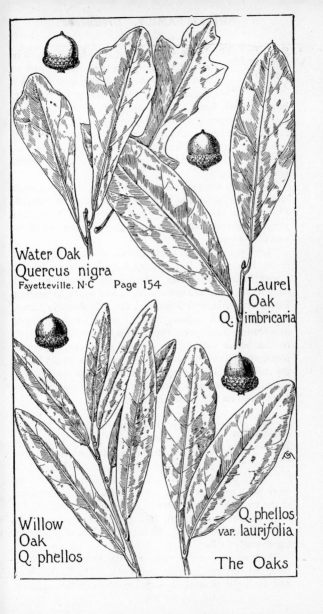

Water Oak
Quercus nigra
Fayetteville. N·C   Page 154

Laurel
Oak
Q. imbricaria

Willow
Oak
Q. phellos

Q. phellos
var. laurifolia

The Oaks

**Slippery Elm
Red Elm
*Ulmus fulva***

A commonly slim and characteristically rough tree, rough in bark and leaf, 40–50 and rarely 70 feet high, with a trunk diameter of 1–4 feet, having an irregular, broad-topped figure. Bark dark gray brown, deeply furrowed perpendicularly, very rough-scaly, the under layers ruddy brown, the innermost layer next the wood buff white, aromatic, and very mucilaginous, used medicinally for its demulcent quality. The twigs rough, grayish, hairy.

The leaves are extremely rough above. deep yellowish olive green, lighter and sometimes rusty-downy beneath. Flowering in March–April. Fruit nearly round in outline, winged, without hairy fringe, ripening in spring, at intervals of 2–4 years.

The Slippery Elm is found in rich alluvial soil, and on rocky hillsides; it is distributed from Orleans Island. Lower St. Lawrence River, west through western Que. and Ont. to N. Dak. and eastern Neb., and south to western Fla. central Ala. and Miss. and the San Antonio River, Tex. The wood is heavy, hard, strong, coarse-grained, durable in contact with the soil, easy to split, and dark reddish brown with lighter sapwood; it is used for fenceposts, wheel-hubs, sills of buildings, etc. Weight 43 lbs. to the cubic foot. The mucilaginous inner bark is officinally valuable and possesses a considerable nutritive quality in addition to its demulcent character.

**English Elm
Red Elm
*Ulmus
campestris***

A large tree introduced from Europe, not essentially English, with an oblong, round-topped figure, often massed in two sections, the upper one the larger. It frequently reaches a height of 90 feet or more, with an erect trunk continuing almost to the apex of the tree; the heavy, crooked branches wide-angled; the twigs not drooping. Bark dark gray brown, perpendicularly furrowed with short seams, the ridges angularly or transversely broken.

The leaves are similar to those of the American or White Elm, but very rough on the upper side. The English Elm was formerly planted in large numbers in the eastern

sections of N. E., and is a familiar tree on Boston Common.
Fruit, large, smooth, flat, ovate or nearly round in outline,
and winged. The wood is hard, heavy, and has a finer
grain than that of the American Elm.

A tall and graceful tree 50–70 and
sometimes 120 feet high, with a trunk
diameter of 3–10 feet; the trunk dividing
about one-third of the distance up into
many stout, outwardly curved branches

**American Elm
White Elm**
*Ulmus
americana*

forming a tree with a symmetrical round-topped figure,
the base of which is the apex of an inverted cone, draped
or fringed on the sides with numerous drooping branchlets.
This is the common form as seen in isolation on meadow
land. Bark brown gray, divided by many short, perpendicular furrows into flat-topped ridges, exceedingly
rough and firm; the inner layers whitish, the twigs slender,
generally smooth, the younger ones slightly or densely
downy, light ruddy or yellowish brown, nearly always
drooping.

The leaves are ovate or obovate, abruptly pointed,
sharply double-toothed, 2–4½ inches long, dark or lighter
olive green, roughish or nearly smooth above, paler and
fine-hairy or nearly smooth beneath, the veins whitish,
straight, in high relief, and extending to the very edge;
stems quite short and whitish. Flowering in March–
April. Fruit ovate, winged, smooth (except upon the edge
which is hairy), ½–¾ inches long with incurved points, quite
closing the deep notch, ripe in May or early June.

The White Elm is common in moist, rich soil, especially
on intervales and along the margins of streams, and is
distributed from Newf. west to the north shores of Lake
Superior, and the Saskatchewan River, lat. 54° 30′ at the
eastern base of the Rocky Mts., to the Black Hills, Dak.
western Neb. western Kan., Okla., and the Rio Concho,
Tex., and south to Cape Canaveral and Pease Creek, Fla.
The tree is common throughout the bottom-lands of the
eastern States, and is frequently planted as a street and
shade tree in towns and cities of that region, but of late
years it has suffered such irreparable injury from insect
pests—especially the Elm-leaf beetle (*Galeruca scanthome-*

laena), and the Long-horned beetle (*Saperda tridentata*),—
that it is a question whether it can much longer survive
as an ornamental tree. It has attained its highest development in the fertile meadow lands of the Connecticut
River Valley. The New York Indian name is "Oo-hoosk-
ah"—it slips. The wood is heavy, tough, hard, coarse-
grained, and a pale brown with lighter buff sapwood; it is
used for wheel-hubs, saddle-trees, barrels, boat and ship-
building, and sometimes for furniture; it is not particularly
desirable for fuel. The weight is 40 lbs. to the cubic foot.

Cork Elm
Rock Elm
Ulmus
racemosa

A rather tall tree 50–70 and sometimes
100 feet high, with a trunk diameter of
2–4 feet, the stem generally very straight,
the numerous slender, stiff branches
widely angular with it or nearly horizon-
tal. Bark very rough, perpendicularly deep-furrowed, the
twigs covered with fine hairs or down, the branchlets most
frequently with thick corky ridges unbroken at the junction with the twigs.

The leaves are similar to those of the White Elm, but
with fewer, straighter veins. The flowers appear in April.
Fruit a trifle larger than that of the White Elm.

The Cork Elm is found on river banks, in gravelly or
rich soil, and on calcareous ridges; and is distributed from
eastern Que. west through Ont. northwestern N. H.
southern Vt. northern N. Y. southern Mich. and Wis.
(Lake Mendota near Madison), and northeastern, Neb.
and south to Ky. central Tenn. and southeastern Mo. It
is absent in Me., R. I. and Conn., and rare in N. H. and Vt.
The wood is durable, close-grained but otherwise similar
to that of the White Elm. It is largely used in the manufacture of agricultural implements, chairs, wheel-hubs,
railroad ties, and the sills of buildings. Weight 45 lbs. to
the cubic foot.

Wahoo Elm
Winged Elm
Cork Elm
Ulmus alata

A small southern Elm 30–40 and occasionally 50 feet high, found in situations
similar to those of the foregoing species,
and characterized by its commonly corky-
winged branches. The bark in close, fine,
perpendicular ridges, light gray brown, the branches and
light brown twigs characteristically slender.

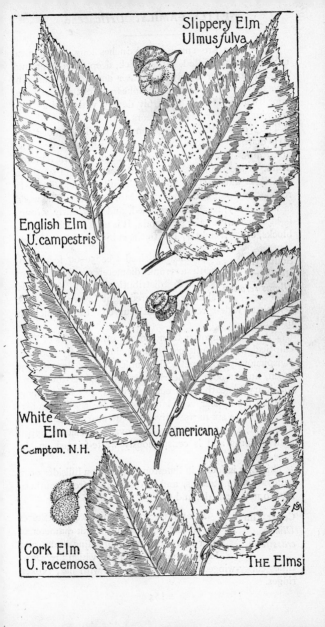

Slippery Elm
Ulmus fulva

English Elm
U. campestris

White Elm

Campton. N.H.

U. americana

Cork Elm
U. racemosa

The Elms

The leaves are small, $1\frac{1}{4}$–$2\frac{1}{4}$ inches long, often quite narrow, sharp-pointed, rather thick, deep olive green and smooth above or nearly so, lighter and downy beneath. The flowers with ovate calyx-lobes not cut to the base, appearing in March; the fruit downy when young, developing at intervals of 2–3 years.

The Wahoo Elm is common on dry gravelly or moist soil. It is distributed from southern Va. south to western Fla. and from southern Ill. and Ind. through western Ky. and Tenn. to the Gulf of Mexico, and west through southern Mo. Ark. and eastern Okla. to Trinity River, Tex. It reaches its finest development in Mo. and Ark. The wood is very heavy, hard, close-grained, and only fairly strong, light brown with paler sapwood. It is used for wheel-hubs, blocks, etc. Weight 47 lbs. to the cubic foot.

Southern Red Elm
Ulmus serotina

A medium-sized tree 50–60 feet high, with a trunk diameter of 2–3 feet, of southern distribution, with thin, and shallowly fissured light brown bark, the branches wide-spreading and curved, the branchlets drooping.

The leaves narrower than those of other species of Elm, elliptical with a prolonged sharp point, scarcely obovate, conspicuously asymmetrical, double-toothed, deep yellow green, and smooth or nearly so above, lighter-toned and soft-hairy beneath, with ocherish veins; 2–3 inches long. The flowers appear very late, not until early September; the calyx has six narrow divisions cut nearly to the base. The fruit, about $\frac{1}{4}$ inch broad, is ovate, one-sided, tipped with 2 horns and is conspicuously white-fringed on the edge.

This Elm is found in limestone regions, on hillsides or in valleys beside streams, and is distributed from southern Ky. to northern Ala. and Ga.

Cedar Elm
Ulmus crassifolia

A large tree of the southwestern States 60–80 feet high, with a trunk diameter of 2 or more feet, with spreading limbs, and long drooping branchlets which are sometimes corky-winged. Bark light brown with flat, broken ridges.

NETTLE FAMILY. *Urticaceae*

The leaves are singularly small for so large a tree, only 1–2 inches long, ovate, dull pointed, often asymmetrical, thick, almost leathery, lustrous dark olive green above, paler beneath and soft-hairy, the ribs ocher yellow, with coarse, not sharp teeth; turning dull golden yellow in autumn. Flowering in August–September. Fruit a small ovate-winged seed notched at the apex, $\frac{1}{3}$ inch long, white-hairy.

The Cedar Elm is common in the bottom-lands of the Mississippi basin, and is distributed from the valley of the Sunflower River, Miss. through southern Ark. and Tex. to Nuevo Leon (Mexico), and in western Tex. from the coast to the Pecos River. It is the common Elm of Texas, and reaches its best development in the valleys of the Guadalupe and Trinity Rivers. The wood is hard, heavy, and strong and is not commercially distinguished from that of other Elms.

Planer Tree
Water Elm
Planera
aquatica

A small southern tree closely allied to the Elms 25–40 feet high, with a trunk diameter of 2 feet. Bark nearly smooth, dark brown gray, the twigs light brown or ocherish.

The Elmlike small leaves 1–2 inches long conspicuously asymmetrical, narrowly ovate, long-pointed, sharply double-toothed, dark green above, strongly veined, paler and smooth beneath. The flowers staminate and pistillate, pale green, in small clusters at the base of the leaves, appearing with the leaves in April. The tiny fruit about $\frac{1}{4}$ inch long, nutlike, leathery, and covered with irregularly cut-lobed bracts.

The Planer Tree is rather common in the swamps of the coastal plain from N. C. (Cape Fear River), to western Fla. and through southern Ala. and Miss. to Tex. (Trinity River); northward it extends through western La. and Ark. to southern Mo. western Tenn. (Brownsville), central Ky. and to the lower Wabash River in Ill. The wood is soft, not strong, and pale brown, the weight 33 lbs. to the cubic foot. It is not commercially valuable.

NETTLE FAMILY. *Urticaceae*

**Hackberry
Sugarberry**
*Celtis
occidentalis*

A tree greatly varying in size, 20–70 and occasionally in advantageous situations 130 feet high, with a trunk diameter of 4 feet. Bearing a superficial resemblance to the Elms. Bark warm light brown, broken into confluent, discontinuous, irregular, shallow ridges, the large limbs, widely divergent, the branches nearly horizontal.

The leaves few-veined with 3 conspicuous ribs diverging from the base, totally unlike the straight-ribbed leaves of the Elm, extremely asymmetrical, commonly irregular-ovate with an attenuated, sharp apex, and often with a lop-sided heart-shaped base, irregularly and coarsely toothed, 2½–4 inches long, light olive green above, paler beneath. Flowers insignificant, pale green, the pistillate solitary or in pairs, the staminate with 5–6 stamens, in tiny clusters, appearing with the expanding leaves in April–May. Fruit a cherrylike, slightly obovoid berry, at first ocher yellow, or ruddy, finally purple black, sweet and edible, about ½ inch long.

Common in rich woods or on river banks from the St. Lawrence River (St. Helen's Island, near Montreal) west to southern Ont., and from eastern Mass. to northwestern Neb. N. Dak. southern Ia. (Boise City), eastern Wash. Ore. (Snake River), western Wash. (Puget's Sound), Nev. (eastern Humboldt Mts.), and N. Mex., and south to Biscayne Bay and Cape Romano, Fla. central Tenn. Mo. eastern Kan. Okla. and eastern Tex. The wood is heavy, rather soft, coarse-grained, compact, and pale yellow. Weight 40 lbs. to the cubic foot.

Celtis occidentalis var. *crassifolia* is a tree occasionally 125 feet high with fine-downy branchlets and leaves 4–6 inches long, heart-shaped at the base, and rather rough on the dark green upper surface. N. J. west to Ind. S. Dak. and Col. and south to S. C.

Celtis occidentalis var. *pumila* is a dwarf form a few feet high, with irregular straggling branches.

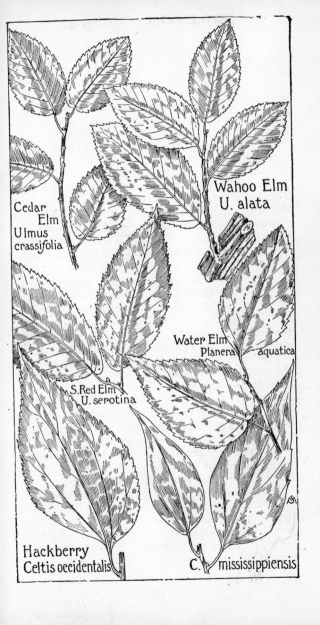

Cedar
Elm
Ulmus
crassifolia

Wahoo Elm
U. alata

Water Elm
Planera aquatica

S. Red Elm
U. serotina

Hackberry
Celtis occidentalis

C. mississippiensis

NETTLE FAMILY. *Urticaceae*

Mississippi Hackberry
Celtis mississippiensis

A small southern tree the bluish olive bark of which is covered with warty excrescences; otherwise similar to the foregoing, but the leaves quite toothless, or with very few teeth, attenuate-pointed, asymmetrical and rounded at the base, altogether smooth. Flowers on slender hairy stems, in tiny clusters, blooming in February–March. Fruit similar but a trifle smaller and bright orange red, darker when fully ripe.

Found in rich, wooded bottom-lands, from southern Ind. and Ill. through Ky. Tenn. and Ala. to Biscayne Bay, Fla., and through Mo. Ark. and Tex. to Nuevo Leon (Mexico). The common Hackberry of the Ohio and Mississippi basins, rare in the Gulf States, though frequent in La. and Tex. The wood is similar to that of C. *occidentalis*, and is not commercially distinguished from it.

Osage Orange
Maclura pomifera

A medium-sized, thorny tree 30–50 feet high, confined to the Southwest, but in frequent cultivation, and commonly used for hedges. Bark very light brown, the branchlets, especially the lower ones, beset with straight, sharp thorns ¾ inch long, accompanying the leaves.

The leaves broadly ovate or elliptical-ovate, abruptly sharp-pointed, toothless, thin, smooth when mature, lustrous deep green above, paler beneath, about 3–4 inches long. Flowers staminate and pistillate on separate trees, the staminate in loose, short, rounded clusters, the pistillate in a dense spherical head 1 inch in diameter, at first beset with the numerous long hairlike styles, finally developing a large orange like fruit 2½–4 inches in diameter, with a tuberculate green and golden yellow surface, the fleshy texture within filled with a milky juice.

The Osage Orange grows in the rich soil of bottom-lands from Kan. and southern Mo. to northern Tex., and is not infrequently spontaneous in the Atlantic States. The wood is bright orange ocher color, strong, firm, and durable, the weight 48 lbs. per cubic foot. It is not commercially important.

A small tree 25–40 feet high, a native of China and Japan in common cultivation in the middle Atlantic and Southern States, and not infrequently an escape. Bark light gray brown and nearly smooth, the branches divergent.

Paper Mulberry
Broussonetia papyrifera

The large leaves are very similar to those of the Red Mulberry, broadly ovate, or commonly three-lobed, often asymmetrically so, or even two-lobed, the notches rounded at their bases which sometimes are set with subordinate points, light green, and more or less harsh above, paler beneath and fine-hairy, the edge set with coarse blunt teeth; 4–7 inches long. Flowers staminate and pistillate on separate trees, the staminate in soft, flexible, pale green catkins 2–3 inches long, the pistillate in densely hairy, globular heads ⅔ inch broad, holding many ruddy fleshed seeds within.

The Paper Mulberry is a frequent escape to roadsides in the vicinity of old estates from southern N. Y. to Ga. and Mo. In Asia the bark is manufactured into paper, hence the popular name.

A widely cultivated, medium-sized tree 20–50 or rarely 65 feet high, with a short trunk 2–4 feet in diameter, and

Red Mulberry
Morus rubra

spreading stout limbs forming a rounded head; the twigs slender and ruddy brown or olive brown. It is largely planted in the southern States for its fruit which is a much esteemed food for pigs and poultry. Bark dark brown with a ruddy tinge, scored perpendicularly into narrow, flat, scaly ridges, which break horizontally, and curl upward at the tips.

The light green leaves broadly heart-shaped, often cut into 2–3 round-notched abruptly pointed lobes, coarsely toothed, rough above, downy and slightly paler beneath, 4–6 inches long. Flowers staminate and pistillate on the same tree, or not infrequently on separate trees, the staminate in drooping, greenish catkins, the pistillate, short and compact, finally forming a succulent dark purple blackberrylike fruit 1 inch long; a juicy, cloyingly sweet berry. June–July.

On intervales or in rich open woods, from western Mass.
and Conn. west through southern Ont. to the Daks. eastern
Neb. and Kan., and south to Fla. (Biscayne Bay and Cape
Romano), and the valley of the Colorado River, Tex.
It reaches its best development in the lower Ohio basin.

White Mulberry
Morus alba
A similar, smaller tree but 40 feet high,
imported from China in the especial
interest of the silkworm. Bark light
gray brown deeply furrowed into confluent, sinuous ridges
ocher brown beneath, the twigs lighter than those of *M.
rubra*, generally very pale brown.

The leaves somewhat asymmetrical, heart-shaped, with
roundish, coarse teeth, sometimes deeply cut into 5-6
lobes, mostly smaller than the preceding, 2-5 inches long,
thin, smooth, lustrous light green above, pale beneath.
Flowers as in *M. rubra*, the staminate about 1 inch long.
Fruit a similar berry, but white or tinged with magenta,
insipid and inferior to that of the other species. July-
August. In common cultivation, often an escape on
roadsides, and more or less naturalized. Me. and Ont.
south to Fla. The wood of both species soft, compact,
durable, and light ocher yellow; weight 37 lbs. per cubic
foot.

Morus celtidifolia is an extreme southwestern species,
with ocher-colored twigs and small leaves similar to those of
M. alba. From Tex. (south from the Colorado River and
mountains west in the State), and southern N. Mex. to
Ariz. (Santa Rita Mts.), and south.

SANDAL-WOOD FAMILY. *Santalaceae.*

A small, mostly tropical family, including a few trees
or shrubs with alternate-growing, toothless leaves, and
staminate and pistillate or polygamous flowers borne on
separate plants. The fleshy fruit with but one seed.

Buffalo-nut
Oil-nut
*Pyrularia
pubera*
A straggling shrub 4-13 feet high, with
many slender light brown, divergent
stems. Parasitic in nature, often flourish-
ing on the roots of *Calycanthus*.

The leaves elliptical or narrowly obo-

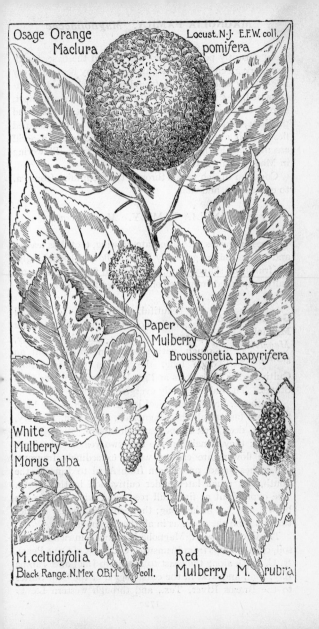

Osage Orange
Maclura
Locust. N.J. E.F.W. coll.
pomifera

Paper
Mulberry
Broussonetia papyrifera

White
Mulberry
Morus alba

M. celtidifolia
Black Range. N. Mex. O.B.M. coll.

Red
Mulberry M. rubra

vate, abruptly pointed, narrowed toward the base, toothless, dark green above, paler and very veiny beneath, very
fine-downy when young, soft and smooth when old, short-
stemmed, 2–4 inches long. Flowers pale green, in short,
spare, terminal spikes $1\frac{1}{2}$ inches long, staminate and
pistillate, the latter finally developing a pear-shaped
fleshy fruit about 1 inch long, permeated with an acrid
essential oil, leathery, light brown when ripe. Flowering
in May. Fruit ripe in September.

Common in rich woods through the mountains from Pa.
to central Ga. and Ala.

MAGNOLIA FAMILY. *Magnoliaceae.*

Trees or shrubs with alternate-growing, toothless leaves,
and perfect, large, generally fragrant flowers borne singly;
the fruit cone-shaped, containing several fleshy seeds eventually suspended from the cone by threadlike connectors.

**Great-flowered
Magnolia**
*Magnolia
grandiflora*
A beautiful, large tree 50–70 and
occasionally 90 feet high, with a trunk
diameter of $4\frac{1}{2}$ feet. Bark brown gray,
rough, with short, thin scales about an
inch long, the boughs wide-spreading.
Cultivated in the streets and gardens of cities in the Gulf
States. The only perfectly evergreen species.

The large, broadly elliptical leaves are 5–8 inches long,
toothless (as are all the Magnolias), evergreen, leathery,
lustrous deep green and smooth above, rusty-downy
beneath; they remain on the tree two years. The large
lilylike flowers are creamy white, exceedingly fragrant,
6–8 inches broad, and bloom from April to June in the
South, but much later under cultivation in the North.
The ovoid fruit at first dull rose pink, when ripe is tan
brown, and 3–4 inches long; the seeds hanging by slender
threads from the pods, as in all the Magnolias.

The Great-flowered Magnolia is common in rich alluvial
soil, or in swamps from Brunswick Co. (west of Cape Fear),
N. C. south along the coast to Mosquito Inlet and Tampa
Bay, Fla., and west in the coast region of the Gulf States
to the Brazos River, Tex., and through western La. to

southern Ark. It reaches its finest development on the bluffs of the lower Mississippi. In Brunswick Co. N. C., its northerly limit, it is confined and grows sparingly within a coastal area barely 25 miles long.

A shrub 3–18 feet high in the North, but a slender tree 70 feet high, with a trunk diameter of 3 feet in South. Bark light brown with small scales, the branches gray brown, and the newer twigs a decided green turning ruddy as they grow older.

**Small Magnolia
Sweet Bay**
*Magnolia
virginiana*

The leaves are light green and smooth above, covered with a whitish bloom beneath, the midrib prominent, broadly elliptical in outline, 4–6 inches long. They are deciduous in the North and fall in November, in the South they are mostly evergreen. The creamy white flowers, about 2 inches long are delicately fragrant, the 6–9 petals broad and obtuse. Blooming in May–June. The ovoid fruit deep magenta pink, 2 inches long.

The Small Magnolia is common in wet or swampy localities, and is distributed from Gloucester (near a station called Magnolia), Mass. where it is reduced to shrub form, Turtle Pond, L. I. Suffolk Co. N. Y. and N. J. to Fla. (Biscayne Bay, on the east coast, Tampa Bay, on the west coast), and west along the Gulf region to Trinity River, Tex. In N. C. where it attains a height of 12–25 feet it is confined to wet land on the coastal plain, excepting a small marginal part of the Piedmont plateau. According to the quality of the soil it takes two rather distinct forms, one a shrub not exceeding 10 feet, the other a fair-sized tree.[1]

The wood is soft, light, close-grained, and of no economic value.

A tall, slender tree commonly 50–60 and occasionally 90 feet high, with a trunk diameter of 4–5 feet. Bark sepia brown or grayish brown, broken into small, thin scales, the ridges narrow and confluent, the stem continuous to the crown of the tree, the branches slender and

Cucumber Tree
*Magnolia
acuminata*

[1] *Vide* Gifford Pinchot in *Timber Trees of North Carolina*, pg. 35.

ascending. The hardiest of the Magnolias. The large leaves are thin, deep green above, lighter and slightly downy beneath, oval, and acute at the tip, 6–10 inches long, widely distributed along the branches. Flowers tulip-shaped, petals obovate, greenish yellow white, 2 inches long, blooming late in May. The fruit is cucumber-like, at first green, finally dull crimson red, about 3 inches long, the seeds orange red.

The Cucumber Tree is common in moist rich woodlands, often on mountain slopes, and is distributed from western N. Y. through southern Ont. to southern Ill., and south along the Alleghany Mts. to Stockton, Baldwin Co. southern Ala. Meridian and Lauderdale, eastern Miss. central Ky. Nashville (and eastern) Tenn., and eastern, southern, and southwestern Ark. In N. C. it is confined to the mountain region, where it develops a height of 80 feet and a trunk diameter of 4 feet. It is thinly scattered in Ky. and Tenn. but attains its greatest proportions in the mountains of the Carolinas and Tenn.

The wood is soft, light (29 lbs. to the cubic foot), close-grained, and of a satiny texture, light ocher yellow in color. It is used for water-pipes, cabinet-making, flooring, etc.

Great-leaved Magnolia
Magnolia macrophylla

A smaller, but a spreading tree 20–40 and sometimes 60 feet high, with a trunk diameter of about 18 inches. Bark light warm gray, shallowly scored, and transversely cut into very small, thin scales.

The leaves are extremely long 1–3 feet, obovate and heart-shaped at the narrowed base, blunt at the tip, deep green and smooth above, whitish and downy beneath; clustered terminally on the branches. The flowers are wide open bell-shaped, also very large, 8–12 inches in diameter, creamy white with a magenta pink stain at the base of each of the 6 blunt petals. Blooming in May and June. The bright magenta rose fruit is broadly ovoid, and 3–4 inches long.

The Great-leaved Magnolia is found in rich valley wood-lands, and is distributed from N. C. (mostly in the moun-

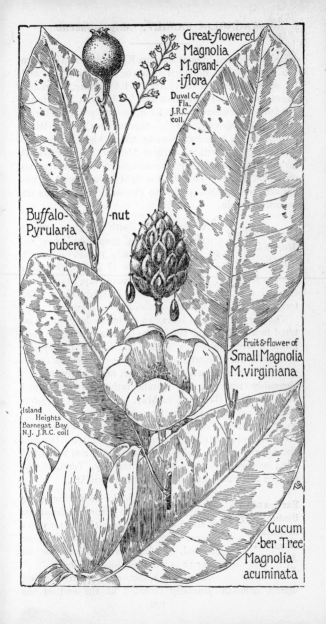

Great-flowered
Magnolia
M. grand-
-iflora

Duval Co
Fla.
J.R.C.
coll.

Buffalo-   -nut
Pyrularia
pubera

Fruit & flower of
Small Magnolia
M. virginiana

Island
Heights
Barnegat Bay
N.J. J.R.C. coll

Cucum
-ber Tree
Magnolia
acuminata

tains) southward to southeastern Ky. middle and western Fla. southern Ala. northern Miss. the Pearl River, La. and to southwestern central Ark. (Hot Spring, Garland, Montgomery and Sebastian Cos.). In N. C. there are but two well-known stations for it, one on the French Broad River near Asheville, and the other on the Catawba River in Lincoln Co., where it grows 15–30 feet high. It reaches its best development in northern Ala. and is cultivated as far north as Boston. It is extensively cultivated as an ornamental tree. The wood is light brown, hard, close-grained, and weighs 34 lbs. to the cubic foot; it has no commercial value.

Umbrella Tree
Magnolia tripetala

A small tree with slender, widely curving, sometimes sprawling branches, 16–25 and occasionally 40 feet high, with a trunk diameter of 18 inches, the stem erect or irregular. The bark light warm gray, smooth and covered with many small blisterlike excrescences. The twigs stout, ruddy tan or greenish brown.

The very large, thin leaves 18–20 inches long, are clustered in a circle at the tips of the branches; they are deep green above, lighter beneath and slightly downy, or eventually they become smooth. The conspicuous cream white flowers 6–8 inches in diameter, are slightly but not agreeably fragrant, the petals rather narrow—broad lance-shaped. Blooming in May. The bright magenta rose fruit ovoid 3½–4 inches long.

The Umbrella Tree is found in rich, moist soil of wooded hillsides, and is distributed from southern Pa. south through the Alleghany Mts. and N. C. to the coast, and to central Ala., westward it extends to central Ky. Tenn. northeastern Miss. and central and southwestern Ark.

Ear-leaved Umbrella Tree Mountain Magnolia
Magnolia Fraseri

A slender tree similar to the foregoing species, 25–30 and in favorable situations 45 feet high, with a trunk diameter of 18 inches; the branches wide-spreading or crooked. Bark brown, smooth, or on older trees with very small scales.

The smooth, lustrous deep green leaves, lighter beneath, similarly crowded at the end of the branches, obovate, pointed at the tip, ear-lobed at the base, 8–15 inches long. The beautiful cream white flowers 3–9 inches broad, the petals obovate and obtuse, clawed at the base, slightly sweet-odored. Blooming in May–June. The similar fruit possibly a trifle longer than that of *M. tripetala*.

The Ear-leaved Umbrella Tree is found beside the streams of mountain valleys, or in mountain woods, and is distributed from southwestern Va. along the mountains through Ky. Tenn. and N. C. to Ala. Miss. (Pearl River), and to the Chattahoochee River, Fla. In N. C. it occurs in abundance in all the counties of the Blue Ridge and on the eastern slopes of these hills. It attains its greatest development beside the tributaries of the Savannah River, and on the slopes of the Black and Big Smoky Mts. But aside from its local abundance it is the least widely distributed of all the Magnolias.

The wood is light, soft, weak, pale brown, and possesses no commercial value. Weight 31 lbs. to the cubic foot. It is a beautiful tree and it has been successfully cultivated as far north as New York City.

A large, handsome tree of great economic value, commonly 50–70 and in woodlands occasionally 190 feet high, with a trunk diameter of 8 feet. The trunk often very straight and continuous to the small, rounded head, the limbs slender, mostly horizontal, curved, somewhat drooping below; the bark brownish gray, often with dark or sepia brown, rounded confluent ridges, the perpendicular furrows short and rather deep. The slender twigs a shining, reddish chestnut brown.

Tulip Tree
White Wood
Liriodendron
tulipifera

The leaves smooth, bright yellow green, lighter beneath, with 4 lobes, cut nearly square across the top, rounded toward the base, toothless, and long-stemmed. They turn a rich russet brown in the fall. The tulip-shaped flowers are pale yellow green, 3–4 inches across, stained orange cadmium within at the base over the 6 obovate petals; the numerous pale greenish anthers long and slender. Blooming in May–June.

The fruit light brown, conelike, finally expanding in a

circle of many divisions (the carpels), each enclosing one or two orange seeds which eventually hang for a while on slender filaments before falling (as in *Magnolia*).

The Tulip Tree is common in rich moist soil, and is distributed from Worcester Co. Mass. R. I. and southwestern Vt. (Hoosic Valley, Pownal), west to Ont. southern Mich. (as far north as the Grand River) and Wis., and south to Fla. Ala. Miss. Ark. and southeastern Mo. The tree is in common cultivation about the suburbs of New York City, but is local only in Conn. In N. C. it is frequent in all parts of the State, and is most abundant on the mountain slopes west of the Blue Ridge where it grows 150 feet high, with a trunk diameter of 10 feet. Asheville is the principal center of industry in the manufacture of White Wood lumber.

The wood is pale greenish or olive-toned buff with whiter sapwood, light (25 lbs. to the cubic foot), soft, close and straight in grain, easily worked, and it does not readily split, warp, or shrink. It is largely used for the interior finish of houses, for construction, cabinet work, boat-building, and wooden ware.

The output of White Wood lumber in N. C. in 1892 was 18 million board feet. The local name is Yellow Poplar.

STRAWBERRY-SHRUB FAMILY. *Calycanthaceae.*

Shrubs with opposite-growing toothless, leaves, and perfect flowers with similar sepals and petals in many series, somewhat confused; the large ovoid fruit similar in character to that of the rose.

Strawberry Shrub Carolina Allspice *Calycanthus floridus*
An aromatic, southern, mountain shrub 4–8 feet high, with many slender ascending stems, and slightly downy branchlets and leaf-stems. Commonly cultivated in parks and gardens.

The leaves elliptical, *not* ovate, sharp-pointed, toothless, short-stemmed, dark green and roughish above, downy and grayish beneath, 2–3 inches long. Flowers 1½ inches broad, dark maroon red, with many incurved linear petals and many very short

Ear-leaved Umbrella Tree
Magnolia Fraseri
Similar leaf of
M. macrophylla
25 ins.
long

Flower petal
M. Fraseri

Umbrella Tree
M. tripetala

Tulip Tree
Liriodendron tulipif-
era

stamens, having the odor of sweet strawberries when crushed. April–May. Fruit ovoid, nodding, leathery-coated, much larger than that of the rose.

Commonly in the rich soil of hillsides and along streams from Va. to N. C. S. C. Ga. Fla. Ala. and Miss.

Smooth Straw-berry Shrub
Calycanthus fertilis
A very similar shrub 3–6 feet high, with smooth branchlets, and similar elliptical leaves commonly larger, 2½–7 inches long, sharp-pointed, rarely blunt, bright green and rough above, paler and smooth beneath. The similar flowers smaller, dull green ruddy-stained, or maroon, and odorless, or very slightly fragrant Fruit obovoid, smooth, about 2 inches long.

In similar situations from Franklin Co. Pa., south in the Alleghany Mts. through N. C. and Tenn. to northern Ga.

Sweet Shrub
Calycanthus occidentalis
A larger Californian shrub 5–9 feet high, with large (sometimes 6 inches long), perfectly ovate leaves, rounded or slightly heart-shaped at the base, rough above, downy beneath. The larger fragrant flowers, 2½ inches broad, an intense maroon red, fading to an ocher brown with age. Fruit 1½ inches long, cuplike, with a spiky crown.

Along streams in the North Coast Range and the Sierra Nevadas, in Shasta, Sonoma, Napa, Lake, and Tulare Cos. Cal.

CUSTARD APPLE FAMILY. *Anonaceae.*

Trees or shrubs with alternate-growing toothless leaves, and perfect flowers with 3 sepals, about 6 petals, and many stamens; the fruit large and fleshy.

Papaw
Custard Apple
Asimina triloba
A shrub or small tree 10–40 feet high, with a maximum trunk diameter of about 10 inches. Bark commonly light sepia brown, deep ruddy gray and smooth when young, rough and with ashen patches when old; the branches slender and spreading.

The large leaves 6–12 inches long, olive green, obovate, toothless, abruptly pointed at the broad tip, and smooth. Flowers borne singly, nearly $1\frac{3}{4}$ inches broad, deep dull magenta red, with 3 large sepals, and 6 petals set in 2 ranks. Blooming in March–April.

The cylindrical fruit fleshy, 3–5 inches long, at first green, finally dull sepia brown, sweet and edible in October especially after frost, borne 2–4 in a pendulous cluster; the single fruit weighing half a pound or more.

The Papaw is found in swampy or alluvial rich soil, and is distributed from western N. Y. and eastern Pa., west to the north shores of Lake Huron, southern Mich. northeastern Io. southeastern Neb. and eastern Kan., and southward to central Fla. and the Sabine River, Tex. It is rather rare on the Atlantic seaboard, but very common in the Mississippi Valley, reaching its best development in the Ohio Basin and along the streams of southern Ark. In N. C. it is common in the northeastern and central sections of the State.

The yellowish wood is light, soft, and of no economic value. Weight about 24 lbs. to the cubic foot. The tree is unpleasantly odorous in all its parts when bruised.

Pond Apple
Annona glabra

A similar southern species 30–40 feet high, with wide-spreading, crooked branches and dark ruddy brown bark.

The leaves broadly elliptical, pointed, leathery, bright green above, paler beneath, 3–5 inches long. Flowers pale dull yellowish white.

Fruit inverted pear-shaped, yellow with brown blotches, 3–5 inches long, ripe in November, edible but flatly insipid.

The Pond Apple is found in wet situations in southern Fla. on the shores of the east coast from Biscayne Bay to Cape Malabar, and on the west coast from Pease Creek to Caloosa River.

BARBERRY FAMILY. *Berberidaceae.*

A small Family including the shrub *Berberis*, with alternate-growing, simple or compound leaves, and perfect flowers with (generally) 6 sepals, petals, and stamens—

the rule applying to *Berberis* alone. Fruit a one-seeded or few-seeded scarlet berry.

American Barberry
Berberis canadensis

A low shrub 1-5 feet high, with slender terra-cotta brown branchlets, smooth, and spiny.

The small leaves long-obovate, rounded at the tip, with small, spare, slightly spiny-tipped, circularly incised teeth, or nearly toothless, deep lustrous green above, paler beneath, smooth, 1-2 inches long. Flowers small, waxy light gold yellow, in small drooping clusters, with 6 notched petals and as many stamens. June. Fruit a generally one-seeded, cardinal scarlet, ovoid berry, about $\frac{1}{3}$ inch long, in clusters. September. Frequent in the Alleghany Mts., from Va. south to Ga. and in Mo.

European Barberry
Berberis vulgaris

The common Barberry of Europe, imported into this country and planted for hedges but now largely supplanted by *Berberis Thurnbergii*, a remarkably beautiful Japanese species, the berries of which are bright shining scarlet.

Leaves reduced to thorns scattered on the newer twigs, finally obovate with fine bristle-tipped teeth, dark lustrous green, 1-2 inches long. Flowers similar to the foregoing, but in profuse clusters, the petals *not* notched. May-June. Fruit cardinal or dark scarlet, ellipsoid, slightly acid. Often preserved as a jam or jelly.

Running wild throughout southeastern N. E. generally near the coast, in thickets and on sterile or sandy ground.

Trailing Mahonia
Berberis aquifolium

A very beautiful, low, trailing shrub of the Rocky Mts. and the northwestern coast, with compound leaves of about 5 (3-7) ovate, hollylike leaflets, extremely dark lustrous green to bronzy green above, paler and smooth beneath, changing in autumn to dull reds and yellows, 1-2 inches long, spiny-edged. Flowers waxy gold yellow in erect, small terminal clusters. June Fruit a purple blue globular berry, $\frac{1}{4}$ inch in diameter.

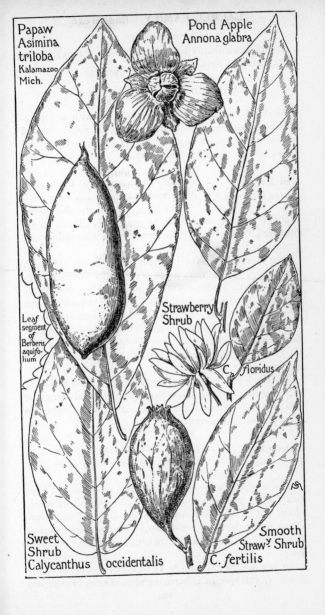

Papaw
Asimina
triloba
Kalamazoo
Mich.

Pond Apple
Annona glabra

Leaf
segment
of
Berberis
aquifo-
lium

Strawberry
Shrub

C. floridus

Sweet
Shrub
Calycanthus   occidentalis

Smooth
Straw.y Shrub
C. fertilis

LAUREL FAMILY. *Lauraceae*

In open woodlands from western Neb. throughout the
Rocky Mts. to Ariz. Also in B. C.

LAUREL FAMILY. *Lauraceae.*

More or less aromatic trees or shrubs with alternate-
growing, toothless leaves, and perfect, or staminate and
pistillate flowers (on separate plants as in *Sassafras* and
Litsea). Fruit a one-seeded berry.

Red Bay   A medium-sized southern tree 50–70
Persea Borbonia feet high, with a trunk diameter of 3
            feet. The wide-spreading greenish brown
branches forming an irregular-topped tree. Bark deeply
furrowed, ruddy brown; the newer twigs also ruddy and
smooth.

The evergreen leaves narrowly and bluntly elliptical,
laurellike, dark lustrous green above, paler beneath, altogether smooth (at least when older), toothless, 2–6 inches
long, and aromatic when bruised. Flowers perfect, with
12 stamens, growing in small, mostly terminal spikes; inconspicuous, pale yellow or cream white. Fruit, a lustrous
dark violet black, ovoid berry about $\frac{1}{2}$ inch thick, with
the persisting withered calyx beneath; the thickened stems
ruddy.

The Red Bay is common on the coastal plain from Va.
to Biscayne Bay and Cape Romano, Fla., and along the
gulf to the Brazos River, Tex.; northward it extends
through La. to southern Ark.

Swamp Bay   A similar but smaller tree about 35
Persea pubescens feet high, with velvety-hairy branchlets
            and brown bark.

The similar leaves attenuated, and more or less fine-
hairy when young, 3–7 inches long, smooth above when
older, but persistently fine-hairy beneath. The flower-
stems and calyx also fine-hairy. The nearly spherical
berry similar, bluish with a bloom, but smaller $\frac{1}{3}$–$\frac{1}{2}$ inch
long.

In swamps from southern Va. to Fla. and Miss. The
wood of both species is hard, durable, strong, brittle, and

close-grained. It varies from bright mahogany red to lighter terra-cotta, and is used occasionally for interior finish and cabinet work. Weight 40 lbs. to the cubic foot.

A tree 15–50 or occasionally 120 feet high, with a trunk diameter of 7 feet; often reduced to a shrub at the northern limits of its range. The yellow green

Sassafras
*Sassafras
variifolium*

twigs and the foliage are distinctly fine-hairy when young, and also aromatic and mucilaginous. Bark on older trees extremely rough, light brown, broken into incontinuous, flattened, confluent, and sinuous ridges, on younger trees cracked into short blocks, buffish in the crevices. The ascending limbs very irregular.

The leaves variable, ovate or elliptical, blunt-tipped, some two-lobed (mitten-shaped), others three-lobed, lustrous deep green above, paler beneath and altogether smooth when mature, 2–5 inches long, aromatic when crushed. The insignificant flowers greenish yellow, staminate and pistillate on different trees, clustered in small tassels, appearing with the developing leaves in April. Staminate flowers with a six-pointed calyx and 9 stamens, the pistillate with an ovoid ovary which finally develops into an ovoid berrylike fruit $\frac{1}{2}$ inch long, deep slaty blue, on a thickened, fleshy, crimson red stem, ripe in August.

The Sassafras is common in rich woodlands from southern Me. (Wells and North Berwick) southern N. H. and Bellows Falls, Vt., west to southern Ont. central Mich. eastern Ia. eastern Kan. and Okla., and south from southern N. E. to Fla. and the Brazos River, Tex. It is absent in the northerly and scarcely common in the more southerly portions of N. E. In N. Y. it is common and is named "Wah-eh-nak-kas," Smelling Stick, by the Onondaga Indians. It reaches its finest development in southwestern Ark. and Okla. In N. C. it rarely exceeds a height of 50 feet and is most common on the coastal plain and the Piedmont plateau; in Va. it ascends to 3000 feet in the mountains. The wood is light, soft, weak, brittle and coarse-grained, and is slightly aromatic. It is dull orange brown and is largely used in boat-building, cooperage, and fencing; the weight is 31 lbs. to the cubic foot. A strongly aromatic oil is distilled from the bark, twigs, and roots.

White Sassafras
Sassafras variifolium var. *albidum*[1]   A distinct variety described by Nuttall in 1818. The twigs are from their early development smooth, and often have a slight bloom.

The early leaves are also nearly (or quite) smooth; later they show no hairiness whatever. The whiter roots according to Nuttall possessing a stronger flavor, but according to John Uri Lloyd possessing a bitter taste with a less aromatic quality![2] A tree mostly of upland regions, among the hills from western N. E., south to N. C.

California Laurel
Umbellularia californica   A Californian shrub or tree, in thickets 10–15, and in the forest 50–80 feet high, with a trunk diameter of 3 feet. Bark thin, dark ruddy brown and scaly, on young trees smoother and gray brown. A tree with a narrow crown and slim ascending branches, in the open the crown rounded and the branches long and thick. Often a many-stemmed shrub in crowded clumps on the margins of streams or in narrow gulches of dry foothills.

The leaves lustrous deep yellow green, smooth, paler beneath, laurellike, elliptical, 3–5 inches long, persisting for 2–5 years, and possessing a strong camphoric odor sufficiently pungent to cause sneezing when they are crushed. Flowers similar to those of the preceding species. Fruit resembling an olive, yellowish green and fleshy, containing a single seed. Ripe in October.

The California Laurel has a restricted range from south-western Ore. (Umpqua River, Coos Co.), southward through the coast ranges and the Sierras (from the head of Sacramento Valley) to southern Cal., climbing to an altitude of 4000 feet. Wood very heavy when green (about 63 lbs. to the cubic foot), hard, fine-grained, and rich tan brown in color; valued for cabinet work and interior finish

[2] *Vide* Fernald in *Rhodora*, Vol. XV., pg. 14, January, 1913.
[3] *Vide* Lloyd in *Bull. Lloyd Libr.*, No. XVIII., pg. 77 (1911).

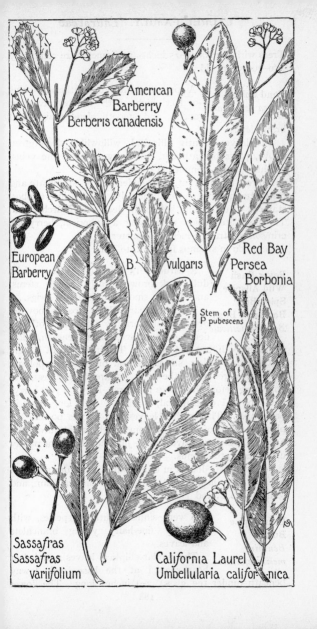

American
Barberry
Berberis canadensis

European
Barberry

B. vulgaris

Red Bay
Persea
Borbonia

Stem of
P pubescens

Sassafras
Sassafras
variifolium

California Laurel
Umbellularia californica

LAUREL FAMILY. *Lauraceae*

Trees with trunks 20–25 inches in diameter are commonly 150–200 years old.

Pond Spice
Litsea geniculata

A spreading shrub of southern swamps 6–9 feet high, with widely divergent branches and smooth, slender, zigzagged branchlets.

The leaves bluntly elliptical, willowlike, deep green above, paler beneath and fine-hairy only on the veins, toothless, short-stemmed, 1–2½ inches long.

Flowers insignificant, pale golden yellow, staminate and pistillate on different trees, the calyx divided into 6 lobes, stamens 9; expanding before the leaves in March–April. The pistillate flowers developing a spherical, berrylike, crimson red fruit, ¼ inch in diameter.

Common in swamps from Va. to Fla.

Fever Bush
Wild Allspice
Spice Bush
Benjamin Bush
Benzoin aestivale

A shrub 7–15 feet high, with upright dull, dark brown, nearly smooth stems, and slender, smooth light brown twigs.

The leaves narrowly or broadly obovate, or elliptical, abruptly pointed, toothless, deep green above, paler beneath, altogether smooth, 2–5 inches long. The insignificant flowers waxy golden yellow, staminate and pistillate, or polygamous, clustered about the twigs, apparently stemless, and appearing before the leaves in March–May. Fruit berrylike, obovoid or elliptical, scarlet, ¼ inch long, ripe in September. The crushed leaves and berries possess the pleasant odor of Gum Benzoin which is obtained from *Styrax Benzoin* a native tree of Java and Sumatra wholly unrelated to this genus.

Found in woodlands in damp situations from southern Me. through Ont., west to Mich. and eastern Kan., and south to N. C. and Tenn.

Hairy Spice Bush
Benzoin melissaefolium

A very similar southern species, with distinctly fine-hairy young branchlets and leaves.

The similar elliptical leaves rounded or heart-shaped at the base, and downy beneath (under the glass), 2–4 inches long. The flower

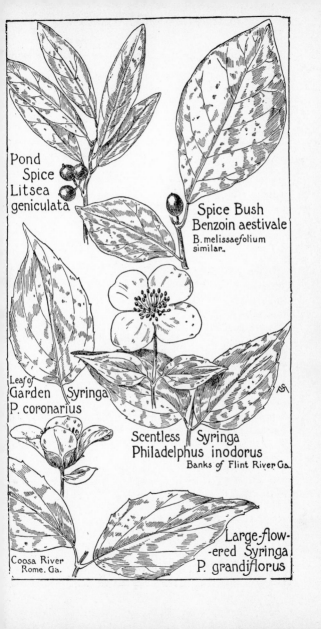

Pond
Spice
Litsea
geniculata

Spice Bush
Benzoin aestivale
B. melissaefolium
similar.

Leaf of
Garden Syringa
P. coronarius

Scentless Syringa
Philadelphus inodorus
Banks of Flint River Ga.

Large-flow-
-ered Syringa
P. grandiflorus

Coosa River
Rome. Ga.

clusters meager and few. February–March. Found on rich bottom-lands or in swamps from N. C. to Ala. and Fla , and west from southern Ill. to southeastern Mo.

SAXIFRAGE FAMILY. *Saxifragaceae.*

A moderate-sized Family nearly related to Rosaceae, including several shrubby members with opposite-growing and toothed leaves (in *Itea* alternate-growing), and perfect flowers with commonly 4–5 petals and as many or twice as many stamens; the fruit in capsule form.

A southern shrub 5–8 feet high, with ascending, light buff brown, slightly roughish stems, and diverging, flexible, smooth branches, the newer twigs light tan yellow. The thin bark of *Philadelphus* is generally more or less shredded.

**Mock Orange
Syringa**
*Philadelphus
inodorus*

The ovate light green leaves, sharp-pointed, a trifle paler beneath, altogether smooth, conspicuously three-veined, toothless or with few spreading teeth, 2–4 inches long. The flowers terminating the branchlets, solitary or in small clusters, white, with 4 (sometimes 5) large, rounded petals and many yellow stamens; odorless. Fruit a many-seeded capsule, ¼ inch long, splitting into several sections.

Common in the mountains from Va. to Ga. and Ala.

A taller, very similar southern shrub 6–11 feet high, but the long, slender curving branches somewhat fine-hairy. The leaves similar, and the larger flowers 1½–2 inches wide, ivory white and odorless.

**Large-flowered
Syringa**
*Philadelphus
grandiflorus*

Generally on river banks or low ground from Va. and Tenn. to Fla., and often cultivated.

The common sweet-scented Syringa of parks and gardens, 8–11 feet high, is a native of Europe. The four-petaled cream white flowers about 1¼ inches broad,

Garden Syringa
*Philadelphus
coronarius*

are borne in similar small clusters. It is sometimes an escape in copses and thickets.

WITCH HAZEL FAMILY. *Hamamelidaceae*

Wild Hydrangea
Hydrangea arborescens

A smooth, wide-branched shrub 2–8 feet high, with slender, light brown twigs. The deep green leaves broadly ovate, or almost heart-shaped, pointed, very coarsely sharp-toothed, paler green beneath, veiny, but smooth or rarely downy, 2–6 inches long. Flowers in rather flat clusters, 2–4 inches broad, those of the margin staminate, with a wide-spread calyx, often all the flowers pistillate. June–July. Fruit a membranous, two-horned capsule, ribbed, and containing many seeds.

Mostly on rocky banks of streams from southern N. Y. and N. J., south to Fla., and west to Ia. and Mo. Common in the valley of the Delaware River. Ascending to 4000 feet in the mountains of N. C.

Hydrangea cinerea

A more southern, similar species, with the branchlets covered with a gray fine-hairiness.

The leaves similar, blunt-toothed and densely gray downy beneath, sometimes nearly white. Found in similar situations from S. C. to Ga., and west to Tenn. and Mo.

Virginia Itea
Itea virginica

A shrub 4–9 feet high, somewhat similar to the preceding. The alternate-growing, elliptical leaves about 2 inches long, abruptly pointed, minutely sharp-toothed, deep green above, paler beneath, altogether smooth. The small white flowers in long, slender clusters, with 5 lance-shaped petals. Fruit-capsule slender, ovoid, two-horned, $\frac{1}{4}$ inch long.

Generally in swamps on the coastal plain from N. J. and Pa. to Fla., and west in the Mississippi basin to Ill. and Mo., and southwest to Tex.

WITCH HAZEL FAMILY. *Hamamelideæ.*

Trees or shrubs with alternate-growing, toothed leaves, the flowers staminate and pistillate on the same plant, or perfect, or polygamous. The fruit in capsule form.

Witch Hazel
Hamamelis virginiana

A tall shrub 10–12 or occasionally a slender, unsymmetrical tree, 26 feet high, with a short trunk 6 inches in diameter, and spreading branches. Bark sepia or

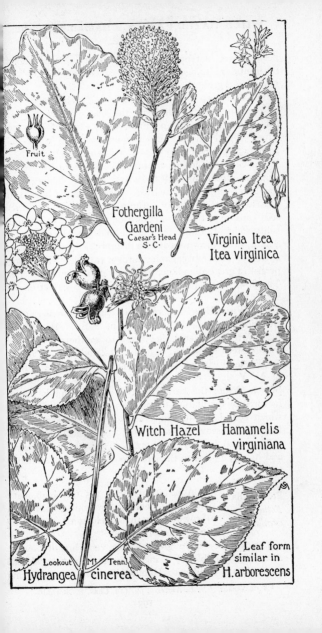

Fruit

Fothergilla
Gardeni
Caesar's Head
S.C.

Virginia Itea
Itea virginica

Witch Hazel   Hamamelis
virginiana

Leaf form
similar in
H. arborescens

Hydrangea   cinerea
Lookout   Mt Tenn.

deep brown, blotched with lighter brown and occasional
horizontal markings, moderately smooth; generally 2–4
trunks in a group.

The dull deep olive green leaves 2–4 inches long, oval
or obovate, asymmetrical at the base, straight-veined
the coarse teeth dull and undulating, the surface corrugated, slightly downy when young, smooth when old,
turning a spotted dull gold yellow in autumn.

The clustered flowers are bright yellow, bearing 4 fertile
stamens alternating with the 4 long, narrow, linear petals,
the latter curled and twisted. The blossoms appear in
touseled clusters in early autumn along with the matured
seed capsule of the previous season, which latter, in time,
splits suddenly down the middle and forcibly ejects the
4 hard, shiny brown seeds to a distance of 15 or sometimes
45 feet! The empty, gaping, brown capsules ⅝ inch long,
persist in great abundance all winter on the bare branches.
The flowers are staminate and pistillate or perfect on the
same tree.

The Witch Hazel is common in copses or woods in wet
situations, and is distributed from N. S. N. B. and the
St. Lawrence River Valley west to southern Ont. Wis.
southeastern Minn. and eastern Neb., and south to northern Fla. and eastern Tex. Among the Onondaga Indians
of N. Y. it is called "Oe-eh-nah-kwe-ha-he" (Spotted
Stick). From the bark and twigs an extract is manufactured by distillation (sometimes called Pond's Extract)
which contains indubitably efficacious, demulcent qualities. The discovery is attributed to an Oneida Indian.[1]

The wood is hard, close-grained, durable, pale brown,
and heavy, 45 lbs. to the cubic foot. It has no economic
value.

Fothergilla
*Fothergilla
Gardeni*

A beautiful shrub 3–5 feet high, with
smooth, ascending, branching, light sepia
brown stems, thickly clustered, the young
twigs densely woolly.

The leathery olive green leaves very broadly ovate,
extremely variable 1½–3 inches long, asymmetrical, the
larger leaves similar to Hamamelis with an undulating

[1] Vide *Shrubs of N. E. America*, pg. 120, Chas. S. Newhall.

edge or with coarse dull teeth, the smaller leaves obovate with an undulating or coarse-toothed apex, and a rounded base scarcely asymmetrical, pale and soft hairy beneath. The fine white flowers in beautiful, pomponlike, terminal clusters 1–2 inches long; stamens slender protruding, white, rarely pale pink. April. The seed-capsule somewhat similar to that of Hamamelis about $\frac{1}{3}$ inch long, ovate, two-lobed, each lobe with 2 short beaks.

In sandy pine lands or low wet ground from Va. to Ga.

Fothergilla major is a similar, taller shrub with ascending, thickly clustered stems, 10–12 feet high.

The leaves larger, 2–4 inches long. The similar flower-clusters often $2\frac{1}{2}$ inches long, the seed-capsule larger.

On mountain slopes from N. C. and S. C. to Ala.

Sweet Gum
Liquidambar
Bilsted
Liquidambar
Styraciflua

A beautiful tree commonly 45–60 and occasionally 140 feet high, with a trunk diameter of 4–6 feet, the stem usually continuing to the rounded crown, the slender branches wide-spreading, horizontal below, ascending at an angle of about 45° above, forming a broadly ovoid figure. Bark gray brown, deeply and perpendicularly furrowed into broad, flat, scaly ridges, the branches frequently set with corklike ridges.

The leaves deep glossy green, 3–5 inches broad, radiately five-pointed (rarely seven), finely round-toothed, the general outline star-shaped, but cut nearly square or shallowly heart-shaped at the base; the stem long and slender. Fragrant when crushed, turning deep yellow, rich red, and dark maroon in autumn. The flowers in an erect or nodding catkin are staminate, those in a rounded, long-stemmed head pistillate. Blooming in May.

Fruit spherical, about one inch in diameter, sepia brown, pendent from a slender stringlike stem, formed of an agglomeration of beaked ovaries, most of their contents abortive, the 1–3 mature seeds falling in autumn. Persisting through the winter.

The Liquidambar is common in rich, wet lowlands, and is distributed from Fairfield Co. Conn., west to southeastern Mo. Ark. and eastern Okla., and south to Cape Canavera and Tampa Bay, Fla. and Trinity River, Tex. The tree is sparingly cultivated in N. E.; in N. C. it is abundant on the coastal plain where its maximum height is 100 feet, but much less frequent on the Piedmont plateau. It attains its fullest development in the Mississippi Basin.

The wood is hard, heavy (weight 38 lbs. per cubic foot), close-grained, and light brown with buff sapwood; it is used for the outside finish of houses, for flooring, barrels, wooden ware. and cabinet making. The resinous sap is employed in the South in the manufacture of chewing gum, and as a medicinal curative for catarrhal trouble.

PLANE TREE FAMILY. *Platanaceæ.*

Trees with alternate-growing, coarsely toothed, angularly lobed leaves, and staminate and pistillate flowers on the same tree; the fruit a spherical head of club-shaped, closely packed nutlets.

Plane Tree
Sycamore
Buttonwood
Platanus
occidentalis

A tall tree 50–80 and in favorable situations in bottom-lands of the Ohio Basin often 150 feet high, with a trunk diameter of 12 feet. The stem often continuing straight or with slight angles to the crown. The branches generally scragged, forming an irregular long-ovoid figure. Bark dull ruddy brown, furrowed at the base of the trunk, smooth and scaly above, the scales broad, flat, peeling off in thin, brittle layers leaving large sharply defined patches of buffish white, brown gray, or pale tan-colored inner bark exposed.

The large light green leaves, 4–9 inches wide, and nearly or quite smooth, have an angularly five-pointed outline and very few coarse teeth; the swollen base of the stem fits caplike over the undeveloped spring buds; turning russet brown in autumn. The staminate and pistillate flowers spherical, on long stems, blooming in May.

The fruit spherical 1–1½ inches in diameter on long wiry stems, solitary or rarely borne in twos, at first green, finally light brown, rough with the pin-head surface of the nutlets. Persisting on the branches through the winter. A similar species, the Oriental Sycamore, *Platanus orientalis*, of Europe, is occasionally planted for ornament in parks and

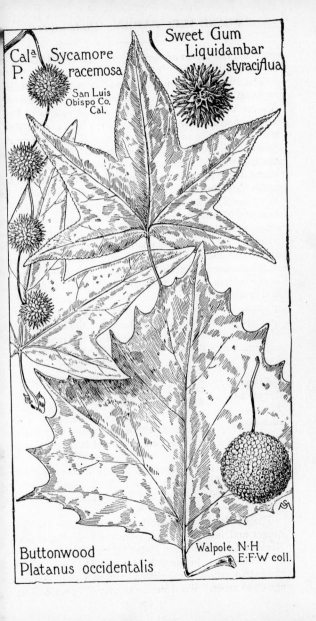

Cal^a Sycamore
P. *racemosa*

San Luis
Obispo Co.
Cal.

Sweet Gum
Liquidambar
styraciflua

Buttonwood
Platanus occidentalis

Walpole. N·H
E·F·W coll.

PLANE TREE FAMILY. *Platanaceae*

gardens; the leaves are smaller, and the fruit is borne i
clusters of 2-4 balls.

The Plane Tree is usually found in rich bottom-land
or moist woodlands, and is distributed from southern Me
Vt. N. Y. and Ont., south along upland valleys to Fla.
and west to southeastern Minn. eastern Neb. eastern Kan
and Tex. (Brazos and Devil's Rivers). It is not a commor
tree in N. E., in Me. it is confined to York Co., in N. H. to
the valley of the Merrimac near the coast; in Vt. it is occa
sional and is found in the Connecticut River Valley as fa
north as Walpole, and in the Hoosic Valley, Pownal. In
the other N. E. States it is frequent but not abundant; nor
is it the largest tree of eastern America as some authors
state, a number of other species develop much taller individuals. In N. C. it attains a height of 90 feet, with a
trunk diameter of 6 feet, on rich alluvial soil or in swamps
of the Piedmont plateau. It attains its best development
in the bottom-lands of the Ohio and the Mississippi basins,
and is also a rapid grower. The wood is heavy, coarse-
grained, hard, strong, and light ruddy brown; it is used
for cigar boxes, ox yokes, furniture, and the interior finish
of buildings, but it chips badly, and decays rapidly when
in contact with the soil. The weight is 35 lbs. to the cubic
foot.

California Sycamore
Platanus racemosa

The Sycamore of the Pacific coast is
not as large a tree; height 40-60 or rarely
80 feet. Bark a dull grayish brown, ridged
at the base of the trunk, gray white,
smooth and thin, with green gray patches
above and on the limbs, peeling off and leaving the upper
parts of the tree white.

The leaves light yellow green, 6-10 inches wide, with
3-5 conspicuous *deep-cut* lobes. Fruit like that of *P.
occidentalis*, paler beneath and densely hairy; several balls
on a stem 5-10 inches long.

The California Sycamore is distributed over the coast
ranges and interior valleys, from the lower Sacramento
River to Lower Cal. (San Pedro Martir Mt.), in the north
up to 2000 feet, in the south to 4000 feet elevation. A
single tree with a trunk diameter of 20 inches shows an
age of 86 years. Wood similar to that of *P. occidentalis*.

ROSE FAMILY. *Rosaceae.*

A large Family of herbs, shrubs, and trees, with alternate growing, toothed leaves commonly accompanied with stipules, and perfect flowers with an equal number of sepals and petals (generally 5) and many stamens; the fruit in various forms, mostly achenes (seeds) with or without a pulpy receptacle.

A tall shrub 4–10 feet high, with ascending light brown stems and *bright tan yellow* slender twigs. The old bark loose, separating into thin strips.

Nine-bark
Physocarpus opulifolius

The leaves dark green, somewhat maplelike with 3 lobes, rounded at the base, or heart-shaped, irregularly round-toothed. Flowers in terminal, nearly spherical clusters, $1\frac{1}{2}$–2 inches broad, white (rarely slightly magenta-tinged), with 5 rounded petals and 20 or many stamens. June. Fruit smooth, pink red inflated pods, usually 3 on a stem in the two-inch-broad cluster, each with 2–4 shiny seeds, the finally pale brown, papery receptacles persisting until winter.

Distributed generally on rocky banks of streams, from Que. and N. E., west to Man. Ill. and Kan., and south to Fla. It climbs to an altitude of 5000 feet on Craggy Mt., Buncombe Co., N. C., and is common in cultivation.

Physocarpus opulifolius var. *intermedius* is a western form with the pods permanently fine-hairy. Southern Mich., west to S. Dak. and south to Ala. and Ark.

The common Pear, native of Europe and Asia, occasionally runs wild in thickets and open woods, throughout the eastern States.

Pear
Pyrus communis

The leaves ovate, elliptical, or obovate, abruptly sharp-pointed, very indistinctly toothed or toothless, 2–3 inches long, nearly or quite smooth, olive green above, paler beneath, long-stemmed. Flowers white, not sweet in odor. April–May. Fruit yellow green, depauperate, reduced to about $1\frac{3}{4}$ inch length, the texture peculiarly abounding in gritty cells (cellular sclerosis); the same condition exists in the Quince.

ROSE FAMILY. *Rosaceae*

Siberian Crab Apple
Pyrus baccata

A small tree common in cultivation and an occasional escape to thickets and borders of fields, from Me. to Conn.

The leaves elliptical, abruptly pointed or long sharp-pointed, fine dull-toothed, leathery dark olive green. Flowers fragrant, white and rose pink. Fruit ¾–1 inch thick, dull yellow with rosy cheek. Introduced from Europe.

Narrow-leaved Crab Apple
Pyrus angustifolia

A small tree 15–20 feet high, with a trunk diameter of about 9 inches, the twiglets hardened and thornlike, as sometimes in the common Apple.

The leaves narrowly or broadly elliptical, coarsely scollop-toothed or toothless, sometimes shallowly lobed, lustrous dark green above, paler beneath, altogether smooth. Flowers crimson pink, fragrant, in clusters of 3–7. Fruit oblate-spheroidal, green yellow, hard and acid, ¾–1 inch thick. In thickets beside watercourses, from N. J., west to Ill. and Kan., and south to Fla. and La.

American Crab Apple
Pyrus coronaria

A small, round-topped tree similar to the common Apple, established locally in the northern States, about 15–25 feet high. Bark light brown gray, the trunk short, with spreading, irregular, warm gray limbs.

The leaves dark green, broadly or narrowly ovate, variable in size, about 3 inches long, with coarse double teeth, often with 4–5 points or lobes on either side. Flowers extremely sweet, white and pink. May. The fruit oblate-spheroidal, sweet-odored, bright green, about 1½ inches in diameter; very astringent.

Mostly in thickets or hedges from Ont. and Mich., south to N. J. and S. C.

Western Crab Apple
Pyrus ioensis

A similar western species with thornlike twiglets, and ovate or long-ovate leaves, dull olive green above, paler and densely fine-hairy beneath, coarsely round-toothed, often with several shallow lobes, about 2–3 inches long, the stems woolly. The similar flowers in groups of 2–3, the calyx woolly. Fruit similar.

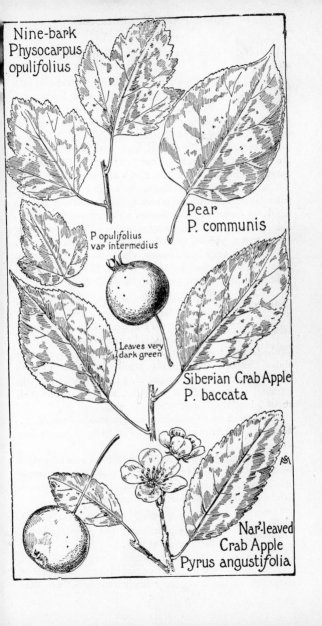

Nine-bark
Physocarpus
opulifolius

Pear
P. communis

P opulifolius
var intermedius

Leaves very
dark green

Siberian Crab Apple
P. baccata

Nar²-leaved
Crab Apple
Pyrus angustifolia

Distributed from Minn. Wis. and Ill. to Kan. Okla. La. and Ky.

Apple
Pyrus Malus
This familiar fruit tree, introduced into the United States and Canada, has become established in many localities; it is especially common along watercourses, which have been the most effective means of distributing the seed. A low tree 20-30 or occasionally 40 feet high, with wide-spreading, heavy limbs and gnarled branches beset with thornlike growths. Bark gray brown, rough and irregularly scaly.

The leaves rigid, leathery, dark olive green above, paler beneath, ovate or obovate, finely toothed, and irregularly clustered. The flowers white, pink-striped, variable, with 5 petals and many stamens. Fruit commonly green, green yellow, or red. Introduced from Europe. The wood is very hard, heavy, close-grained, and tough. It is highly esteemed for tool handles. The color is rich reddish brown, weight 50 lbs. to the cubic foot.

Chokeberry
Pyrus arbutifolia
A shrub 3-9 feet high, with clustered, slender, dark brown stems and twigs.

The leaves elliptical, ovate, long-ovate, or obovate, abruptly pointed, finely toothed, the teeth glandular-tipped, deep olive green above, smooth and densely woolly beneath. Flowers white or crimson magenta-tinged, ½ inch broad, in mostly terminal clusters. Fruit berrylike, a bright garnet red, about ¼ inch thick; astringent.

Common in moist situations and in woods from N. Y., west to O. and Ark., and south to Fla. Often intergrading with—

The var. *atropurpurea* Robinson, a form generally with smaller obovate leaves, and larger claret red or purple black fruit, ¼-⅖ inch in diameter, in smaller clusters. Common from central Me., south and west.

Black Chokeberry
Pyrus melanocarpa
A shrub closely resembling the preceding species in habit, but generally lower, about 2-4 feet high.

The similar leaves obovate or elliptical, abruptly acute-pointed or scarcely pointed, narrowed at the base, very finely round-toothed, dark

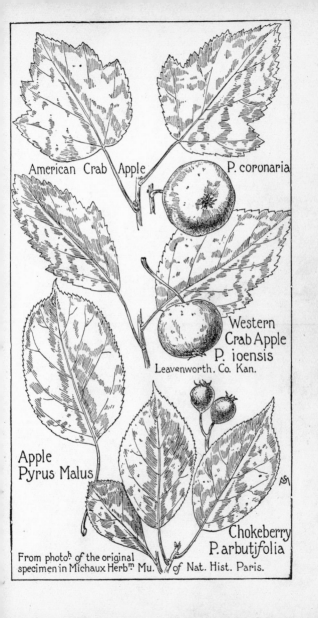

American Crab Apple   P. coronaria

Western
Crab Apple
P. ioensis
Leavenworth. Co. Kan.

Apple
Pyrus Malus

Chokeberry
P. arbutifolia

From photo^h of the original
specimen in Michaux Herb^m Mu. of Nat. Hist. Paris.

green above, paler beneath, altogether smooth. Flowers also similar. Fruit huckleberrylike, very dark purple, or quite black, not as astringent as the last. April–June.

Found in similar situations or on rocky uplands, common throughout the North from Lab. and N. S. to Minn., and South through the Alleghany Mts. to Fla. climbing to an altitude of 6000 feet in the Great Smoky Mts., N. C.

A beautiful and ornamental small tree 15–20 and in favorable situations 30 feet high, with a trunk diameter of 8–15 inches, but in high altitudes reduced to a shrub; the branches slender and ascending, the **American Mountain Ash** *Pyrus americana* foliage thin, scarcely umbrageous. Bark a neutral or brown gray, smooth, on older trees rough with horizontal excrescences; the twigs smooth, pale brown with conspicuous scattered gray dots.

Leaves compound, with 13–15 elliptical, taper-pointed (occasionally less acute), sharply double-toothed, deep bright green leaflets, paler beneath, and almost or quite smooth when old, the stems bright red, darker above, the buds ruddy, sticky-shiny and smooth.

The white flowers in broad flat-topped clusters, with 5 rounded petals and many stamens. May–June. The fruit bright, shining coral red, or deep scarlet, about the size of a small pea on slender, spreading dark red stems, in crowded clusters about 5 inches broad; very acid to the taste, ripe in late August or early September, persisting into the winter.

The Mountain Ash is found in cool mountain woods, on river banks, and in swamps from Newf. west to Lake Winnipeg, Man., and south to Conn. northern and western N. Y. the Great Lake region, and through the Alleghanies to N. C. and eastern Tenn. It is common on all the mountain slopes of Me. N. H. Vt. and Mass. at an altitude of 1000–3000 feet; it is rare in R. I. but locally common on dry ledges, in rocky woods or on the margin of swamps and ponds in the northern hilly townships of Conn. Wood close-grained, not very soft, buffish or pale brownish white, weight 34 lbs. to the cubic foot; it has no economic value.

Elder-leaved Mountain Ash
Pyrus sitchensis

A similar but smaller tree 6–15 feet high, with distinctly broader, mostly obtuse-tipped leaflets, in outline resembling those of the Elder, nearly if not wholly smooth, oblong or ovate lance-shaped, with single or double, much coarser, more widely spreading teeth, a trifle paler beneath, and firmer in texture. The flowers similar but larger, $\frac{3}{8}$ inch broad. June–July. Fruit very much larger, $\frac{5}{16} - \frac{7}{16}$ inch in diameter.

Pyrus sitchensis is common in mountain woods and along the shores of cold rivers and lakes, from southern Greenland and Lab. to the mountains of northern N. E., and westward along the northern shores of the Great Lakes to Little Slave Lake, through the Rocky Mts. to Alaska, and southward in the mountains to the Yosemite Valley, Cal. and N. Mex. It is found on the slopes of Mt. Moosilauke and other of the White Mts. N. H. where it climbs to an altitude of over 4000 feet.

European Mountain Ash Rowan Tree
Pyrus Aucuparia

The European Rowan Tree is in extensive cultivation in the parks and gardens of this country, and it has become established in many localities through the eastern States in several agricultural forms.

The leaflets are narrowly oblong, not taper-pointed, but rather obtuse-pointed, and pale green beneath with a permanent, fine, white hairiness—under the glass; the tips of the terminal buds are also distinguished by the white, hairy down. Fruit about the size of that of the preceding variety, mostly over $\frac{3}{8}$ inch in diameter, and bright scarlet; the clusters more rounded and smaller than those of *Pyrus americana*.

Round-leaved Shadbush
Amelanchier sanguinea

A straggling shrub 3–8 feet high, with slender, curving stems, not treelike in character of growth.

The leaves are not round, but very broadly elliptical or bluntly ovate, rounded or often slightly heart-shaped at the base, comparatively (with *A. canadensis*) coarse-toothed, light green and

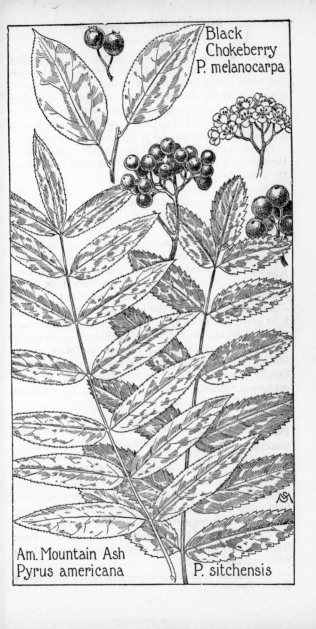

Black
Chokeberry
P. melanocarpa

Am. Mountain Ash
Pyrus americana

P. sitchensis

smooth, the veins many, close together, and terminating at the teeth. $1\frac{1}{4}$–$2\frac{1}{4}$ inches long. Flowers with 5 strap-like white petals, in loose clusters like those of *A. laevis*, appearing 11–14 days later, but the sepals spreading almost horizontally, curving backward on the fruit. May. Fruit spherical, huckleberrylike, large, purple black with a bloom, very sweet and juicy, ripe in August–September.

Found on gravelly soil from Me. Vt. and western Mass. through N. Y. Que. and Ont. to Mich., and south along the mountains to N. C. and Ala.

The common name originated from the fact that the tree is in bloom contemporaneously with the first run of shad.

Low Juneberry
Amelanchier humilis

An upright little shrub of the North, 1–4 feet high, growing in patches, with slender, straight stems; a new species.

The leaves oblong-elliptical or sometimes long-ovate, rarely obovate, narrowed or *very* slightly heart-shaped at the base, coarsely dull-toothed, light green and smooth, 1–2 inches long. Flowers small and numerous in terminal or lateral clusters, sepals nearly horizontal but curled back. Fruit purple black with a bloom, sweet and juicy, broadly vase-shaped rather than exactly spherical. Found in dry, open rocky places in calcareous regions, from Vt. and Ont. to N. Y. (not as far south as Albany), O. Minn. and Neb.[1]

Flowery Shadbush
Amelanchier florida

A western shrub 2–10 feet high with slender ascending branches and twigs.

The leaves broadly elliptical or broadly oval, sometimes slightly heart-shaped at the base, very coarsely *round-toothed* (the points abruptly sharp) to the middle or somewhat below, light green above, altogether smooth. Flowers in dense, small, erect clusters, with narrow petals, the sepals rolled back but not abruptly, triangularly lance-shaped. Fruit large, broadly vase-shaped, purple black with a bloom when mature.

[1] *Vide* Wiegand, in *Rhodora*, vol. xiv., July, 1912. "Amelanchier in E. N. America."

ROSE FAMILY. *Rosaceae*

Found in dry soil from western Ont. to B. C. Mich. S.
Dak. Neb. N. Mex. and Cal.

A stiff upright shrub 1–4 feet high, growing in patches like *A. humilis*, with slender stems.

Long-rooted Shadbush
Amelanchier stolonifera. **Wiegand.**
Amelanchier spicata. **Britton & Brown** *in part*[1]

The leaves broadly elliptical or ovate, with a slight point, the base sometimes slightly heart-shaped, rarely a trifle obovate, the teeth comparatively coarse, but less so than in *A. florida*, altogether smooth, 1–2 inches long, deep green. The small flowers in short, dense, erect clusters, sepals lance-shaped as in *A. florida*. Fruit also similar, purple black with a bloom, sweet, and good-flavored. Generally found along river banks on the coastal plain; ascending to the summits of mountains in Vt. and western Mass., also near Albany, and at Lake George, N. Y., along the crest of the Hudson River Palisades, N. J., and on the shores of Lakes Erie and Huron, and at Wellesley, Mass.

Another upright shrub with slender stems, growing in extremely close bushy clumps, 7–24 feet high, with generally madder purple gray twigs.

Oblong-leaved Shadbush
Amelanchier oblongifolia

The leaves are not oblong but absolutely elliptical, or sometimes narrowly obovate, blunt-tipped and fine-toothed nearly to the base, deep green, smooth, about 1–2 inches long. Flowers small, petals short, sepals erect or irregularly spreading, becoming nearly erect in fruit. Fruit purple black with a bloom, sweet and edible.

Found in swamps or on low ground, on the coastal plain from southern Me. to S. C. Augusta, Ga. (?) and Mobile, Ala. (?)

The *Amelanchier nantucketense* of Bicknell,[2] an erect, much branched shrub only on Nantucket Island, does not appear to be a distinct species; the reflex lance-shaped

---

[1] *Vide* Britton and Brown's *Ill. Flora of the Northern U. S.,* vol. ii., p. 238 (1897). In ed. II., p. 292 (1913) probably not *A. spicata* (Lamarck) C. Koch.

[2] *Vide* Bicknell, in *Bulletin Torrey Bot. Club.,* vol. xxxviii., pg. 453, 'Flowering Plants of Nantucket."

sepal corresponds with *A. stolonifera*, but other characters correspond with *A. oblongifolia*, suggesting a hybrid origin. Only a consensus of botanical opinion can prove the Nantucket plant unique. The type species is found near Reed Pond.

Shadbush
Juneberry
Serviceberry
Amelanchier
canadensis

A shrub or small tree 8–25 or occasionally 40 feet high, with a trunk diameter of 16 inches. Bark gray variegated with *sepia brown striping,* on older trees narrowly furrowed into flat, scaly ridges, on young trees greenish gray, quite smooth, and slightly streaked. Commonly forming a group of several stems, but not infrequently with a single trunk. The slender twigs madder brown with a slight gloss.

The lustrous deep green leaves are distinctly elliptical, or slightly obovate, sharp-pointed, about 2–3½ inches long, sharply and finely toothed, heart-shaped or rounded at the base, woolly on the veins beneath, the slender woolly stems nearly an inch long, often ruddy-tinged. In early autumn the leaves turn a rusty red. The white flowers in long loose clusters, with 5 straplike petals ⅔ inch long, and many yellow stamens, the sepals finally sharply reflexed. Blooming before the leaves have fully unfolded, in April–May. The fruit a dry, edible berry, lacking distinct flavor, resembling a huckleberry, varying in color from crimson through magenta to dark or black purple, according to the stages of development; ripe in June. This species is distinguished from *A. laevis* by the woolly sepals, leaf veins, and stems, and the finer toothed leaves.

Found on hillsides and in dry open woodlands, and distributed from Me. (Washington Co.) and western N. H., west to Io. Kan. and Mo., and south generally on dry banks and hills to Ga. and La. The wood is very hard, heavy (50 lbs. to the cubic foot), strong, and brown tinged with red. It is used for tool handles, cabinet work, and (under the name of lance-wood) for fishing rods, umbrella handles, and canes.

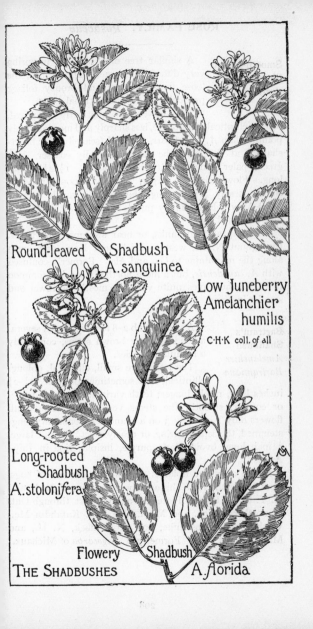

Round-leaved   Shadbush
A. sanguinea

Low Juneberry
Amelanchier
humilis

C·H·K coll. of all

Long-rooted
Shadbush
A. stolonifera

Flowery   Shadbush
THE SHADBUSHES   A. florida

ROSE FAMILY. *Rosaceae*

Smooth-leaved Shadbush
Amelanchier laevis

A similar tree or shrub, but in spring very different in general appearance, the loose flower-clusters and bronzy foliage producing a less conventional effect.

The leaves are distinctly elliptical, oblong-elliptical, or obovate, less sharply and more abruptly pointed than *A. canadensis*, rounded (scarcely ever heart-shaped) at the base, the teeth decidedly coarser, dark green, paler beneath, altogether *smooth*. 1½–2½ inches long. Flower-clusters larger, flexible, drooping; petals showy, nearly ¾ inch long, the reflexed sepals *narrow*. April–May. Fruit finally purple or black with a bloom, long-stemmed.

On damp wooded banks, or near swamps, from Newf. throughout N. E., west to Mich. and Kan., and south along the mountains to Ga. and Ala. Formerly confused with *A. canadensis*, but a more northerly species, common in N. E; the leaves quite variable, mostly narrower and smaller in Newf.

Bartram's Shadbush
Amelanchier Bartramiana

A small shrub 2–8 feet high, with several ascending, gray brown stems, commonly a mountain species.

The leaves are small, elliptical, oblong-elliptical, and sometimes obovate, 1¼–2¼ inches long, rarely longer; teeth variable, sharp and fine, or coarser, smooth, the stems very short. The small flowers only 1–2 rarely 3 on a branchlet, commonly long-stemmed, the sepals flaring, or nearly erect. Fruit large, ½ inch long, ovoid, dark purple, insipid, ripe in July–August.

Found on moist uplands and on the borders of bogs, from Lab. and Newf. through the mountains of N. E. and N. Y. to the Pocono Plateau, Pa., and west through Ont. to northern Mich. and Minn. On Mts. Katahdin Me., Washington, Moosilauke, and Monadnock, N. H., and Mansfield, Vt., etc. Formerly *A. oligocarpa* of Michaux.

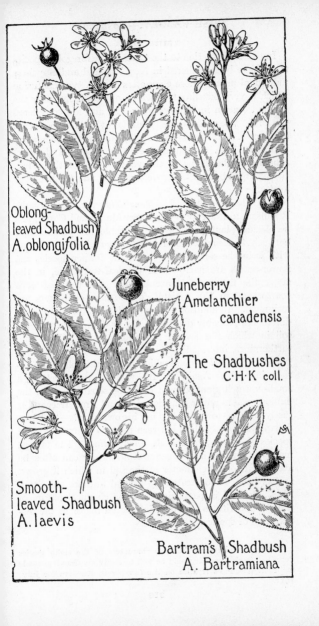

Oblong-
leaved Shadbush
A. oblongifolia

Juneberry
Amelanchier
canadensis

The Shadbushes
C·H·K coll.

Smooth-
leaved Shadbush
A. laevis

Bartram's Shadbush
A. Bartramiana

ROSE FAMILY.—*Rosaceae.*

In contradistinction to the types of the foregoing species there have been gathered in New England and elsewhere individual plants whose characters show a type-confusion which is very puzzling.[1] Such plants are found near the railroad station in Bellows Falls Vt., and are considered by Prof. Wiegand to be possible hybrids between *A. laevis* or *A. canadensis* and *A. humilis* or *A. stolonifera.* However, to a certain degree, they resemble *A. Bartramiana* in the shape of the young fruit, of the calyx, the enlarged base of the style, and the fine teeth of the leaves.

Also the so-called *A. oblongifolia* var. *micropetala,* Robinson, a dwarf form of eastern Mass., and Conn., is a perplexing plant probably attributable to hybrid origin between *A. oblongifolia* and *A. stolonifera* which grow along with it in the same locality. In the former species the flower-petals are narrow and the leaf-teeth fine, in the latter the flower-petals are broader and the leaf-teeth coarser and in the varietal forms these characters are reciprocal. In addition to such variations there are other differences probably due to the dry or damp nature of the soil in which the several individuals grow. There are, furthermore, intermediate forms between the var. *micropetala* and *A. oblongifolia* which still further place the variety in doubt. Again Mr. Bickwell's *A. nantucketense,* a small-flowered plant, cannot easily be separated from the dubious plants under consideration, and Prof. Wiegand is justly entitled to call it—to use his own words—"a Mendelian phase of a hybrid between the two common coastal species *A. stolonifera* and *A. oblongifolia.*" The fact is, many differences in the genus *Amelanchier* can often be attributed to the character of the soil in which it grows. It has been demonstrated by several authors and Prof. M. L. Fernald in particular that the chemical nature of the soil constitutes a strong, influential factor in the distribution of species.

[1] To fully understand the type characters of the eight species described in this book it would be well to study my drawings made for Prof. Wiegand's treatise on *Amelanchier* in Rhodora for July, 1912.

CRATAEGUS

An extremely difficult and complex genus separated by botanists into many divisions comprehending about 200 species. The subtle distinctions of leaf-form, anther-color, number of stamens, and character of fruit, etc., are more or less precarious, but are recorded herewith after an impartial study of living and pressed specimens in field and herbarium. Although several authors are responsible for the nomenclature and classification adopted, as a rule I have followed the lead of W. W. Eggleston who is a most conservative and reliable guide. The descriptions, however, are independently untechnical and must prove valuable or not according as they stand or break down under the test.

The Hawthorns are mostly flat-topped trees, irregular in limb and branch, the shrubby form generally showing ascending and the tree form spreading branches, but no rule is possible in this direction.

1. The leaf-lobes when they are small and shallowly cut are called points; the ribs invariably terminate at these points.

2. The white flowers, as a rule, are unpleasantly odored and bloom in May; the fruit ripens in October unless otherwise specified.

3. The fruit is commonly deep red or scarlet red, but never pure scarlet as in *Cornus Canadensis;* often it is suffused with orange, becoming a dull orange scarlet, and often it is with a bloom approaching a purer red. The definition nearly spherical means a sphere flattened at axis or circumference—either or both, but in general a square-shouldered figure.

4. The wood is uniformly reddish brown, hard, and heavy, weighing 40–53 lbs. to the cubic foot; it is commercially valueless.

OXYACANTHAE. Fruit small, red, with but one nutlet.

English Hawthorn
White Thorn
Crataegus monogyna

A beautiful small tree or tall shrub commonly 15 and occasionally 35 feet high, round-headed and broad in figure, with a dark brown trunk. Thorns about $\frac{1}{2}$ inch long.

Leaves about $1\frac{1}{2}$ inches long, lustrous deep green above, lighter and fine-hairy beneath, with 3–15 (commonly 5) lobes, and few teeth. Flowers in rounded clusters, white or pale pink, anthers pink. Double flowered varieties common. Fruit in clusters, very small, nearly spherical, red, with but one nutlet. September. Common in parks and private grounds, and a frequent escape. Formerly called *C. oxyacantha* with which it was confused.

CRUS-GALLI. Fruit deep red or dull orange, with 1–3 deeply grooved nutlets (3–5 in *C. Canbyi*).

Cockspur Thorn
Crataegus Crus-galli

A commonly cultivated tree about 25 feet high, with buff gray trunk and wide-spread branches.

Leaves 1–3½ (commonly 2) inches long, obovate or elliptical, wedge-shaped at the base, sharply toothed above the middle, obscurely toothed or toothless toward the stem, dark green and lustrous above, pale beneath. Flowers white, anthers pink, slightly fragrant, $\frac{5}{8}$ inch in diameter; with 10 stamens. Fruit nearly spherical, brown green or dull red. Common in sandy or swampy soil, from Montreal, southern Ont., the shores of Lake Champlain, the Hudson River Valley N. Y., Nantucket, Mass. and Conn., west to Mich. and southeastern Kan. and south to Ga. The following varieties of this thorn are more or less sparingly distributed: var. *pyracanthifolia* with acute-pointed leaves and small bright red fruit. Northern Del. to O., occasional; var. *capillata*, leaves thin, and fruit with solitary nutlet. Wilmington, Del.; var., *oblongata*, fruit oblong or ellipsoidal, bright red. Del. and eastern Pa.; var. *exigua*, fruit ellipsoidal, deep red, and with a solitary nutlet. Conn.; var. *prunifolia*, leaves very large, $2\frac{1}{2}$ inches wide. 5 inches long, the prolific fruit deep,

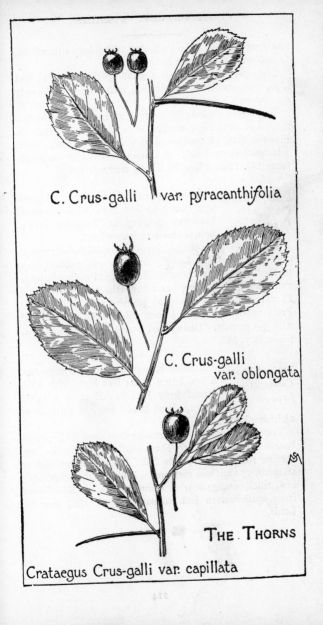

C. Crus-galli var. pyracanthifolia

C. Crus-galli var. oblongata

THE THORNS

Crataegus Crus-galli var. capillata

lusterless scarlet; the branches drooping, decumbent. Occasional. Cultivated in the North.

Crataegus schizophylla is a small species about 10 feet high, with numerous thorns 1–2½ inches long, found only on Martha's Vineyard, Mass.

The leaves obovate or ovate 1–2¼ inches long, wedge-shaped at the base, coarsely toothed at the apex, smooth. Flowers with 10 stamens and magenta anthers. Fruit ⅓ inch thick, dark red. A species too close to the many-formed *C. Crus-galli* to be wholly trustworthy.

Canby's Thorn
Crataegus Canbyi

An infrequent eastern species. A small tree about 20 feet high, with ascending branches forming an irregular crown. Spines about 1¼ inches long.

The leaves spoon-shaped, broader toward the tip, wedge-shaped toward the base, pointed or not pointed, fine-toothed, with or without shallow lateral points, smooth and dark green above, paler beneath, 1–2½ inches long. Flowers small with about 20 stamens and pink anthers. Fruit nearly spherical, ½ inch thick, light crimson red, with 3–5 nutlets. Distributed from eastern Pa. to Chesapeake Bay, Md.

Fruitful Thorn
Crataegus fecunda

Another infrequent but western species. A small tree 15–24 feet high, with wide-spread gray branches forming a broad crown. Bark brown gray. Thorns about 2¼ inches long.

The leaves similar to but broader than those of *C. Canbyi*, lustrous green, irregularly sharp-toothed, 1¼–3 inches long, turning rusty yellow in the fall. Flowers with about 10 stamens, the anthers magenta. Fruit nearly spherical, ½ inch thick, orange scarlet, borne profusely. Distributed from southwestern Ind. to southeastern Mo., near St. Louis.

214

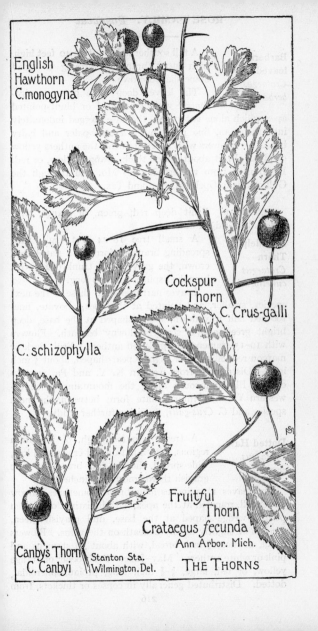

English
Hawthorn
C. monogyna

Cockspur
Thorn
C. Crus-galli

C. schizophylla

Fruitful
Thorn
Crataegus fecunda
Ann Arbor. Mich.

Canby's Thorn
C. Canbyi

Stanton Sta.
Wilmington. Del.

THE THORNS

Barberry-leaved Haw
Crataegus berberifolia

A tall southern Haw, often 40 feet high, with stout branches forming a broad dome-shaped crown.

The leaves deep olive green, wedge-shaped with a rounded or blunt-pointed apex which alone is toothed, the base merged indefinitely into the stem, fine rough-hairy above, paler and hairy beneath. Flowers with 10–20 stamens, the anthers yellow or pink. Fruit about $\frac{2}{3}$ inch thick, orange yellow, or red. Distributed from western Ky. to Mo. and through the Gulf States to Opelousas, La. and Tex.

PUNCTATAE. Fruit deep red, green, or orange, with 2–5 shallow-ridged nutlets.

Philadelphia Thorn
Crataegus cuneiformis

A small tree 18–24 feet high, with spreading branches forming a flat-domed crown, the gray brown trunk often with branched spines 7 inches long.

Leaves narrower than those of the next species, smaller, and pointed at the apex, obovate, fine-toothed half way down, wedge-shaped at the base, deep bright green above, scarcely downy beneath. Flowers with 10–15 stamens and pink red anthers. Fruit dark or maroon red, ellipsoid or slightly pear-shaped, about $\frac{1}{3}$ inch long. Distributed from western N. Y. and Pa. west to central Ill., and south along the mountains to southwestern Va. An intermediate form between the next species and *C. Crus-galli*, requiring further study.

Dotted Haw
Crataegus punctata

A tree 15–30 feet high, of mountain regions, with a flat-domed crown and low, wide-spread, thorny, gray branches. The grayish thorns mostly $1\frac{1}{2}$ inches long.

The leaves $1\frac{1}{2}$–3 inches long, broad, sometimes narrow and small, rounded at the apex, with indistinct or uneven points, wedge-shaped at the base, dull grayish green, smooth or slightly downy beneath on the veins. Flowers small, at most $\frac{3}{4}$ inch broad, with about 20 stamens and pink or white anthers. May–June. Fruit ocher or orange yellow, or red, large, $\frac{5}{8}$–$\frac{7}{8}$ inch long, prolate-spheroidal, dotted. Distributed generally in copses or thickets, from

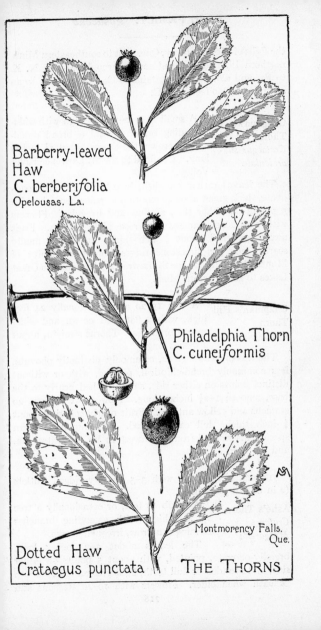

Barberry-leaved
Haw
C. berberifolia
Opelousas. La.

Philadelphia Thorn
C. cuneiformis

Dotted Haw
Crataegus punctata

Montmorency Falls.
Que.

THE THORNS

the Falls of Montmorency, Que. west to southeastern Minn. northern Ill. and Io., and south through western N. E. to Pa. and along the mountains to Ga. It ascends to an altitude of 5000 feet in N. C.

Caughnawaga Thorn
Crataegus suborbiculata

A small tree 12–18 feet high with wide-spreading branches, and a broad dome-shaped crown, the thorns about 1½ inches long. Confined to the St. Lawrence River Valley.

The leaves rather roundish, broad-elliptical or broad-ovate, dark green above, smooth and paler beneath, with 5 points on either side, shallow and irregular. Flowers with about 20 stamens and rose pink anthers. Fruit nearly spherical about ½ inch thick, dull green, finally scarlet red. On limestone ridges from the vicinity of Montreal, Que. along the St. Lawrence River and the Great Lakes to southeastern Mich.

Chapman's Hill Thorn
Crataegus collina

A tree 15–20 and occasionally 24 feet high, with a flattened crown and wide-spread branches. Thorns straight, about 2 inches long.

The leaves yellow green, commonly distinctly obovate, less commonly broad-elliptical, pointed, with or without distinct points on either side, sharp-toothed nearly to the base, smooth 1–2¼ inches long. Flowers with about 20 stamens and yellow anthers. Fruit nearly spherical about ⅜ inch thick, dull cardinal red. A common southern species, distributed from southwestern Va. to central Ga. and northern Miss.

VIRIDES. Fruit red, with 3–5 shallow ridged nutlets (2 in *C. Margaretta*).

Ashe's Thorn
Crataegus Margaretta

A shrub 10 feet, or occasionally a tree 25 feet high, with ascending branches forming a narrow, irregular crown.

The leaves about 1–2 inches long, broadly-obovate, pointed, with about 5 points on either side, and rounded or dull teeth, light green above, smooth beneath when older. Flowers with 10–20 stamens and

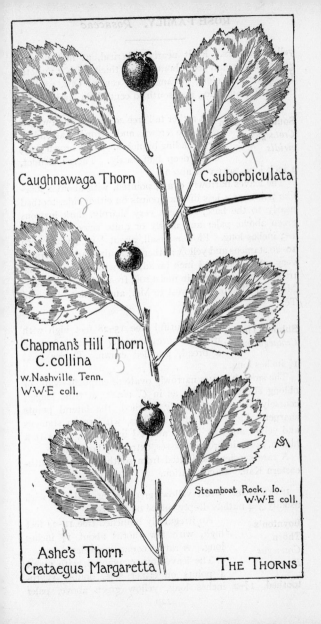

Caughnawaga Thorn

C.suborbiculata

Chapman's Hill Thorn
C. collina
w.Nashville. Tenn.
W·W·E coll.

Steamboat Rock. Io.
W·W·E coll.

Ashe's Thorn
Crataegus Margaretta

THE THORNS

yellow anthers. Fruit nearly spherical, at first bronzy green, finally dull red, about ½ inch thick, with 2 nutlets. In woods and along streams from central Ont. west to central Io. and Mo., and south to central Pa. and W. Va.

Southern Thorn
Crataegus
viridis

A rather tall tree 20–34 feet high with a domelike crown and strongly ascending or spreading branches. Bark brown gray, often deep buff, scaly. Thorns slender, 1 inch long, scarce or absent.

The leaves narrowly ovate, pointed, with about 2 lobe-like points or 4 less distinct points on either side, toothed nearly to the base, but not very sharply, dark lustrous green above, paler and nearly or quite smooth beneath, 1–3 inches long. Flowers small, about ½ inch wide, with 10–20 stamens and yellow anthers. Fruit nearly spherical, very small scarcely ¼ inch broad, red with a bloom. Distributed over lowlands in moist soil, from Chesapeake City, Md. and Clayton, Va. west to Mo., and south to Fla. and Tex.

Shining Thorn
Crataegus nitida

A beautiful tree 15–28 feet high with irregular spreading gray branches forming a broad, rounded crown. Thorns rare, 1½ inches long.

The smooth leaves narrowly ovate or elliptical-ovate, or oblong elliptical, nearly as in *C. viridis*, a trifle longer, coarsely and more sharply toothed, the lateral points sharper. Flowers in large clusters, with 10–20 stamens and yellow anthers. Fruit about ½ inch thick, red with a bloom, borne in prolific masses, extremely beautiful.

A rare species distributed from southern Ill. to southeastern Kan. In cultivation.

INTRICATAE. Fruit yellow, greenish, or dull red, with usually 3–4 nutlets deeply ridged on the back.

Boynton's
Thorn
Crataegus
Boyntoni

An irregularly branched tree 12–24 feet high, with few thorns about 1¾ inches long. A rather common species.

The leaves ovate, pointed, with about 4 points on either side, doubly sharp-toothed, 1¾–2 inches long, yellow green above, paler

Southern Thorn
C. viridis
Kinston. N·C· W·W·E coll.

Shining Thorn
Crataegus nitida

Arnold Arboretum
Jamaica Plain. Mass.

Boynton's
Thorn
C. Boyntoni

THE THORNS

beneath and smooth. Flowers with 10–15 stamens and yellow anthers. Fruit about ⅓ inch thick, orange red or dull red. Commonly distributed on banks of streams from eastern Mass. west to southern Ont. and central Mich., and south to S. C. and central Tenn. Formerly *C. foetida* of Ashe.

Yellow-fruited Thorn
Crataegus pallens

A species similar to the foregoing, with many slender, straight thorns about 1¾ inches long.

The leaves ovate, with 3 shallow but conspicuous divisions on either side, scarcely sharp-pointed, bluntly toothed, smooth, yellow green, paler beneath, 1¼–2 inches long. Flowers with 10–20 stamens and pink anthers. Fruit nearly ½ inch thick, ocher yellow. Distributed along the hills of southern Pa. south among the mountains of Va. W. Va. and N.C.

Alleghany Thorn
Crataegus straminea

A shrub with irregular branches, 7–10 feet high. Thorns few, straight, dark brown, 2–3 inches long.

The leaves ovate or broadly elliptical, pointed, with 3–4 points on either side, finely sharp-toothed, yellow green above, smooth. Flowers with about 10 stamens, and yellow or often pink anthers. Fruit pear-shaped or ellipsoid, ⅓ inch long, yellow green. Distributed over rocky hillsides from western Vt. west to southern Mich., and south from Conn. to Del. northern Ala. and southern Mo.

Scarlet Haw
Crataegus pedicellata
Sargent

A shrub or small tree 10–30 feet high, with irregular, spreading pale gray brown branches. Thorns stout, curved, about 1¾ inches long, dark brown.

Leaves ovate, wedge-shaped at the base, or nearly so, commonly with 2 distinct lobes on either side, or with about 4 less prominent points, olive green above paler beneath, rough-hairy on both sides, 1–2¾ inches long. Flowers with about 10 stamens, the anthers light yellow. May–June. Fruit nearly spherical, about ⅖ inch thick, crimson maroon.

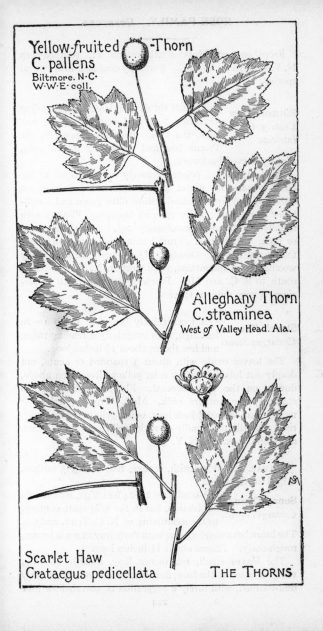

Yellow-fruited-Thorn
C. pallens
Biltmore. N.C.
W.W.E. coll.

Alleghany Thorn
C. straminea
West of Valley Head. Ala.

Scarlet Haw
Crataegus pedicellata

THE THORNS

From eastern Mass. southwestern Vt. southeastern
N. Y. western Pa. to N. C. Formerly confused with several
species.

Biltmore Haw
*Crataegus
intricata*

A small shrub with irregular, spreading
branches, 7–10 and occasionally 14 feet
high, the twigs generally zigzagged, the
thorns few and about $1\frac{3}{4}$ inches long,
slightly curved backward.

The leaves ovate, pointed, scarcely wedge-shaped at the
base, *broad*, with about 4 somewhat rounded lobes on
either side, sharply toothed, yellow olive green and rough-
hairy above, paler and very hairy beneath. Flowers with
usually 10 stamens (occasionally 20), the anthers yellow
or pink. May–June. Fruit $\frac{1}{3}$ inch thick, greenish ocher,
finally red brown. October. Distributed through rocky
woodlands on mountains, from western N. E. and N. Y.
south to S. C. and Mo. Formerly confused with *C. coccinea*, a very dubious species.

Stone's Thorn
Crataegus Stonei

A local, thickly branched shrub 10–20
feet high, with irregularly spreading twigs,
and few thorns about $1\frac{1}{2}$ inches long.

The leaves ovate with about 3 rounded or acute, not
deeply cut lobes on either side, yellow olive green above,
downy on the veins beneath. Flowers with about 10
stamens, the anthers pink. May. Fruit spherical or
nearly pear-shaped $\frac{1}{2}$ inch long, ocher yellow suffused with
red. Distributed usually on rocky soil from central Mass.
and Conn. to eastern N. Y.

FLAVAE. Fruit greenish, orange, red, with 3–5 nutlets,
ridged on the back.

Sunny Thorn
Crataegus aprica

A small tree 15–24 feet high, common in
cultivation, but in the wild state confined
to the mountains of N. C. Tenn. and Ga.
The branches ascending, the bark dark gray or sepia brown,
rough-scaly. Thorns about $1\frac{1}{2}$ inches long.

The leaves small, 1–2 inches long, broadly obovate,
wedge-shaped at the base, indistinctly and very irregularly
dull-toothed, with rarely a suggestion of one shallow lobe

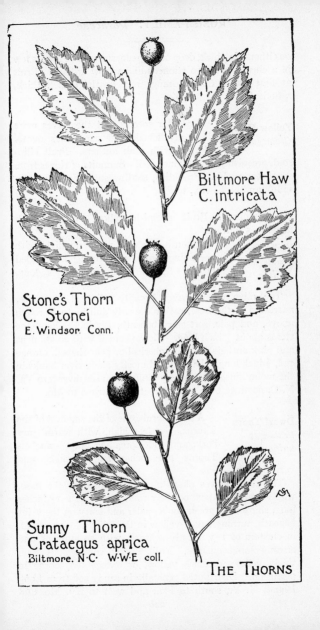

Biltmore Haw
C. intricata

Stone's Thorn
C. Stonei
E. Windsor. Conn.

Sunny Thorn
Crataegus aprica
Biltmore. N·C· W·W·E coll.

THE THORNS

on either side, thick, deep olive green, smooth. Flowers few in a cluster, with 10 stamens and yellow anthers. Fruit at first green, finally orange red, nearly ½ inch thick, spherical.

Yellow Haw
Crataegus flava

A similar species, but the leaves more distinctly lobed, and sometimes ovate. Flowers with pink anthers. Fruit ellipsoid, greenish yellow stained red. Summits of ridges from southeastern Va. (Franklin), southwestern Va. (Fayetteville), and N. C. etc., to Fla.

PARVIFOLIAE. Fruit greenish yellow or red, with usually 5 nutlets.

Vail's Thorn
Crataegus Vailiae

A southern shrub 5–10 feet high, with ascending branches forming a rounded crown. Spines about 1½ inches long, slender.

The olive green leaves broadly elliptical or ovate, narrowed at the base, rather coarsely dull-toothed, rough above, and pale, soft-hairy beneath, 1–2 inches long, the stems about ¼ inch long. Flowers small with 20 stamens and pink anthers. Fruit spherical or pear-shaped, orange red, ⅓ inch long. Distributed mostly along river banks in the mountains, or on rocky bluffs, from southwestern Va. N. C. northwest Ga. Ala. (Greensboro), west to Mo.

Dwarf Thorn
Crataegus uniflora

A small shrub, one of the smallest of the Thorns, 3–9 feet high, with warm gray bark, and wide-spreading gray branches. Thorns 1–2 inches long, straight and very slender.

The small leaves obovate, wedge-shaped at the base, with a rounded apex, coarsely round-toothed, 1–1⅓ inches long, shiny deep green above, paler and hairy on the veins beneath, turning russet yellow in the fall. Flowers small, in clusters of 1–3, mostly solitary, with 20 stamens and cream-colored anthers. Fruit nearly spherical, ⅓ inch thick, yellow, greenish yellow, or orange red, borne in profusion. Distributed generally in sandy soil from Long Island, N. Y., south to Fla., and west to Ky. Mo. and

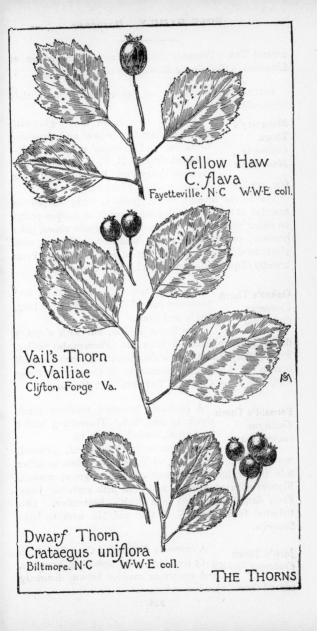

Yellow Haw
C. flava
Fayetteville. N·C   W·W·E coll.

Vail's Thorn
C. Vailiae
Clifton Forge Va.

Dwarf Thorn
Crataegus uniflora
Biltmore. N·C   W·W·E coll.

THE THORNS

ROSE FAMILY. *Rosaceae*

central Tex. Formerly confused with *C. tomentosa* of Linnaeus. (See *Gray's Manual* 7th ed. p. 467.)

ROTUNDIFOLIAE. Fruit red, with usually 3–4 nutlets shallowly ridged.

Macauley's Thorn
Crataegus Macauleyae

A small tree 12–18 feet high, with sparingly slender, brown and drooping branches, and greenish gray bark, distributed through N. Y. (Chapinville, and Genesee Valley Park, Rochester). Thorns few, straight and slender, about 1 inch long.

The leaves broadly ovate, pointed, wedge-shaped or rounded at the base, with several small or shallow points on either side, sharply toothed, bright green above, paler beneath, and smooth, $1\frac{1}{2}$–$2\frac{1}{3}$ inches long. Flowers with about 20 stamens and small Naples yellow anthers. Fruit broadly ellipsoid, dark red, $\frac{1}{2}$ inch long. November.

Oakes's Thorn
Crataegus Oakesiana

A similar tree with ruddy twigs and numerous curved thorns 1–$1\frac{1}{2}$ inches long, ruddy and stout.

The leaves similar, but with about 5 distinctly sharp points on either side. Flowers also similar. Fruit slightly pear-shaped or ellipsoid, about $\frac{3}{4}$ inch long, dull orange red. August. Common in the Connecticut River Valley, in Essex Co., Vt. Too close to *C. Macauleyae*.

Fernald's Thorn
Crataegus laurentiana

A profusely branched northern shrub about 15 feet high. Thorns 2–3 inches long, stout, curved, red brown.

The leaves ovate-elliptical, pointed, wedge-shaped at the base, with 4–5 acute points on either side (upper half), sharp-toothed, yellow green, smooth. Flowers with 10 stamens and flesh pink anthers. June. Fruit dark red about $\frac{1}{2}$ inch thick. September. Distributed from Newf. N. S. Que and Me. west to Lake Superior.

Jack's Thorn
Crataegus Jackii

A narrowly distributed Canadian shrub 9–15 feet high, with spreading branches, and numerous madder brown, distinctly curved thorns $1\frac{1}{2}$–2 inches long.

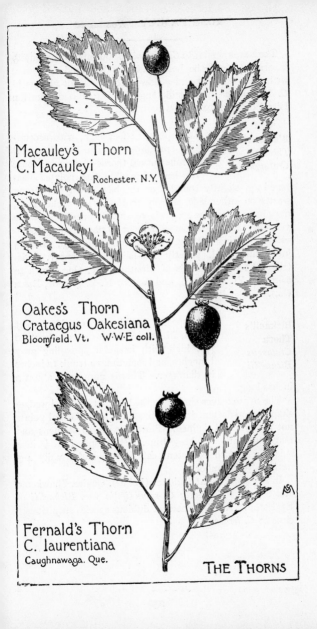

Macauley's Thorn
C. Macauleyi
Rochester. N.Y.

Oakes's Thorn
Crataegus Oakesiana
Bloomfield. Vt.   W·W·E coll.

Fernald's Thorn
C. laurentiana
Caughnawaga. Que.

THE THORNS

The leaves similar to *C. Macauleyae* but abruptly pointed, tapering toward the base, and round-toothed. Flowers with 5–10 stamens and yellow anthers. Fruit also as in *C. Macauleyae*, but a trifle angled. Distributed from the Island of Montreal to southern Ont.

Blanchard's Thorn
Crataegus irrasa
A shrub 9–12 feet high, with ascending or spreading grayish branches, and numerous curved thorns 1½–3 inches long.

The leaves broadly ovate, pointed, flattened or slightly rounded at the base, with 4–5 strong points on either side, sharply toothed, 1¼–2 inches long, dark lustrous yellow green above, slightly fine-hairy on the veins beneath. Flowers with about 20 stamens and cream-colored or pink anthers. Fruit nearly spherical, about ⅓ inch thick, red, slightly fine-hairy. September. Distributed from the Falls of Montmorency, Que. south to southern Vt. (Pownal), and eastern N. Y. (Keene, Essex Co.).

Bicknell's Thorn
Crataegus Bicknellii
A species found *only* on Nantucket Island, Mass. A shrub or tree about 10 feet high with irregular spreading gray branches, and sometimes a trunk 12 inches in diameter. Thorns numerous, about 2 inches long.

The ovate leaves similar to the last, but rounded wedge-shaped, not flattened at the base, the acute lateral points not always well defined. Flowers with 10 stamens and magenta anthers. May–June. Fruit spherical ⅓ inch thick, red, with persistent calyx-lobes, and usually 4–5 nutlets. September.

In dry thickets at Quidnet (Polpis), Quaise, Shawkemo and Squam. Formerly *C. rotundifolia* var. *Bicknellii* of Eggleston. A still somewhat dubious species suspiciously close to *C. irrasa*.

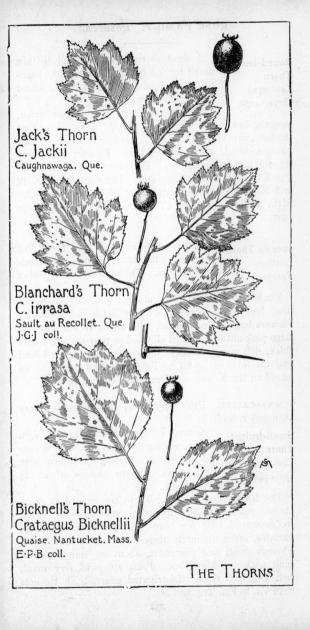

Jack's Thorn
C. Jackii
Caughnawaga. Que.

Blanchard's Thorn
C. irrasa
Sault au Recollet. Que.
J·G·J coll.

Bicknell's Thorn
Crataegus Bicknellii
Quaise. Nantucket. Mass.
E·P·B coll.

THE THORNS

Round-leaved Thorn
Crataegus chrysocarpa

A shrub or tree 8–25 feet high, with a round-topped head, conventionally beautiful foliage, and numerous thorns about $1\frac{1}{2}$–$2\frac{1}{2}$ inches long.

The leaves deep shiny yellow green, smooth, ovate, sharp-pointed, broadly wedge-shaped at the base, with about 4 distinct points on either side, slightly round-toothed, $1\frac{3}{4}$–$2\frac{3}{4}$ inches long. Flowers with 5–10 stamens and yellow anthers. Fruit nearly spherical, about $\frac{1}{3}$ inch thick, orange red, and soft. Distributed from N. S. and N. B. west to Saskatchewan, Neb. and the Rocky Mts., and south to N. C. Formerly *C. rotundifolia* in part.

Jones's Thorn
Crataegus Jonesae

A rare shrub or small tree 12–20 feet high, with a flat-domed crown, and spreading branches. Thorns about $1\frac{1}{2}$–$2\frac{1}{4}$ inches long.

The leaves similar in color and shape to *C. chrysocarpa* but much longer, 2–4 inches long, brownish fine-hairy beneath. Flowers large, 1 inch broad, with about 10 stamens and large pink anthers. Fruit ellipsoid or pear-shaped, $\frac{5}{8}$ inch thick, rich pure red. September. On Mt. Desert Island and the adjacent coast to Falmouth, and inland to an island on the Kennebec River near Skowhegan, Me.

MICROCARPAE. Fruit very small, with 3–5 nutlets very shallowly ridged.

Small-fruited Thorn
Crataegus spathulata

A small southern tree 12–25 feet high, with spreading branches and small wedge-shaped leaves. Bark gray brown with tiny scales. Thorns slender about $1\frac{1}{2}$ inches long.

The leaves very small, $\frac{3}{4}$–$1\frac{1}{2}$ inches long, dark green above, paler beneath, altogether smooth when older, wedge-shaped, with few blunt, *scolloped* teeth at the tip, variable, often distinctly three-lobed and 1 inch broad. Flowers small and numerous, about 20 stamens, with pink anthers. May–June. Fruit spherical *very* small, red, $\frac{1}{5}$–$\frac{1}{4}$ inch thick. Distributed generally in thickets from Va. to Fla. Tex. and Mo.

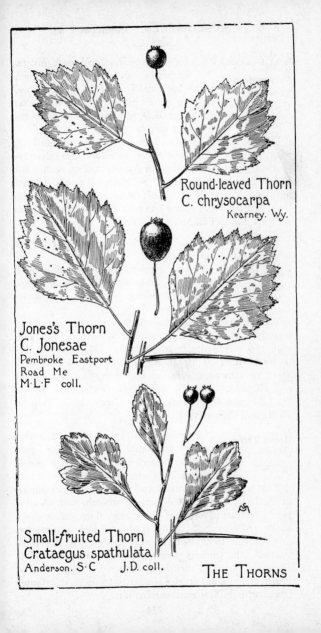

Round-leaved Thorn
C. chrysocarpa
Kearney. Wy.

Jones's Thorn
C. Jonesae
Pembroke Eastport
Road Me
M·L·F coll.

Small-fruited Thorn
Crataegus spathulata
Anderson. S·C   J.D. coll.

THE THORNS

ROSE FAMILY. *Rosaceae*

APIIFOLIAE. Fruit red, with commonly 2 smooth nutlets.

Parsley-leaved Thorn
Crataegus Marshallii

A southern shrub or tree 6–20 feet high, with horizontally spreading branches, forming an irregular, flat-topped figure; the leaves small, parsleylike, the few thorns 1 inch or more long.

The beautiful deep green leaves about $\frac{3}{4}$–$1\frac{2}{3}$ inches long, with about 3 deeply cut lobes on either side, sharply-toothed, pointed-arch-shape in general outline, with a flat base. Flowers with about 20 stamens and deep red anthers. March–April. Fruit ovoid, small, about $\frac{1}{4}$ inch long, scarlet red. Along streams in wet places, from southern Va. to Fla. Mo. and Tex.

TENUIFOLIAE. Fruit red, with commonly 3–4 nutlets strongly ridged on the back.

Bosc's Thorn
Crataegus flabellata

A rare species, 10–20 feet high, with ascending branches and shining twigs. Thorns numerous, 1–4 inches long, sometimes branched.

The beautiful leaves deep green, $1\frac{1}{4}$–$2\frac{1}{2}$ inches long, broadly ovate, pointed, rounded or flattened at the base, with 5–6 very acute points on either side, sharply fine-toothed, either slightly hairy or smooth. Flowers with about 10 stamens, the clusters with many blossoms. Fruit red, ellipsoidal, about $\frac{1}{2}$ inch long. September. In the St. Lawrence River Valley near Montreal, at Walpole, N. H., and Crown Point, N. Y.

Grove Thorn
Crataegus lucorum

A shrub or small tree 7–18 feet high with nearly horizontal or spreading gray branches. Bark smooth and gray brown. Thorns few about $1\frac{1}{4}$ inches long.

The leaves broadly ovate, broad wedge-shaped or rounded at the base, finely double-toothed, smooth, with about 4 very small acute lobes on either side, deep yellow green above, paler beneath. Flowers about $\frac{3}{4}$ inch in diameter, calyx similar to that of the next species, with about 20 stamens, the anthers pure red. Fruit pear-shaped or ellipsoidal, nearly $\frac{3}{4}$ inch long, deep red. September. A rather rare western species similar to the next, distributed from northern Ill. to southeastern Wis.

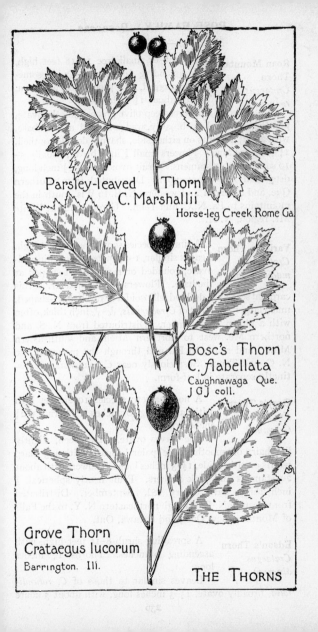

Parsley-leaved Thorn
C. Marshallii
Horse-leg Creek Rome Ga.

Bosc's Thorn
C. flabellata
Caughnawaga Que.
J G J coll.

Grove Thorn
Crataegus lucorum
Barrington. Ill.

THE THORNS

ROSE FAMILY. *Rosaceae*

Roan Mountain Thorn
Crataegus roanensis

A shrub or small tree 10–18 feet high, with ascending branches. Twigs somewhat zigzagged, olive green or ocher brown. Thorns about 1¼ inches long.

Leaves deep olive green, smooth, ovate, pointed, rounded or broadly wedge-shaped at the base, with about 4 points on either side, sharply double-toothed, 1¼–3 inches long. Flowers small ⅝ inch broad, usually 5–10 sometimes 20 stamens. Fruit ovoid, nearly ½ inch long, deep dull red. September. Distributed from southern Que. and northern and western N. E. to Wis. south in the mountains to Pa. N. C. and Tenn. Common in the White Mt. region, N. H.

Variable Thorn
Crataegus macrosperma

A similar species sometimes 24 feet high. Leaves similar, 1–2½ inches long, elliptical-ovate, rounded or rarely heart-shaped at the base. Flowers a trifle broader. Fruit cardinal scarlet to dull red, ellipsoidal or rarely pear-shaped, much larger than that of *C. roanensis*, $\frac{7}{16}$–$\frac{9}{16}$ inch thick, often with a bloom. September. Distributed from N. S. and northern Me. west to northern Mich. and southeastern Minn., and south to Pa. and through the mountains to N. C. and Tenn. Suspiciously near *C. roanensis* but distinctly separate in leaf-form.

Gray's Thorn
Crataegus Grayana

A northeastern species 10–20 feet high with ascending branches. Thorns 1–2¼ inches long.

The leaves ovate, olive green, slightly fine-hairy or smooth above, paler beneath, with 4–5 sharp points on either side, 1½–3 inches long. Flowers with about 20 stamens and pink anthers. Fruit nearly spherical, ⅔ inch thick, dark cherry red. September. Distributed from western N. E. through northeastern N. Y. to the Falls of Montmorency, Que., and Ottawa, Ont.

Edson's Thorn
Crataegus alnorum

A spreading shrub 8–15 feet high, with ascending branches. Thorns 1¼ inches long.

Leaves similar to those of *C. rotundifolia*, broadly ovate, 1½–3 inches long, with about 5 acute

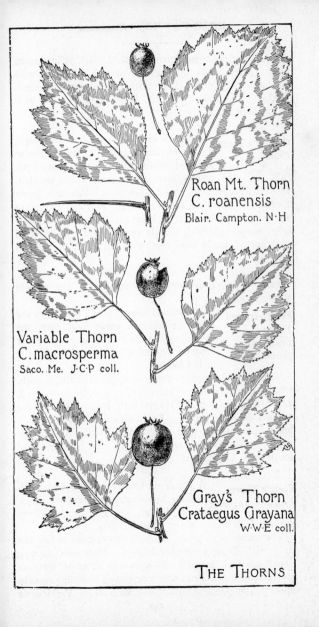

Roan Mt. Thorn
C. roanensis
Blair. Campton. N·H

Variable Thorn
C. macrosperma
Saco. Me. J·C·P coll.

Gray's Thorn
Crataegus Grayana
W·W·E coll.

THE THORNS

points on either side, sharply toothed, dark yellow green above, paler beneath, altogether smooth. Flowers with 20 stamens. Fruit ½ inch thick, deep pure red. September. Distributed from N. E. south to Pa., and west to southern Mich.

Gruber's Thorn
Crataegus populnea
A shrub or small tree 8–18 feet high, with spreading branches forming a flatish rounded crown. Thorns 1–2 inches long.
The olive green leaves ovate, pointed, with a flattened base, about 4 points on either side, finely toothed, smooth, 1½–2 inches long. Flowers with 5–10 stamens and pink anthers. Fruit scarlet red, about ½ inch long, nearly spherical, slightly pear-shaped. Distributed over bottom-lands from southern Ont. south to Pa. and Del.

PRUINOSAE. Fruit red, with commonly 4–5 nutlets strongly ridged.

Frosty-fruited Thorn
Crataegus pruinosa
A common species 10–18 feet high; the trunk or stems a warm light gray, the ascending branches forming an irregular crown. Thorns often curved back, 1–2 inches long.
The leaves deep green, ovate or elliptical-ovate, smooth, with 3–4 shallow-cut points on either side, finely-toothed, 1½–2½ inches long. Flowers with 10–20 stamens, the anthers pink or yellow. Fruit oblate-spherical, ⅝ inch broad, scarlet red with a bloom. Distributed through rocky woodlands from western N. E. west to Mich., and south to N. C. and Mo.

Fretz's Thorn
Crataegus rugosa
A shrub or tree 10–20 feet high with ascending branches, and zigzagged twigs. Thorns slender, straight or backward curved, dark brown, about 1¾ inches long.
The leaves olive green, ovate, pointed, flattened at the base, with about 3 rounded lobes on either side, sharply double-toothed, smooth. Flowers with about 10 stamens and pink anthers. Fruit nearly or quite ½ inch thick, oblate spherical, deep red. Distributed from N. E., N. Y. (Moore's

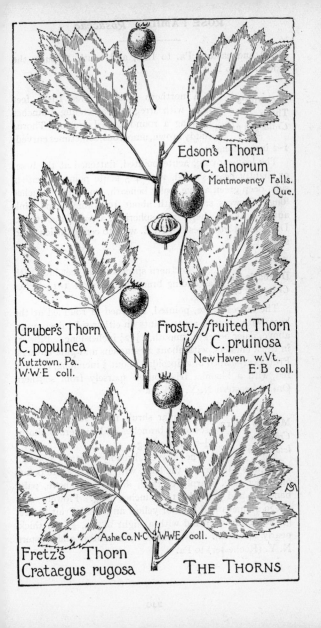

Edson's Thorn
C. alnorum
Montmorency Falls.
Que.

Gruber's Thorn
C. populnea
Kutztown. Pa.
W·W·E coll.

Frosty- fruited Thorn
C. pruinosa
New Haven. w.Vt.
E·B coll.

Ashe Co. N·C W·W·E coll.

Fretz's Thorn
Crataegus rugosa

THE THORNS

Mills) and eastern Pa. to Ind., and south through the mountains to N. C.

Beckwith's Thorn
Crataegus filipes

A northern shrub or tree 10–24 feet high with irregular, ascending branches forming a round-topped crown. Thorns ruddy brown, numerous, sometimes curved, 1–2 inches long.

The leaves ovate, acute pointed, flattened at the base, or slightly heart-shaped, with 4–5 acute points on either side, deep green above, paler beneath, smooth, 1–2 inches long. Flowers small, with about 10 stamens and pink anthers. Fruit cherry red, spherical, about ½ inch thick. Distributed from western N. E. west to central Mich., and south to Pa.

Dunbar's Thorn
Crataegus beata

A northern species 12–20 feet high with ascending branches. Thorns 1–1½ inches long.

The leaves ovate, pointed, flattened or rounded at the base, with about 4 acute points on either side, deep green above, paler beneath, smooth, 1½–2½ inches long. Flowers in thick clusters, with about 20 stamens and pink anthers. Fruit pear-shaped or ellipsoidal, about ⅗ inch long, crimson red with a bloom. Distributed sparsely from southern Ont. to western N. Y. and Pa.

Maine's Thorn
Crataegus leiophylla

A similar shrub 10–15 feet high, with ascending branches and numerous thorns 1¼–2 inches long.

The leaves broadly ovate, pointed, sometimes flattened at the base, with about 4 acute points on either side, sharply toothed, deep green above, paler beneath, and smooth, 1¼–2 inches long. Flowers with 10–20 stamens and pink or yellow anthers. Fruit at first green, finally deep red with a slight bloom, ½ inch thick, nearly spherical. Distributed from central and western N. Y. (Rochester) to Pa.

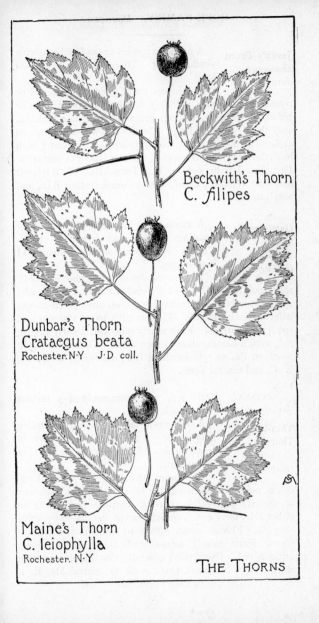

Beckwith's Thorn
C. filipes

Dunbar's Thorn
Crataegus beata
Rochester. N·Y   J·D coll.

Maine's Thorn
C. leiophylla
Rochester. N·Y

THE THORNS

Jesup's Thorn
Crataegus Jesupi

A northern species 12–20 feet high, with similar habit. Thorns about 1½ inches long.

The leaves ovate, pointed, flattened or rounded at the base, with 4–5 distinctly deep-cut lobes or points on either side, deep green above, paler beneath, smooth, 1½–2½ inches long. Flowers with about 10 stamens and red anthers. Fruit mostly pear-shaped about ⅔ inch long, dark red, slightly angled, without bloom at maturity. Distributed from western Vt. (Twin Mts., W. Rutland) and East Windsor, Conn., west to southwestern Wis., and south to Pa.

Gattinger's Thorn
Crataegus Gattingeri

A shrub 10–15 feet high with ascending branches forming an irregular crown. Thorns numerous, slender, about 1¾ inches long.

The leaves almost triangular (deltoid), sharp-pointed, with about 3 rounded lobes on either side, sharply-toothed, 1–2 inches long, deep olive green above, paler beneath, smooth. Flowers with 10–20 stamens and small pink anthers. Fruit nearly spherical, slightly angled, red, with a bloom, about ½ inch thick. Distributed from southern Pa. west to southern Ind., and south to W. Va. N. C. and central Tenn.

COCCINEAE. Fruit red, with commonly 4–5 nutlets slightly ridged on the back.

Thin-leaved Thorn
Crataegus villipes

A tree 20–30 feet high with ascending gray branches, and gray brown bark in small scales. Thorns very few, 1½–2 inches long.

The large leaves 1½–3½ inches long, ovate, pointed, rounded at the base, with about 5 distinct or scarcely perceptible coarsely sharp-toothed points on either side, olive green, smooth except the fine-hairy veins beneath. Flowers small with 5–10 stamens and red anthers. Fruit mostly pear-shaped about ½ inch long, crimson red. Distributed generally over damp mountain slopes, from Montreal, Que., south to central Me. R. I. N. Y. Pa. and through the mountains to S. C

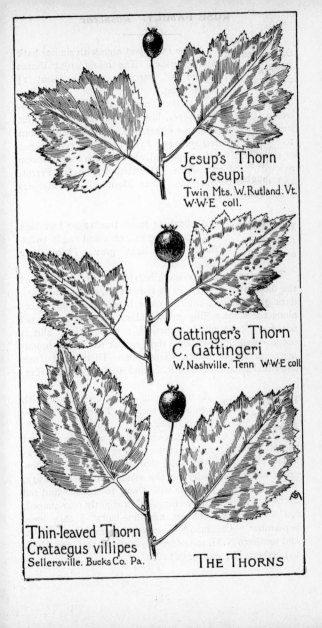

Jesup's Thorn
C. Jesupi
Twin Mts. W. Rutland. Vt.
W·W·E coll.

Gattinger's Thorn
C. Gattingeri
W. Nashville. Tenn W·W·E coll

Thin-leaved Thorn
Crataegus villipes
Sellersville. Bucks Co. Pa.

THE THORNS

Oblong-leaved Thorn
Crataegus anomala

A tree 15–20 feet high with similar bark and branches. The many stout thorns brown red, strongly curved about $1\frac{1}{4}$ inches long.

The large leaves 2–3$\frac{1}{4}$ inches long, similar to those of *C. villipes*, but with several distinct but irregular sharp points on either side. Flowers with about 10 stamens and red anthers. Fruit distinctly pear-shaped or sometimes nearly ellipsoidal, about $\frac{3}{8}$ inch long, crimson red with a bloom, edible. Distributed from Isle Perrot, and Caughnawaga, Que. (near Montreal), to Me. (?) Mass. Conn. (?) and N. Y.

Eggert's Thorn
Crataegus coccinioides

A shrub or small tree 12–20 feet high with spreading branches and ruddy twigs. Bark warm light gray. Thorns 1–2 inches long.

The leaves ovate, pointed, heart-shaped or flattened at the base, with 4–5 points on either side, sharply toothed, dark green above, slightly paler beneath, and fine-hairy along the veins. Flowers with about 20 stamens and red anthers. Fruit nearly spherical, a trifle oblate, almost obtuse-angled, $\frac{3}{4}$ inch long, dark scarlet red with a prominent, persistent calyx. September. Distributed from Montreal Island south to R. I., and west to Mo. and Kan.

Pringle's Thorn
Crataegus Pringlei

A tree about 18–24 feet high, with ascending branches. Thorns curved 1–$1\frac{3}{4}$ inches long.

The leaves broadly ovate, abruptly and sharply pointed, rounded at the base, with about 4 shallowly cut points on either side, sharp-toothed, bright yellow green above, fine-hairy on the veins and paler beneath, 2–3 inches long. Flowers with about 10 stamens and red anthers. Fruit broadly ellipsoidal or slightly pear-shaped, red with a slight bloom, and fine-hairy, $\frac{5}{8}$ inch long. September. Commonly distributed from Mass. (?) Vt. and southern N. H. west through southern Ont. and Mich. to northern Ill., and south to Pa.

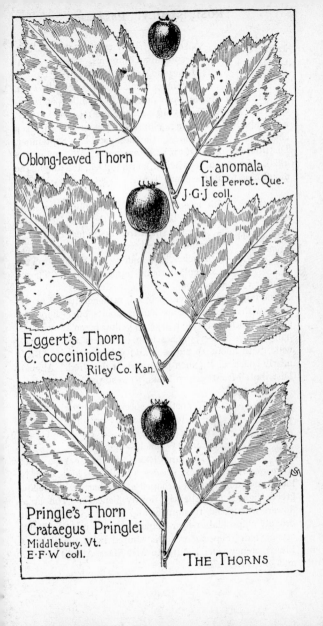

Oblong-leaved Thorn

C. anomala
Isle Perrot. Que.
J·G·J coll.

Eggert's Thorn
C. coccinioides
Riley Co. Kan.

Pringle's Thorn
Crataegus Pringlei
Middlebury. Vt.
E·F·W coll.

THE THORNS

Tatnall's Thorn
Crataegus albicans

A shrub or small tree 10-20 feet high, with spreading branches. Thorns about 1¼ inches long, slightly curved.

The leaves similar to those of *C. Pringlei*, but flattened at the base, or slightly rounded or heart-shaped. Flowers with 5-10 stamens and rose red anthers. Fruit about ½ inch long, ellipsoidally pear-shaped, deep cherry red with a bloom, the flesh edible. September. Distributed from western Vt. Mass. and Conn. (among the hills), west to southern Mich., south to Del., and among the mountains to northeastern Tenn.

MOLLES. Fruit large, red, with commonly 4-5 nutlets shallowly ridged on the back.

Arnold's Thorn
Crataegus Arnoldiana

A rare, small tree 15-20 feet high, with ascending and spreading brown gray branches, and buff twigs, which form an irregular round-topped crown. Thorns curved, 1½-2 inches long.

The larger ovate leaves pointed, rather flattened at the base, with six acute, conspicuous points on either side, sharply toothed, a trifle hairy and yellow green above, fine-hairy beneath, 2-3⅞ inches long. Flowers about ¾ inch wide, with about 10 stamens and yellow anthers. Fruit nearly spherical ⅝-¾ inch thick, bright deep red. August. Distributed from eastern Mass. to western Conn.

Emerson's Thorn
Crataegus submollis

A northern species, commonly a tree 18-30 feet high with spreading branches forming a dome-shaped crown. Thorns curved 1½-3 inches long.

The large leaves similar to those of *C. Arnoldiana* and the next species, 1¾-4 inches long, sharply lobed and broadly wedge-shaped at the base, deep yellow green, lighter and slightly downy beneath. The large flowers with about 10 stamens and yellow anthers. Fruit broadly ellipsoidal or pear-shaped, about ⅝ inch long, dull orange red. September. Distributed from the Falls of Montmorency, Que., south to Me. Mass. Albany, N. Y., and southern Ont.

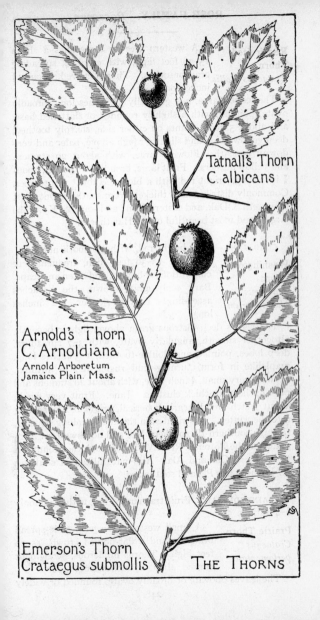

Tatnall's Thorn
C. albicans

Arnold's Thorn
C. Arnoldiana
Arnold Arboretum
Jamaica Plain. Mass.

Emerson's Thorn
Crataegus submollis   THE THORNS

Red-fruited Thorn
Crataegus mollis
A western tree or sometimes a shrub 15–38 feet high, with crooked, spreading gray branches. Thorns curved, about 1½ inches long.

The leaves large, 2–5 generally 3½ inches long, broadly ovate, pointed, with a slightly rounded or flattened base, and about 5 acute points on either side, sharply toothed, deep yellow green and slightly rough above, paler and very downy beneath. Flowers large, with about 20 stamens and yellow anthers. Fruit large, broadly ellipsoidal, about ⅞ inch long, bright red with a bloom, edible. September. Commonly distributed in thickets from southern Ont. west to eastern S. Dak. and eastern Kan., and south to Ky. The largest and most beautiful of the Hawthorns.

CORDATAE. Fruit bright red, with 5 smooth nutlets.

Washington Thorn
Crataegus phaenopyrum
A tree 15–30 feet high, frequently in cultivation for hedges, and often an escape. Bark scaly gray brown, the branches ascending. Thorns slender 1–2 inches long.

The leaves deep lustrous green above, lighter beneath, altogether smooth, angularly ovate, with 3–7 spreading, deep lobes, pointed and double-toothed, 1–3 inches long, maplelike in form, turning dull russet red in autumn. Flowers very small, ⅜ inch wide, with about 20 stamens and pink anthers; in thick clusters. June. Fruit very small, about ¼ inch broad, nearly spherical, bright red, persisting into the winter. Distributed in thickets, or along streams, through southern Ill. southern Mo. and northwestern Ark., and from the Potomac River Valley through the mountains to northern Ga. and Ala. Also naturalized in southern N. J. Bucks Co. Pa. and southward.

BRAINERDIANAE. Fruit translucent red, with commonly 2–4 nutlets.

Prairie Thorn
Crataegus pertomentosa
A small western tree with wide-spread branches and a flat-domed crown, 15–20 feet high. Thorns numerous, straight or curved, about 2¼ inches long.

The leaves obovate or broadly ovate, rounded or widely

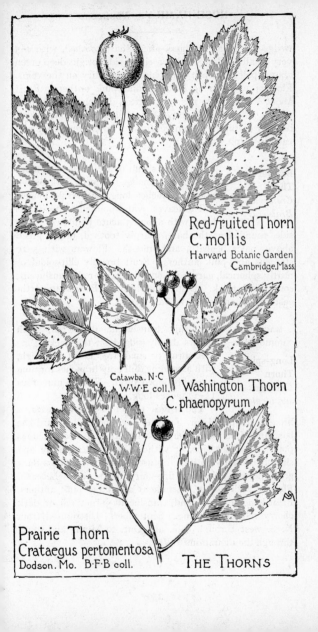

Red-fruited Thorn
C. mollis
Harvard Botanic Garden
Cambridge. Mass.

Catawba. N·C
W·W·E coll.

Washington Thorn
C. phaenopyrum

Prairie Thorn
Crataegus pertomentosa
Dodson. Mo. B·F·B coll.

THE THORNS

wedge-shaped at the base, finely sharp-toothed, with 4–5 very small shallow points on either side, bright deep green above, paler beneath and densely fine-hairy on the veins. Flowers with 10–15 stamens and pink anthers. Fruit about $\frac{1}{3}$ inch thick, nearly spherical, dull cherry or garnet red, nearly translucent, soft. Distributed on stony barrens of prairies from central Io. to western Mo. and eastern Kan.

Brainerd's Thorn
Crataegus Brainerdi

A similar shrub or tree, but with more ascending branches. Thorns dark brown about $1\frac{1}{2}$ inches long, or a trifle longer. The leaves ovate, pointed, 2–$2\frac{3}{4}$ inches long, with about 5 acute points on either side, rounded at the base, sharply toothed, bright green above, paler beneath, and smooth. Flowers with 5–20 stamens and pink anthers. Fruit broadly ellipsoidal or nearly spherical, garnet red or deep cherry red, translucent, soft, $\frac{1}{3}$ inch thick. Distributed from N. E. west to northeastern Io., and south to Pa.

MACRACANTHAE. Fruit translucent dark red, with commonly 2–3 nutlets deeply ridged on the back.

Long-spined Thorn
Crataegus succulenta

A shrub or small tree 12–24 feet high, with ascending dull gray branches forming a round-topped head. Thorns numerous $1\frac{1}{2}$–$3\frac{1}{2}$ inches long. The leaves $1\frac{1}{4}$–3 inches long, ovate or broadly elliptical, or obovate, asymmetrical toward the base and often wedge-shaped; with about 4 inconspicuous points on either side, or without points, irregularly and sharply double-toothed, obtuse pointed, lustrous dark green above, paler and fine-hairy on the veins beneath. Flowers with about 10 stamens and large pink anthers. Fruit $\frac{1}{3}$ inch or less broad, translucent garnet red or dark cherry red, and shining. September. Distributed from N. S. west through Que. and Ont. to Minn., and south through the mountains to Va.

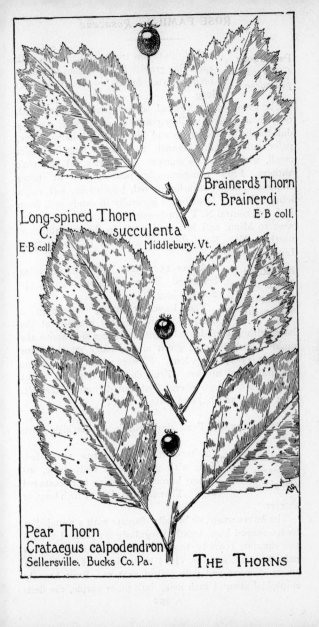

Brainerd's Thorn
C. Brainerdi
E·B coll.

Long-spined Thorn
C.   succulenta
E·B coll.   Middlebury. Vt.

Pear Thorn
Crataegus calpodendron
Sellersville. Bucks Co. Pa.

THE THORNS

ROSE FAMILY. *Rosaceae*

Pear Thorn
*Crataegus cal-
podendron*

A shrub or low tree 9–20 feet high, with spreading grayish buff branches forming a broad crown. Spines few, about 1½ inches long.

The leaves ovate-elliptical, scarcely sharp-pointed, with or without several shallow points on either side, coarsely dull-toothed, olive green and slightly rough-hairy above, paler and fine-hairy beneath, 2–3½ inches long. Flowers small, with about 20 stamens (sometimes 10) and pink anthers. Fruit conspicuously pear-shaped, at times ellipsoidal, nearly translucent red, ⅓ inch long, soft, calyx lobes reflexed. Distributed generally in sandy soil, from L. I. and central N. Y. northeastern N. J. and eastern Pa. west to Minn. and Mo., and south in the mountains to northern Ga. Formerly confused with *C. tomentosa* of Linnaeus.

**New River
Thorn**
*Crataegus
neofluvialis*

A tree 15–30 feet high with spreading branches. Thorns numerous, curved, 1½–2 inches long.

The leaves rhombic, suggesting a diamond figure, slightly rounded at the base, with 4–5 graduated points on either side above the middle, dark lustrous green above, hairy on the veins beneath, 1½–2¾ inches long. Flowers with 15–20 stamens and small pink anthers. Fruit dark red spherical, about ⅓ inch thick. September. Distributed from western Vt. west to Wis. and Io., and south to N. C.

DOUGLASIANAE. Fruit dark purple or blackish, with 3–5 nutlets.

Douglas's Thorn
*Crataegus
Douglasii*

A far-north shrub or tree 12–38 feet high, with gray brown scaly bark, ascending branches and shiny terra cotta red twigs. Thorns small about 1 inch long, or shorter.

The leaves ovate, or broadly obovate with a rounded or wedge-shaped base, mostly irregularly six-pointed toward the summit, coarsely toothed, dark green above, much paler beneath, smooth, 1¼–2½ inches long. Flowers with 10–20 stamens and pale yellow anthers. Fruit broadly ellipsoidal about ⅓ inch long, dark plum purple, the flesh

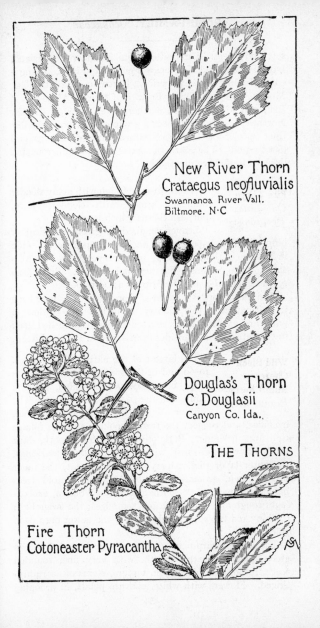

New River Thorn
Crataegus neofluvialis
Swannanoa River Vall.
Biltmore. N·C

Douglas's Thorn
C. Douglasii
Canyon Co. Ida..

THE THORNS

Fire Thorn
Cotoneaster Pyracantha

soft and sweet. Distributed from Thunder Bay Island, Lake Huron, and Keweenaw Peninsula, Mich., Michipicoten Island, Lake Superior, Bozeman, Gallatin Co., Mont., Valley of North Fork of Coeur d' Alene Mts., Ida., and Umatilla Co., northern Ore., through the far Northwest. This concludes a group of over 60 fairly distinct species of *Crataegus* with a more or less general distribution. The southern species are too numerous and dubious to deserve mention!

Fire Thorn
Cotoneaster
Pyracantha

A shrub 3–7 feet high with many slender branches armed with slender, sharp, purplish thorns ¾ inch long.

Leaves small, deep green, elliptical or bluntly lance-shaped, with finely scolloped teeth, 1¼–2 inches long, thin, leathery, mostly evergreen. Flowers small, white, in small, flat terminal clusters. Fruit deep scarlet about the size of a large pea; berrylike.

The Fire Thorn is a native of Europe, and has long been in cultivation in this country for hedges and borders in parks and gardens; it has escaped and has established itself in thickets and on roadsides from southern Pa. southward.

Wild Black Cherry
Rum Cherry
Prunus serotina

The largest of the native Cherry trees, 40–60 and in the southern portions of its range often 90–100 feet high, with a trunk diameter of 1–2 or more feet. The contour of the tree is unconventional, irregular, and rugged, the trunk crooked, and the foliage thin and drooping. Bark on young trees smooth, dark ruddy brown, or greenish, with strong horizontal markings, the outer layer thin, papery, and translucent, the inner bright green, aromatic, and tonic bitter, on old trees blackish brown, or on southern trees, red brown, exceedingly rough and scaly with reflexed edges; the twigs light or shiny red brown, strongly dotted, the newer ones deep gold ocher.

The leaves sharp-pointed, long elliptical, dark lustrous green, paler beneath, smooth, with very fine, rounded teeth, rather thin leathery in texture, stems often ruddy-tinged. Flowers with white, obovate petals, in drooping

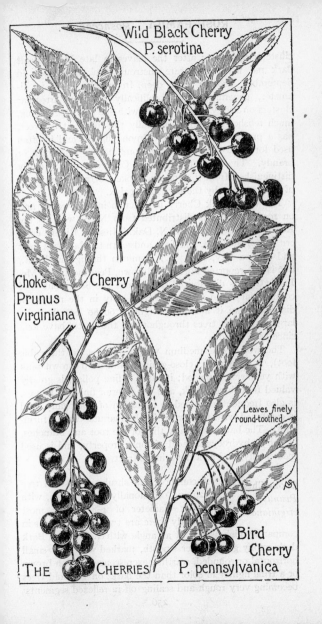

Wild Black Cherry
P. serotina

Choke Cherry
Prunus
virginiana

Leaves finely
round-toothed

Bird
Cherry
P. pennsylvanica

THE CHERRIES

clusters; appearing after the leaves in late May. Fruit dark red when immature, lustrous black when ripe in September, broader than deep, frequently $\frac{1}{2}$ inch in diameter, generally borne prolifically in long, irregular clusters on ruddy stems, always with the calyx persisting, much relished by birds, especially the robin; it is sweet, has a prussic acid or bitter almond flavor, and is often used for its tonic property in combination with rum or brandy. The fruit of the Black Cherry is always easily distinguished from that of the Choke Cherry in any stage of development by the persistent calyx.

The Wild Black Cherry is common in rich woods and on roadsides and is distributed from N. S. west to the Kaministiquia River, Can. N. Dak. (Missouri River), eastern Neb. Kan. Okla. and Tex., and south to Matanzas Inlet and Tampa Bay, Fla. It is common throughout N. E., but is not reported north of Oldtown, Penobscot Co., Me. In N. C. it is distributed throughout the State, but is of commercial value and importance only in the mountain district where it attains a height of 60–80 feet; but the largest and best trees throughout all the States have long since been felled.

The wood is of medium weight (36 lbs. to the cubic foot), hard, strong, close-grained and deep brown pink with yellowish sapwood; it takes a fine polish, is greatly valued for cabinet work, and the interior finish of houses, is also frequently stained in imitation of mahogany, and is combined with that wood in the manufacture of furniture. The bark, especially that of the root and branches, is rich in hydrocyanic acid of tonic property, and is used medicinally, and as a flavoring extract.

Choke Cherry
Prunus virginiana

A common, tall shrub, or a small tree 10–20 and occasionally 30 feet high, with a trunk diameter of 4–8 inches; most frequently there are two or three stems in company which ascend at an angle with each other. Bark dark smoky gray, rather smooth, marked with very small horizontal or rounded, wartlike excrescences buffish brown or a trifle lighter in color than the bark; on very old trees becoming very rough and scaling off in reflexed segments' the twigs brown gray buff-dotted, slender, a trifle rank-odored when crushed, but with the prussic acid flavor which characterizes the twigs of the Black Cherry.

The leaves distinctly widest above the middle, or obovate, abruptly pointed, very finely sharp-toothed, thin, not leathery, medium or yellow olive green, smooth throughout. The flowers in thick white cylindrical clusters, petals rounded, appearing in late spring after the leaves, not very pleasant in odor, but dainty in appearance. Fruit in thick, drooping clusters, in early summer yellow red-tinted, in late summer translucent ruby-red, with a strong resemblance to currants, ripe in September, turning to dark rich red, very astringent, the calyx absent on the fruit.

The Choke Cherry is common in almost all soils, in copses, beside roads, along river banks and in rich woods from Newf. and Lab. west to Minn. Hudson Bay, the Mackenzie River, lat. 62° and the northern coast region of British Columbia, and south to southern Ga. La. and Tex. It is common throughout N. E., and is found on the wooded slopes of the White Mts., and on the spurs of Mt. Katahdin at an altitude of 4000 feet. The wood is hard, close-grained, light brown, and commercially valueless. The twigs are very frequently infected by a fungus disease called Black Knot (*Plowrightia morbosa*), to which the other Cherries are also liable.

The var. *leucocarpa* is a form with short, thick flower-clusters, and sweeter dull golden yellow fruit. It is known only at Dedham, Mass.

A single-stemmed shrub or a small delicate branched tree 12–20 and occasionally 40 feet high, with a trunk diameter of 4–15 inches, the apex commonly narrow-ovoid, or rarely broadly rounded. Foliage thin. Bark ruddy brown, smooth or nearly so, with few or many horizontal rust-colored lines or dots, rather glossy, often purplish when young; on old trees rather rough with semi-detached grayish bark; the twigs slender, ruddy or purplish brown, smooth, often glossy, sparingly dotted.

Wild Red Cherry
Bird Cherry
Pin Cherry
Prunus pennsylvanica

The leaves lance-shaped or narrowly elliptical, extremely sharp-pointed, very finely and sharply toothed, lustrous light yellow green, paler beneath, altogether smooth, with short, slender, generally ruddy stems, drooping, somewhat similar to those of the peach, undulating in outline. Flowers tiny, white, rarely pinkish, delicate, separate, in long-stemmed lateral clusters preceding or developing with the leaves in May. Fruit tiny, translucent ruby red, about the size of a pea, on very long simple (unbranched) stems, borne few in a cluster, very sour, but relished by the birds. Ripe in August–September.

This Wild Cherry is common on rocky woodlands and beside stone walls, in clearings, and on burned-over land from Newf. and Lab. (Strait of Bellisle), west to Hudson Bay (Big River), south Indian Lake, and British Columbia (eastern slopes of coast ranges in Fraser River Valley), to Mich. (Ionia Co.), and south to Pa. along the Alleghany Mts. to western N. C. and eastern Tenn. northern Ill. central Iowa, and the eastern slopes of the Rocky Mts., Col. It is common throughout N. E., and climbs to an altitude of 4500 feet on Mt. Katahdin, Me. and to the same elevation on Mts. Moosilauke and Lafayette and other of the White Mts., it is less common near the seacoast. The wood is light, soft, close-grained, and light brown; it is commercially valueless.

American Sloe Porter's Plum
Prunus alleghaniensis

A straggling shrub, or sometimes a small tree 3–16 feet high, with a trunk diameter of 5 inches, with few if any thorns. Bark brown, rough, scaly branches irregular, twigs smooth with age.

The leaves long ovate or elliptical, sharply pointed, finely toothed or double-toothed, deep green above, paler beneath, smooth, 2–3½ inches long. Flowers as in *P. americana*, white. Fruit dark purple with a bloom, long-stemmed, broadly ovoid, nearly ½ inch long, slightly acid, the stone ridged on one side, grooved on the other, ripe in August.

Mostly in copses and sandy barrens, from Jewett City, eastern Conn. to the Alleghany Mts. in Pa.

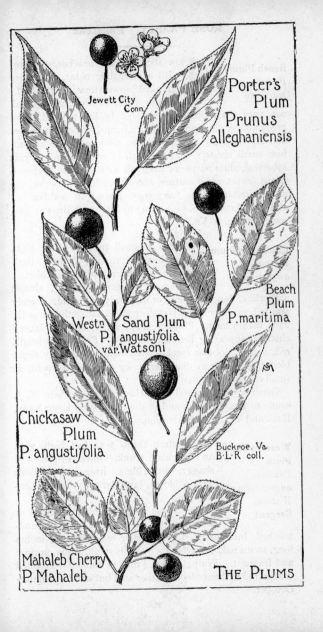

Jewett City
Conn.

Porter's
Plum
Prunus
alleghaniensis

Beach
Plum
P. maritima

Westn Sand Plum
P. angustifolia
var. Watsoni

Chickasaw
Plum
P. angustifolia

Buckroe. Va.
B.L.R coll.

Mahaleb Cherry
P. Mahaleb

THE PLUMS

ROSE FAMILY. *Rosaceae*

Beach Plum
Prunus maritima

A low shrub of sea beaches, 1–5 feet high, with a straggling habit, and more or less crooked brown stems, dotted buff. The leaves ovate or broadly elliptical, not very sharp-pointed, but sharply fine-toothed, olive green above, paler and fine-hairy beneath, the stems short and also hairy, 1–2¼ inches long. Flowers white, in profuse small clusters, about ½ inch or more broad. Fruit spherical, plum purple or magenta with a bloom, ½–¾ inch broad, sweet when mature, often used for a preserve, the stone similar to the foregoing. Found on sea beaches and sand dunes N. S. (according to Britton & Brown), and southern Me. to Va.

Chickasaw Plum
Prunus angustifolia

A shrub or small tree 7–25 feet high, the branchlets with a few thorns. Bark brown, trunk slender, with close scales. The leaves extremely narrow, almost willowlike, lance-shaped, or narrowly elliptical, sharply pointed, very finely toothed, deep green, altogether smooth, 2½–4 inches long. Flowers small, white, in small lateral clusters, appearing before the leaves. Fruit deep bright red, nearly globular (prolate spheroidal), with very slight bloom, ½–¾ inch in diameter, juicy and slightly acid, in small clusters. September.

Generally on dry soil in thickets, from southern N. J. south to Fla. and Ala. and in the Mississippi lower basin, Kan. and Tex. In cultivation.

Western Sand Plum
Prunus angustifolia var. Watsoni
Sargent

A western shrub 3–12 feet high, with an irregular trunk. Bark brown and shaggy, branchlets irregular, smooth with a bloom, lavender gray, with thorn-like tips. The leaves ovate, pointed, rounded or wedge-shaped at the base, finely round-toothed, lustrous deep green, paler beneath, 1–1½ inches long, stems red, ½ inch long. Flowers small, white, profuse and fragrant. Fruit globular, ⅔ inch in diameter, subdued orange red without bloom, rather acid but edible. August–October.

ROSE FAMILY. *Rosaceae*

Along streams in thickets, from southern Neb. to central Kan. (along the Sabine River, about 10 miles from Ellis), and Okla. Occasionally cultivated.

A shrub or small tree 12–24 feet high, from Europe (the Caucasian provinces), in cultivation, and a not infrequent escape. Bark light brown nearly smooth.
Mahaleb Cherry. Perfumed Cherry *Prunus Mahaleb*

The small leaves nearly round, very broadly ovate and abruptly pointed, deep green, smooth, *very* finely round-toothed, slender-stemmed, 1–1½ inches long, fragrant when crushed. Flowers white, small, in small rounded clusters. Fruit globular, maroon or maroon black, nearly ½ inch thick, slightly bitter. July.

Found by the roadsides and river banks from Ont. to N. Y. Penn. and Del. The wood is hard, red brown, fragrant, and is used in Europe for cabinet work and tobacco pipes.

A low northern shrub erect in habit, 1–4 feet high, with pale brown, smooth or often slightly downy branches, common in wet sandy soil, or on banks, and usually in thickets.
Appalachian Cherry *Prunus cuneata*

The leaves olive green above, lighter beneath, obovate, rounded or rarely acute at the tip, narrowed or wedge-shaped at the base, thin, finely toothed over the upper half of the edge, 1–3 inches long. The small white flowers in groups of 2–4. Developing in April–May with the leaves. Fruit a small purplish black cherry, ⅓ inch in diameter, ripe in August, insipid.

The Appalachian Cherry is distributed from southern Me. west through N. H. and Vt. to Minn., and south to N. C.

A prostrate, spreading shrub of sandy or rocky shores 1–5 or more commonly 2 feet high, with rough, brown gray, scraggy stems, and bright red brown new twigs, slender and smooth.
Sand Cherry *Prunus pumila*

Leaves blunt lance-shaped, a trifle broader near the pointed tip, sharply toothed over the upper three-quarters of the edge, bright olive green above, paler beneath, and altogether smooth, $1\frac{1}{4}$–$2\frac{1}{4}$ inches long, the whitish stems about $\frac{1}{2}$ inch long. Flowers like those of the preceding species. Blooming in April–May. Fruit resembling that of the Choke Cherry, borne singly or in small clusters on very slender stems, scarcely exceeding in length the diameter of the fruit, which is insipid, soft, and reddish black when ripe in August.

The Sand Cherry is commonly found on sandy river beaches or rocky banks from eastern Que. west to northern Ind. Wis. and the shores of Lake Winnipeg, Man., and south to Pa.

European Bird Cherry
Sweet Cherry
Mazzard Cherry
Prunus avium

A European Cherry with a slender and narrow figure reaching a height of 50–70 feet, with a trunk diameter of 1–$2\frac{1}{2}$ feet, the stem continuing to the crown, the slender branches ascending. Bark deep red brown strongly marked with long, horizontal gray buff excrescences, the twigs a lustrous red brown. The leaves light green, obovate or elliptical-obovate, pointed, sharp-toothed, smooth, about $3\frac{1}{2}$ inches long. Flowers large, white, with long petals. Fruit deep red (sometimes yellow), juicy and sweet.

The Mazzard Cherry is in common cultivation (in several improved varieties), in many localities it has escaped to thickets or hedgerows.

Pie Cherry
Morello Cherry
Sour Cherry
Prunus Cerasus

A small cherry tree 15–30 feet high, with a trunk diameter of 8–12 inches; the slender branchlets drooping, the short trunk dividing into widely diverging branches forming a rounded head. Bark ruddy brown, gray brown when old, smooth, but strongly marked with elongated horizontal excrescences. The leaves obovate, slightly rounded or wedge-shaped at the base, abruptly sharp-pointed, double-toothed, the teeth fine and indistinct toward the base, deep green, paler beneath, altogether smooth. Flowers white, large, with petals over $\frac{1}{2}$ inch long. Fruit round, translucent red, about $\frac{5}{8}$ inch in diameter, sour but excellent in flavor when

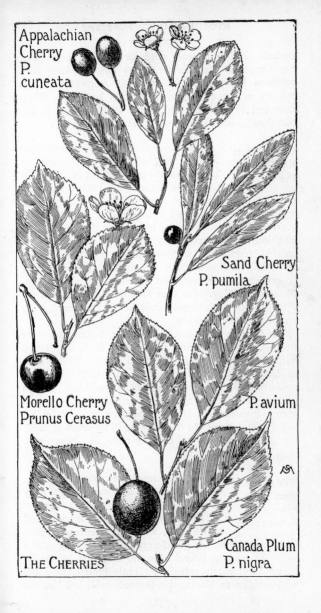

Appalachian
Cherry
P.
cuneata

Sand Cherry
P. pumila

Morello Cherry
Prunus Cerasus

P. avium

THE CHERRIES

Canada Plum
P. nigra

cooked. It is commonly used for pies, as the popular name implies. The Morello Cherry was introduced from southern Europe, and is commonly cultivated in this country in several improved varieties known as Montmorency, Early Richmond, Louis Phillipe, etc. It has occasionally escaped to roadsides and hedges.

Canada Plum
Red Plum
Prunus nigra

A shrub or small tree 6–12 sometimes 25 feet high, with a trunk diameter of 4–8 inches, the general form distorted like that of an apple tree. Bark brown with slight horizontal markings, thin, scaly, very greatly roughened with age, the brown twigs slender, smooth, set at nearly right-angles with the branchlets; thorns about an inch long. The leaves very broad, obovate, abruptly-pointed, rounded or wedge-shaped at the base, doubly and finely scollop-toothed, the teeth tipped with tiny brown glands (through the glass), light olive green. Blooming in May. Fruit an inch in diameter, deep red without bloom, flattened ovoid or nearly round, very sour, but useful in cooking.

The Canada Plum is found beside the road and along streams, in thickets and fence-rows. It is distributed from Newf. west through the St. Lawrence River Valley to Lake Manitoba and Wisc., and south throughout northern N. E. northern N. Y. and eastern Mass., though it is rare near the coast, where it has undoubtedly escaped from cultivation. It is not uncommon in northern Vt. and N. H. among the mountains. The wood is hard, heavy, close-grained, and a ruddy mahogany brown with paler sapwood.

Wild Goose
Plum
Prunus
hortulana

A similar small tree with spreading, irregular boughs, and very rough scaly bark.

The leaves narrow, ovate lance-shaped or elliptical, with an attenuated point, finely round-toothed, gland-tipped, smooth, 4–5 inches long. Flowers in lateral clusters, blooming in April-May. Fruit nearly spherical, slightly prolate, deep red with little or no bloom, thin-skinned, acid, but like the foregoing excellent for preserving. On rich alluvial soil from Tenn. and Ill. to Mo.

A shrub or small tree closely resembling the Canada Plum, in cultivation often 30 feet high, the trunk dividing not far above the ground, the branches angular or curved, scragged, set with slender thornlike twigs. Bark light brown gray, with thin scales.

Wild Plum
Prunus americana

The leaves elliptical-ovate or obovate, attenuately pointed, sharply and doubly toothed, the teeth not glandular tipped. Flowers as in the foregoing species; fruit also similar, about $\frac{7}{8}$ inch in diameter, but the skin rather thick and tough. Ripe in August–September.

Mostly on bottom-lands and the margins of woods, from Conn. south to Fla., and west to Col.

The var. *mollis* is a form with the under surface of the leaves permanently soft-hairy. It is found in the southwest from Io. to La. and Tex.

The Peach Tree, from Asia, in common cultivation in this country, is often an escape on bottom-lands and in thickets. A small tree with rough-scaly, gray brown bark, and madder purple twigs.

Peach
Prunus Persica

The leaves elliptical lance-shaped, attenuately pointed, sharply fine toothed, rather thickish, shiny bright green, smooth, curved and characteristically drooping. Flowers light crimson pink. Fruit velvety skinned, with juicy pulp, $1\frac{1}{2}$–2 inches in diameter. Southern N. Y. to N. C.

PULSE FAMILY. *Leguminosae.*

A large family including several tribes of trees with beautiful alternate, compound leaves, and commonly butterflylike flowers (with wings and standard). Fruit a bean pod.

A low shrub without thorns (most of the Acacias are thorny) 2–4 feet high, confined to the prairie lands and dry bluffs of Mo. (McDonald Co.), Kan. Ariz. and Tex.; also in Mexico.

Prairie Acacia
Acacia angustissima var. hirta

The doubly compound leaves with 8–15 pairs of secondary stems bearing 18–40 bluntly linear leaflets, bluish green without gloss. Flowers very small yellow or salmon color, in globular clusters about ¾ inch in diameter, with many prominent stamens; proceeding from the base of the leaves. Fruit a linear pod 1–2 inches long.

Kentucky Coffee-tree
Gymnocladus dioica

A remarkably rough, coarsely branched tree with equally remarkable, crooked, coarse twigs, and long compound leaves. Its usual height is 40–60 and in favorable environment 90–100 feet, with a trunk diameter of 3 feet. Bark exceedingly rough, very light brown, or dark brown, thin-scaly, without distinctly perpendicular seams, the boughs and spreading branches conspicuously rough and scaly.

The dull deep green leaves doubly compound, with about 9 more or less broadly ovate, pointed, toothless leaflets on each subsidiary stalk, odd or even in distribution, and a pair of single leaflets at the base of the main stalk.

The flowers are staminate and pistillate on separate trees, or perfect, in terminal, nodding clusters, nearly white, with 5 petals and twice as many stamens; the pistillate flowers with a rudimentary ovary. Blooming in May and June.

The fruit a broad, clumsy, leathery, dark brown pod, 4–9 inches long, pulpy inside, with several seeds, persisting on the tree all winter.

The Kentucky Coffee-tree is common in rich woods or alluvial soil, and is distributed from central N. Y. (Cayuga and Seneca Lakes), Pa. (Conococheague Creek, Franklin Co.), west through southern Ont. (Pelee Island, Lake Erie), southern Mich. (Maple River, Clinton Co., Fish Creek, Montcalm Co., and Grand River), Minn. eastern Neb. and Kan. southwestern Ark. Okla. (longitude 96°), and south generally between the Mississippi River and the Alleghany Mts. to eastern and central Tenn. (Nashville). The range has been extended by escapes from cultivation.

The wood is soft, strong, coarse-grained, durable, and light brown. It is used for fence posts, general construction, and cabinet-making; it weighs 43 lbs. per cubic foot.

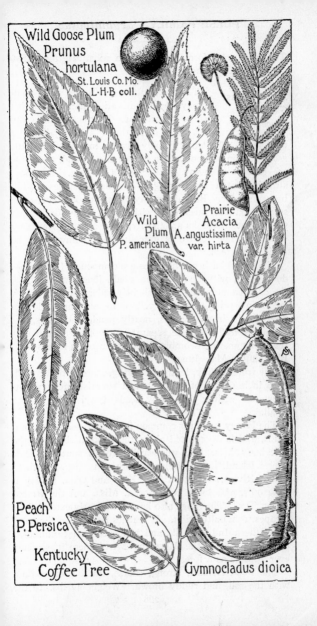

Wild Goose Plum
Prunus
    hortulana
St. Louis Co. Mo.
L·H·B coll.

Wild
Plum
P. americana

Prairie
Acacia
A. angustissima
var. hirta

Peach
P. Persica

Kentucky
Coffee Tree

Gymnocladus dioica

The seeds were formerly used as a substitute for coffee, and called Coffee-nuts.

Honey Locust
Gleditsia
triacanthos

The Honey Locust is a tree more commonly seen in cultivation than in its native wilds. It grows 40–60 or occasionally 140 feet high, and attains a trunk diameter of 6 feet. The trunk usually divides into several stout, ascending limbs about 12 feet from the ground, and these are beset with many thick clusters of long, branching, straight (often three-pronged) thorns or spines, ruddy brown in color. Bark dark grayish brown, on young trees smooth, on older ones rough with broad, jagged dark sepia ridges; not all trunks are thorny, some are comparatively smooth. The foliage is graceful and plumy, like the Maidenhair fern.

The dull, bluish green leaves are compound (sometimes doubly so), with about 18–22 small, long-ovate leaflets, the edge tremulously lined, slightly paler beneath, yellow green in spring, turning yellow in autumn. Flowers greenish, in inconspicuous, nearly pendent clusters, the staminate and pistillate separate and often on different trees, or sometimes combined in one cluster, 3 inches long. Blooming in May–June.

The fruit a shiny, leathery-looking, maroon brown pod, 8–16 inches long, often twisted; a sweetish green yellow substance within; the many seeds grayish, bony and small.

The Honey Locust is common in the rich soil of bottomlands, and is distributed along the western slopes of the Alleghany Mts. Pa., westward through southern Ont. (Pelee Island, Lake Erie), and southern Mich. (north to Raisin River), to eastern Neb. Kan. and Okla. (to longitude 96°), and south to Ga. Ala. Miss. and the Brazos River, Tex. The range also has been greatly extended by escapes from cultivation. It reaches its best development in southern Ind. and Ill., and has become naturalized at all points east of the Alleghany Mts., where it scarcely ever appears as a forest tree.

The wood is hard, strong, coarse, durable in contact with the soil, and ruddy brown. Weight 42 lbs. to the cubic foot. It is variously used for fence posts, wheel-hubs, and for general construction.

A tree common in the swamps of the **Water Locust** Mississippi basin and the South, 25–40 or *Gleditsia* rarely 50 feet high, with a trunk diameter *aquatica* of about 2 feet, and mostly unbranched, slender thorns on the gray brown, rough bark of the straight ascending stem. The leaves similar to those of the preceding species, but coarser, and a slightly deeper green, the leaflets ovate, elongated ovate, or sometimes nearly lance-shaped, not easily distinguished from those of *G. triacanthos* because *very variable*, the edge distinctly round-toothed.[1] The similar flower-clusters rather long; blooming in July. The *ovate* pods 1–1½ inches long, asymmetrical, slender stemmed, in loose clusters, one-seeded, without pulp, and with a spinelike tip, usually light brown.

The Water Locust is confined to deep swamps, and is distributed in the coast region from S. C. south to Fla. (Matanzas Inlet and Tampa Bay), and along the Gulf to the Brazos River, Tex., northward it extends through the Mississippi Basin to western La. southern Ark. and Mo. central Tenn. and Ky. and southern Ill. and Ind. The wood is very hard, light ruddy brown, and weighs 46 lbs. to the cubic foot. It is largely used for fencing, but has no commercial value.

A small, slender, southern tree 15–25 **Redbud. Judas** and in the South occasionally 50 feet **Tree** high, with a trunk diameter of about 10 *Cercis* inches, the irregular branches forming a *canadensis* broad, unbalanced figure. Bark deep (sometimes ruddy) brown, irregularly broken, (not perpendicularly furrowed) into small, thin scales; the twigs slender, and ruddy brown.

The dark green leaves are almost perfectly heart-shaped, with a rather flat base, smooth and glossy above, paler

[1] The descriptions in Britton and Brown's *Flora* and Gray's *Manual* apparently do not agree, but the leaves are certainly very variable. The definitions above are based upon specimens from various localities.

and smooth or very slightly downy beneath; the five stronger ribs radiate from the extreme base of the leaf. The flowers appear before the leaves, clustered along the slender branchlets; they are a ruddy or crimson magenta, small and bean-blossomlike; the profuse bloom appears in April–May.

The fruit is a flat beanlike pod about $2\frac{1}{2}$ inches long, $\frac{5}{8}$ inch wide, with few small, flattened seeds.

The Redbud is found along the borders of streams on gravelly banks, or on rich bottom-lands, and is distributed from the Delaware River, N. J. west through southern Ont. to the Grand and Raisin Rivers southern Mich., and south to Tampa Bay, Fla. and along the Tennessee River to Madison Co. to Cullman and Tuscaloosa Cos. north and western Ala., then to Miss. La. eastern Mo. and Okla. and the Brazos River, Tex.

The slender, magenta-flowered tree is a familiar and beautiful object on the banks of the upper Potomac River, western Md., in springtime, and also along the Tennessee River in Ala., where it is often associated with the white bloom of Amelanchier canadensis. It is in common cultivation as an ornamental tree as far north as Boston. The wood is hard, heavy (42 lbs. to the cubic foot), close-grained, and a deep ruddy brown. It has no commercial value.

Yellow Wood
Virgilia
Cladrastis
lutea

A beautiful medium-sized tree 35–40 and sometimes 50 feet high, with a trunk diameter of 3 feet; in the open attaining a full, rounded figure, with large ascending limbs diverging from the smooth trunk at a point about 8 feet above the ground. Bark grayish brown, thin, smooth like the Beech, but often wrinkled and knobby in places, resembling an elephant's hide; the many slender twigs are ruddy brown.

The leaves are compound, with 5–11 ovate or obovate, pointed, toothless leaflets, bright yellow green above, lighter beneath, very nearly smooth; the caplike base of the stem enclosing the next season's bud. The cream white flowers resembling sweet peas, in terminal drooping clusters 10–15 inches long, are conspicuously beautiful

Honey Locust
Gleditsia
triacanthos

Water
Locust
G. aquatica

Yellow Wood
Cladrastis lutea

Cercis

Redbud
canadensis

and fragrant. Blooming in May–June. The fruit is a small flat beanlike pod 2–4 inches long, containing a few ellipsoidal flattened, bony seeds.

The Yellow Wood is found in the rich soil of bottom-lands, and along mountain bluffs, and is distributed from the Kentucky and Dick Rivers, central Ky. southward locally through central and eastern Tenn. (the Great Smoky Mts. in Cocke and Sevier Cos.), Cherokee Co., the extreme westerly corner of N. C., and the Tennessee River Valley, near Sheffield, Colbert Co. northern Ala. and eastern Mo. It is a rare and distinctively local tree, confined to river valleys and to high, calcareous knolls of mountain slopes. It is in common cultivation in the North as far as New York. There is a remarkably beautiful specimen at Dosoris, L. I. and another at Ridgewood, N. J.; the height of the latter is fully 50 feet.

The wood, at first yellow, finally becomes light brown; it is hard, heavy (40 lbs. to the cubic foot), close-grained, satiny-surfaced, with buff white sapwood. It has no especial commercial value, and a very limited number of uses beyond that of fuel. It yields a rich yellow dye.

Dyer's Green-weed. Woad-Waxen. Whin
Genista tinctoria

A low, branching shrub 10–25 inches high, naturalized from Europe, and occasionally found on dry hills; the stems and branches erect, nearly or quite smooth.

The leaves lustrous light green 1–1½ inches long, lance-shaped, acute at the tip, toothless. The bright yellow flowers resembling bean-blossoms in terminal clusters 1–2 inches long, slender, petals about ½ inch long. The fruit a slender, flat, several-seeded pod about one inch long.

The Woad-Waxen is common on sterile or sandy ground and is distributed from southern Me. (the shore) south to eastern Mass. and southeastern N. Y. "It grows in greatest profusion on Cape Cod, and is a conspicuous, bright and beautiful member of the varied flora of the moorlands."[1]

[1] In a communication received from Charles Arthur King, Plainfield, N. J.

A small shrub of Europe, naturalized in the eastern States, 2–4 feet high, with wiry, rigid, olive green, ascending stems, smooth and angular.

Scotch Broom
Cytisus scoparius

The small compound leaves with 3 obovate leaflets, the upper leaves often single, about ½ inch long, light green, smooth. The flowers bright light golden yellow, like small sweet-pea blossoms, with broad petals, the keel obtuse and curved inward, solitary or in pairs, nearly an inch long. Fruit a flat pod 1–1½ inches long, curved, smooth on the surface, long-hairy on the edge, brown.

On sandy soil and in waste places from N. S. and south-eastern Mass. to Va. and possibly farther south.

A small shrub introduced from Europe and established locally on the Atlantic Seaboard, 2–5 feet high, with thickly clustered, slender, rigid stems.

Furze. Gorse
Ulex europaeu

The rudimentary leaves needlelike or thornlike, dark green, very spiky in appearance, ⅓–⅔ inch long, the lowest leaves often lance-shaped. Flowers small, sweet-pealike about ⅔ inch long, light golden yellow, the calyx large, ocherish yellow and downy, the standard ovate, slightly split down the middle, a trifle sweet-odored. Blooming in May–July. Fruit a short pod, about ½ inch long.

Established along the coast locally, generally in waste places from Nantucket, Mass. to southern N. Y. and eastern Va.

A small western and southern shrub 1–4 feet high, with dull light gray slender stems and twigs which are covered with light gray down, making the plant con-spicuously white, velvety-hairy. Very odd and beautiful.

Lead Plant
Amorpha canescens

The light green leaves compound, about 4 inches long, with 21–51 closely crowded, bluntly elliptical or long ovate leaflets about ½ inch long, downy above, and covered with thick white gray down beneath, the leaflets stemless or nearly so. The fine flowers purple or violet, in slender, clustered, terminal spikes 2–6 inches long. Blooming in June–August. Fruit a tiny 1–2 seeded pod, only slightly longer than the small calyx.

PULSE FAMILY. *Leguminosae*

Found on prairies, from Man. Minn. N. Dak. and Ind., south to Kan. Col. La. and N. Mex.

Dwarf False Indigo
Amorpha microphylla

A similar, much smaller species 8–12 inches high, without the gray white hairiness on stem and leaf, or at least nearly smooth throughout. The fragrant flower-spikes about 3 inches long, and commonly solitary. Blooming in June–July.

Prairies, from Man. and Minn. south to Kan. and Col.

False Indigo
Amorpha fruticosa

A tall shrub 6–20 feet high, with warm gray, slender, upright stems, and yellowish gray twigs, similar in many of its characters to *A. canescens*.

The leaves much larger and much less crowded, with 9–23 leaflets, 1–1½ inches long, bluntly elliptical, bristle-tipped, deep green above, paler beneath, distinctly stemmed. Flower spikes 3–6 inches long, generally in clusters of 3 or sometimes solitary, densely crowded with violet florets. May–July. Pod ⅓ inch long, commonly bearing 2 seeds.

On river banks from southern Pa. south to Fla. and west to Saskatchewan, Minn. the Rocky Mts. Col. and Tex. Also cultivated in the eastern (Atlantic) States and not infrequently an escape.

A. fruticosa var. *angustifolia* is a form with narrower, lance-shaped leaflets, and smaller pods ¼ inch long—sometimes less.

From Ia. south to Okla. and Tex.

Locust. False Acacia
Robinia Pseudo-Acacia

A large but slender tree 60–80 feet high, with a trunk diameter of sometimes 4 feet, the rough, sepia brown bark, scored perpendicularly into rounded and confluent ridges with rigid squarish scales, the slender new twigs ruddy tan brown. The slender, nearly horizontal branches forming an irregular, narrowed head.

The compound leaves formed of 9–17 ovate, light blue green leaflets, paler beneath, altogether smooth, toothless and short-stemmed, 1–1¾ inches long. The cream white flowers in drooping, handsome clusters about 6 inches

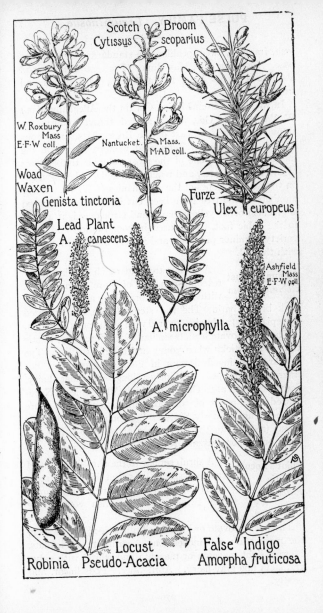

Scotch   Broom
Cytissus   scoparius

W. Roxbury
Mass
E·F·W coll.

Nantucket.   Mass.
M·AD coll.

Woad
Waxen
Genista tinctoria

Furze
Ulex europeus

Lead Plant
A. canescens

A. microphylla

Ashfield
Mass
E·F·W coll.

Locust
Robinia   Pseudo-Acacia

False Indigo
Amorpha fruticosa

long, fragrant, sweet-pealike, the standards yellow at the base. Blooming in May–June. Fruit a slender pod about 2–3 inches long, flat and thin, light brown and smooth.

In woodlands from Marion Co. (in the Alleghany Mts.) W. Va. south to Ga., widely spread through cultivation throughout the U. S. east of the Rocky Mts. indigenous in Ark. Okla. eastern Tenn. and western N. C. (in the mountains). It is one of the most valuable timber trees of the United States, and reaches its highest development on the western slopes of the Alleghanies of W. Va. Large numbers of the tree have been cut in N. C. The wood is greenish ocher yellow, hard, and strong, weight 46 lbs. to the cubic foot. It is used in construction and for a variety of minor purposes, and is very durable in contact with the soil.

Clammy Locust
Robinia viscosa

A similar tree but much smaller, never reaching a height of more than 40 feet, with spreading branches, and less rough dark brown bark. The leaf stems (often characterized by sepia hairs) and twigs covered with a glutinous secretion. The 11–23 ovate leaflets similar to the foregoing, bristle tipped, but sticky when young and a trifle thicker. The similar pink-tinged flowers in dense clusters, but not fragrant. The pod 2–3 inches long, glandular hairy. Southwestern Va. to Ga., in the high Alleghanies. Naturalized as a result of common cultivation in the more northerly and easterly States. Indigenous in N. C. it is found (reduced to the dimensions of a shrub a few feet high) only upon Buzzard Ridge in Macon Co.

Elliot's Locust
Robinia Elliotii

A shrub similar to the shrubby form of the last species 2–5 feet high, the stem ascending and branching near the summit, the twigs especially when young very gray-hairy. The leaflets ovate or broadly elliptical $\frac{5}{8}$–$1\frac{1}{4}$ inches long, the main stalk 4–6 inches long, bearing 11–15 leaflets. Flowers light magenta or magenta and white, with calyx and stem fine gray-hairy. April–May. Pods linear, and bristly.

Found generally near the coast from N. C. to Ga., quite local, very possibly in the vicinity of Highlands, Macon Co. N. C., and on Lookout Mt. near the Tenn. and Ga. line.

A shrub 3–8 feet high, the twigs, branches, and leaf-stems conspicuously bristly-hairy, but in many characters similar to the preceding species.

**Bristly Locust
Rose Acacia**
*Robinia
hispida*

The short-stemmed leaflets about 1–1¾ inches long, broadly elliptical or ovate, 9–13 on the main stalk about 6 inches long. The large flowers rose pink or magenta pink, in rather loose clusters, without fragrance. May–June. The narrow pods bristly-edged.

In the mountains of Va. and Tenn. to Ga. In cultivation and thoroughly established northward.

RUE FAMILY. *Rutaceae.*

Trees or shrubs with pungent aromatic, compound leaves commonly alternate-growing, the flowers polygamous, or staminate and pistillate on different trees.

A bitter aromatic shrub or sometimes a small tree 8–25 feet high, with a trunk diameter of 6 inches, the ascending stems and twigs commonly very prickly, light gray, bluish. Bark smooth. The compound leaves with 5–11 ovate, pointed leaflets including the odd terminal one, toothless or nearly so, deep green, paler beneath, smooth, 1½–2 inches long. The insignificant small flowers greenish yellow, borne at the base of the leaves and appearing before the leaves in April–May. Fruit a small, black, ellipsoid pod ⅙ inch long, with a short stem.

**Prickly Ash.
Toothache-tree**
*Zanthoxylum
americanum*

Common in thin woods, thickets, or on river banks, from western Que. south to Va. and Ky. generally through the mountains, and west to western Ont. Minn. Neb. and Mo. Wood light brown, soft, the weight 35 lbs. to the cubic foot.

Southern Prickly Ash
Zanthoxylum Clava-Herculis

A similar very sharp-prickly-stemmed small tree sometimes 40 feet high, with a trunk diameter of 10 inches.

The leaves similar to the foregoing with 5–17 asymmetrical, generally narrower leaflets, *smooth*, lustrous dark green, paler beneath. Flowers also similar, terminal. Fruit similar, but stemless.

Distributed in sandy soil of the coastal plain from southern Va. to Fla. and west to Tex. and Ark. The classic name is due to the peculiar embossed-club appearance of the trunk in old specimens, the bark being studded with curious, corky, barnaclelike excrescences. The pungent bark has given rise to the name Toothache Tree among the southern negroes.

Hop Tree Shrubby Trefoil
Ptelea trifoliata

A shrub or small tree 10–20 feet high, sometimes with a trunk diameter of 6 inches. Bark dark brown, nearly or quite smooth, and bitter, scaly below.

The compound leaves with 3 ovate, pointed leaflets having few rounded teeth, the stem long, fine-hairy when young, smooth when old, generally with a disagreeable odor; the leaflets 2–4 inches long. The small greenish white flowers with 4–5 lance-shaped petals, also with a disagreeable odor. The fruit hop-like, a much-veined samara (winged seed) $\frac{2}{3}$ inch broad, nearly round, very bitter and used as a substitute for hops.

The Hop Tree grows commonly in rocky woods from Long Island N. Y. west to Ont. and Minn., and south to Fla. Tex. and Mex. It is under cultivation and is established beyond its native limits. The wood is light brown, coarse-grained, and rather heavy, 43 lbs. per cubic foot; it has no commercial value.

QUASSIA FAMILY. *Simarubaceae*.

Trees or shrubs with bitter wood or bark and commonly alternate, compound leaves, the flowers pistillate and staminate on different trees, or polygamous.

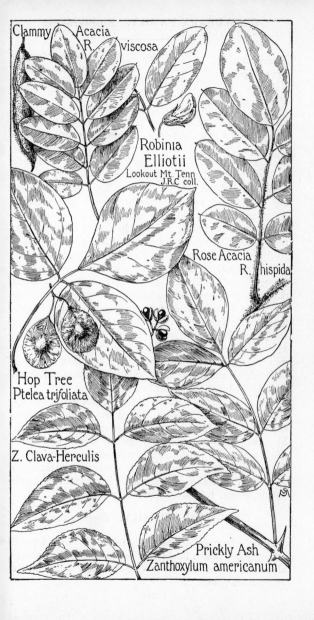

Clammy Acacia
R. viscosa

Robinia
Elliotii
Lookout Mt. Tenn
J.R.C coll.

Rose Acacia
R. hispida

Hop Tree
Ptelea trifoliata

Z. Clava-Herculis

Prickly Ash
Zanthoxylum americanum

Ailanthus
Tree of Heaven
Ailanthus glandulosa

The Ailanthus was brought into this country from China by William Hamilton in 1784 and again from Europe in 1820 by William Prince, of Flushing L. I. The tree attains a medium height of 40–50 and sometimes under favorable circumstances 75 feet, with a trunk diameter of 2–3 feet. It forms a symmetrical rounded figure with widely spreading, stout branches and coarse twigs. Bark brown gray with very shallow, pale buff gray fissures, merging one into another perpendicularly at short distances. The twigs are coarse and blunt, ocher yellow or tan brown with a fine velvety down, and rank-odored when crushed.

Leaves compound 14–28 inches long, with 11–23 narrow, long-ovate, sharp-pointed leaflets, with 3–5 blunt teeth at the base; the long main stem abruptly swollen (resembling a horse's hoof) at the base where it joins the branchlet. Flowers small, yellowish green, in large loose terminal clusters, staminate and pistillate or polygamous, the staminate flowers exceedingly unpleasant in odor, blooming in early June. Fruit in ample clusters of elliptically winged seeds somewhat resembling sea-weed, the wing $1\frac{1}{2}$ inches long, spirally twisted, with one seed in the middle; the clusters are pale green or often magenta-pink-tinged, and in the later dried brown stage remain on the tree well into the winter.

The Ailanthus is a native of China, but it has become naturalized in the eastern United States and southern Ontario, Can. It is a very rapid grower, and spreads freely by suckers. Young saplings frequently flourish on rubbish heaps and in the cracks and crannies of pavements, thriving under apparently unfavorable conditions in the cities of the Atlantic seaboard. The wood is soft, weak, and pale yellow brown; it is not commercially useful.

CROWBERRY FAMILY. *Empetraceae.*

Dwarf evergreen shrubs nearly related in character and aspect to the Heath Family. The leaves crowded, mostly alternate, very small; the flowers staminate and pistillate on separate plants.

A low, spreading, shrubby evergreen common on the barren mountain summits and rocky coasts of the northern States 2–3 inches high, the rough, scraggy stems procumbent, dark brown; branches somewhat gray-powdered, the young branchlets tan brown.

Crowberry
Empetrum nigrum

The leaves tiny, linear, blunt-pointed, about $\frac{3}{16}$ inch long, evergreen, the underside indented longitudinally, smooth, with slight gray-powdery surface. Fruit a dry, black berry (when ripe) about as large as a pea.

The Crowberry is common throughout Arctic America and extends south to the coast of eastern Me. the mountain summits of northern N. E. and N. Y. northern Mich., and west to the coast of Ore.

The var. *purpureum* has dark crimson or purplish berries; not common. The var. *andinum* bears larger crimson or plum purple berries which are more juicy. It is distributed from Newf. to the mountains of Me. and northern N. H.

A small-leaved shrub 5–22 inches high, with many spreading branches almost or quite smooth. The leaves tiny, about $\frac{1}{4}$ inch long, linear, bright deep green, smooth when mature. Flowers in tiny clusters at the tips of the branches, staminate and pistillate on different plants, the latter somewhat showy with prominent madder purple stamens. Fruit a *tiny* dry berry-like drupe, madder brown, scarcely larger than a pin-head.

Broom Crowberry
Corema Conradii

The Broom Crowberry is distinctly local and is found in sandy or sterile soil, mostly near the coast from Newf. and Me. to southeastern Mass., Long Island, N. Y. and N. J. (?) There is one station for it in the Shawangunk Mts., Ulster Co., N. Y. (Britton & Brown).

CASHEW FAMILY. *Anacardiaceae.*

Trees or shrubs with acrid milky or resinous juice, sometimes poisonous, and alternate compound leaves; the flowers often polygamous but mostly regular.

CASHEW FAMILY. *Anacardiaceae*

Staghorn Sumach
Rhus typhina

A tall shrub or small tree of irregular contour and straggling habit, 3–10 and sometimes in the southern part of its range 40 feet high, with a trunk diameter of 5–10 inches, forming at times a characteristically flat-topped and dense thicket set with conspicuous conic clusters of red fruit on the coarse, forking branches. Bark dark brown gray, on young trees smooth, on older ones rough and scaly; the twigs coarse, brittle, ocher brown, the younger ones covered with long soft or velvety, sepia brown hairs, the tips generally winter-killed down several inches; if cut the twigs in spring exude a sticky, milky sap.

The leaves compound with 11–21 oblong lance-shaped leaflets, bright light or deeper green above, pale whitish green beneath, altogether smooth, acute pointed, sharply toothed, conspicuously veined, the soft-hairy stem ruddy-tinged, with an enlarged hooflike base. Flowers whitish green, extremely small, five-parted, in conical clusters, blooming in June–July. Fruit in soft velvety, maroon, conical clusters, composed of many small round green-coated seeds covered with deep red hairs, acid to the taste, ripe in early September.

The Staghorn Sumach, so named because of its velvety forked branchlets which resemble the incipient horns of the stag is common in various soils and localities, and climbs to an altitude of 2000 feet. It is distributed from N. S. west along the St. Lawrence River Valley to southern Ont. and Minn., and south through the northern tier of States and along the Alleghany Mts. to northern Ga. central Ala. Miss. and Mo. It is common throughout N. E. The wood is light, brittle, not very hard, coarsely but beautifully grained, and citron green, or greenish gold ocher in color streaked with brown olive green. It is rarely used for cabinet work, but commonly for the manufacture of souvenirs; the young stems are sometimes used for Maple sap taps; the bark, especially that of the roots, is rich in tannin. The leaves turn a brilliant scarlet, or less frequently yellow in early Autumn.

Rhus typhina forma *laciniata*, Rehder, is a form with leaves very deeply toothed. Common.

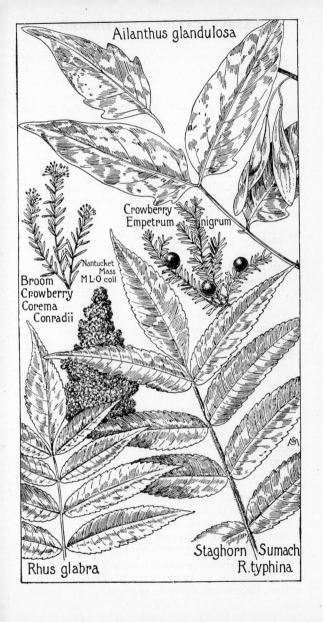

Ailanthus glandulosa

Crowberry
Empetrum nigrum

Broom
Crowberry
Corema
Conradii

Nantucket
Mass
M L·O coll.

Rhus glabra

Staghorn Sumach
R. typhina

Rhus typhina forma *dissecta*, Rehder, is a form with doubly compound leaves. Occasional, but new in cultivation.

Smooth Sumach
Rhus glabra

A similar but much smaller shrub, smooth throughout, 2–10 feet high.

The leaves similar to those of the foregoing species, very whitish beneath and with absolutely smooth stems. The fruit stems possibly a trifle hairy, are generally covered with a slight bloom.

The Smooth Sumach is common in dry situations, and is distributed from N. S. and Me. west to Minn. and B. C., and south to Fla. Miss. and Ariz.

Mountain Sumach
Dwarf Sumach
Rhus copallina

A shrub in the northern part of its range 1½–4 but in the South a tree sometimes attaining a height of 30 feet, the branchlets and twigs soft-hairy, and the sap watery instead of milky white. The twigs also have a balsamic or turpentine flavor to the taste.

The leaves with 9–21, commonly 17 smooth, shining, ovate lance-shaped, nearly always toothless leaflets, the stem *marginally winged* between; the leaflets often asymmetrical at the base.

The Dwarf Sumach is found in rocky situations mostly among the hills, and is distributed from southern Me. south to Manatee and Caximbas Bay, Fla. and west to Miss. Ark. and the San Antonio River, Tex. Also in Cuba.

Poison Sumach
Dogwood
Rhus Vernix

A most poisonous shrub or small tree 5–10 and not infrequently in the southern part of its range 20 feet high, with a trunk diameter of 6–10 inches, the trunk short, forking near the ground, the coarse branches spreading irregularly and producing a round-topped, not a flat head. Bark gray, smooth, or with age rough with conspicuous horizontal or elongated, raised markings.

The leaves compound, with 7–13 thin, smooth, elliptical or obovate, abruptly pointed, toothless leaflets, lusterless light green above, paler green beneath. Flowers blooming in June, insignificant, dull white or greenish, borne in loose, slender clusters, at the junction of leaf-stem and branch. Fruit a small, shiny, greenish, ivory or dull white berry, about the size of a small pea, generally persisting through the winter, in long, slender, pendulous clusters. The species is diœcious—that is, it bears staminate and pistillate flowers on separate trees or shrubs, so not all specimens bear fruit. *Rhus Vernix* is viciously poisonous in all its parts at all times of the year, but especially so at the time of bloom; the poison is an intensely active acid oil which is effective only in direct contact with the skin. Different persons are unequally susceptible to the poison; the most effective remedy is immediately to wash the parts which have come in contact with the plant with thick soap-suds made of strongly alkaline soap, or with alcohol. Binding the parts which have become affected by the poison immediately with cloth bands saturated with extract of Witch Hazel is also efficacious, but the attention of a physician should be directed at once to a case which threatens to become serious.

The Poison Sumach is always found in low, wet ground or in swamps; it is distributed from southwestern Me. west sparingly through southern Ont. to northern Minn. Ark. and western La., and south to northern Fla. and Ala. It is infrequent in southwestern Me., absent in northern and central N. H., very infrequent in Vt., and only occasional in southern N. E. near the coast.

Poison Ivy
Rhus Toxicodendron

A similarly poisonous low shrub with a tendency to climb to a considerable height on trunks of trees, over stone walls and fences, and spreading by running roots over large areas of lowland which is in partial shade.

The leaves composed of three lusterless light green, ovate leaflets with a tendency to droop, toothless or with very few coarse teeth, smooth or with very slight fine-hairiness beneath when young. Flowers in more compact clusters but similar to those of the last species, blooming in June-July. Fruit also similar, often leaden white, lusterless. Common in hedge rows and thickets in wet or dry situations, generally in partial shade, with very nearly the same general distribution as *Rhus Vernix*. Throughout N. E. and most of the U. S. Poisonous in all its parts.

The var. *microcarpa* is a very similar form with smaller berries, scarcely more than ⅛ inch in diameter. Local, western Que. south to Fla. and westward; the distribution very imperfectly known.

Poison Oak
Rhus quercifolia An erect, small shrub 12–20 inches high, of the southern States, also poisonous.

The leaves oaklike, compound, with three (the two lateral ones asymmetrical) ovate, toothless, veiny leaflets with 3–7 lobes, light green above, lighter green beneath, thickly covered with fine hairs. Fruit similar to that of *R. Toxicodendron*, but at first covered with fine hairs, though finally smooth, each berry with a nipplelike projection.

The Poison Oak is found in thin woods and on barren tracts especially near the coast from Va. south to Fla. and westward.

Fragrant Sumach
Rhus canadensis A small straggling shrub 1–6 feet high with aromatic leaves. The leaves compound with 3 ovate leaflets, the lateral ones asymmetrical, the edge coarsely incised with 3–4 scollops on either side, or sometimes three-cleft, olive green above, slightly downy beneath. Flowers in very small clusters, pale yellow or greenish yellow, blooming in March–April. Fruit globular, dull cardinal red, in small clusters, bristly fine-hairy.

In rocky woods from Ont. and western Vt. west to Minn. and Kan., and south to Fla. and La.

Rhus canadensis var. *illinoensis* is a form with branchlets and leaf-stems characteristically fine-downy. Central Ill. only.

Rhus canadensis var. *trilobata* is a western form with small leaflets distinctly and more or less deeply three-lobed, and rather unpleasantly odored, ¾–1½ inches long. Ill. west to S. Dak. Tex. Mon. N. Mex. and Cal. Sometimes called Skunk Bush.

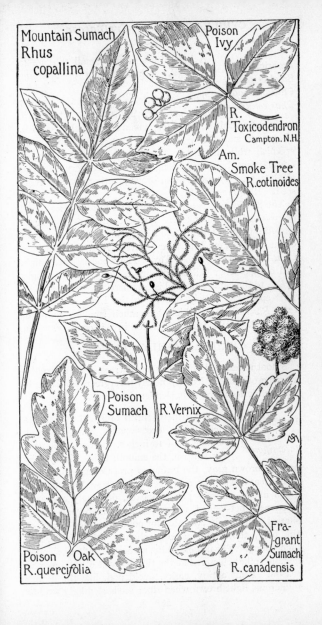

Mountain Sumach
Rhus
copallina

Poison
Ivy

R.
Toxicodendron
Campton. N.H.

Am.
Smoke Tree
R.cotinoides

Poison
Sumach   R.Vernix

Fra-
grant
Sumach
R. canadensis

Poison   Oak
R.quercifolia

CYRILLA FAMILY. *Cyrillaceae*

American Smoke-tree Chittamwood

Rhus cotinoides

A beautiful shrub or small tree 16–40 feet high, with spreading or drooping branches.

The large leaves elliptical, broadly ovate, or slightly obovate, toothless, tapering toward the base, deep green above, paler beneath, altogether smooth, 3–5½ inches long, thin. The small greenish white flowers in large, loose, thin clusters, the flower-stems becoming elongated and feathery in fruit, the latter a very small, sepia brown, leathery coated ovoid seed. Blooming in May.

The Smoke-tree is a rather rare and local species found on wooded river-banks from Cheat Mt. eastern Tenn. and Ala. (north of Tennessee River and on southern slopes of the Cumberland Mts. near Huntsville), to Grand River, Okla. and Medina River, Tex. The wood is soft, tough, and orange-ocher yellow, yielding a rich dye. It weighs 41 lbs. to the cubic foot, and is commercially of little value. This species is closely related to the European Smoke-tree, *Rhus Cotinus*, which has much smaller, rounded, leathery leaves; it is in cultivation in this country.

CYRILLA FAMILY. *Cyrillaceae.*

Smooth stemmed shrubs or small trees, with alternate-growing, toothless leaves, nearly evergreen, and small, regular, perfect flowers in slender clusters.

Leatherwood

Cyrilla racemiflora

A southern shrub or small tree 15–35 feet high, occasionally with a trunk diameter of 10 inches, the bark pale gray or whitish, the smooth twigs silvery gray or pale brown gray, the branches profuse and spreading.

The leaves leathery, evergreen or nearly so, lustrous deep green above, slightly paler beneath, delicately and conspicuously net-veined, altogether smooth, reverse lance-shaped or narrowly obovate, not pointed, wedge-shaped at the base, toothless, the edge slightly rolled back, 2–4 inches long. The flowers white, numerous, in long, slender, flexible spikes clustered at the tips of twigs of the previous season. Fruit a tiny, corky, ovoid pod, like the flowers numerous, light brown when ripe; seeds slenderly ovoid.

The Leatherwood is common along streams and in swamps, from Va. to Fla. and Tex., confined to the coastal plain.

Cyrilla parvifolia is a smaller species, but 3–7 feet tall, the similar leaves narrower, $\frac{3}{4}$–$1\frac{1}{2}$ inches long. The smaller flower clusters $1\frac{1}{2}$–3 inches long. April–May; fruit capsule nearly spherical. In similar situations from Fla. to La. Possibly not separable from *Cyrilla racemiflora* as its characters are scarcely unique.

HOLLY FAMILY. *Aquifoliaceae.*

Shrubs or trees with alternate, often spiny and leathery leaves, and small white, often polygamous flowers, or the staminate and pistillate on different plants.

A shrub or tree 15–30 or occasionally **American Holly** 40 feet high, with a slender brown gray, *Ilex opaca* rather smooth trunk, 10–20 inches in diameter, and spreading slender branches, more or less horizontal or drooping; foliage olive or bronzy green. Bark light gray, or brownish gray, generally smooth, or becoming rough with age; newer twigs smooth ocher brown.

The leaves evergreen, leathery, elliptical, deep olive, or yellow olive green, spiny, but not so much so as the English Holly nor as glossy, or as deep a green, 2–3 inches long. Flowers white, in loose clusters at the bases of the leaves or branchlets, with 4–5 or rarely 6 oval or obovate petals. Fruit scarlet, not glossy, rarely bright yellow, berrylike, about $\frac{1}{3}$ inch in diameter, short-stemmed, persisting through the winter.

The American Holly is generally found in sheltered situations in sandy or moist soil, or near the coast from Mass. (near Quincy) south to Fla. (Mosquito Inlet and Charlotte Harbor), and from southern Ind. through the Mississippi Valley to the Gulf, and through Mo. Ark. and La. to the bottom-lands of eastern Tex. It is not reported from any station in Me. N. H. and Vt., but it is occasional near Quincy, plentiful on Cape Cod, rare on the islands of Naushon and Nantucket, Mass., common locally in R. I., and rare in Conn. The wood is tough, close-grained, fairly

HOLLY FAMILY. *Aquifoliaceae*

hard, pale buff white turning brownish with age, and useful in cabinet making and for the interior finish of houses, the weight is 36 lbs. to the cubic foot. The branches are extensively used for Christmas decorations.

Ilex opaca forma xanthocarpa, Rehder, is a rare form with bright yellow fruit, reported by Mr. E. W. Hervey, from the shores of Buzzard's Bay, Acushnet and Dartmouth, Mass.

Cassena Yaupon
Ilex vomitoria
A southern shrub or small tree 10–18 sometimes 24 feet high, with a trunk diameter of 6 inches.

The small leaves evergreen, leathery, elliptical, obtuse at both ends, round-toothed, lustrous dark green above, lighter beneath, ¾–1½ inches long. Flowers similar to the preceding, but nearly stemless. May. Fruit similar but smaller.

Found in moist woods, and distributed over the coastal plain from southern Va. to Fla. (St. John's River and Cedar Keys), and west along the Gulf to southern Tex. (Matagorda Bay), western Tex. (Rio Blanco River), and west of the Mississippi River, north to southern Ark. The leaves possess a medicinal or emetic property, and are made into a tea by the people of the South. A strong decoction of the leaves formed the famous black drink of the Southern Indians who used it ceremonially.

Dahoon Holly
Ilex Cassine
A similar shrub or small tree, but the trunk often heavier. The evergreen leaves narrowly obovate or elliptical, toothless, or sharply toothed toward the tip, or the edge slightly curved backward, dark green above, lighter beneath with midrib fine-hairy, 2–4 inches long. Flowers similar to the preceding but the stems hairy. May–June. Fruit also like *I. opaca*.

Similarly situated along the coast from southern Va. to Fla. (Biscayne and Tampa Bays), and along the Gulf to western La.

Ilex Cassine var. *myrtifolia* is a form with much smaller, narrower leaves ¾–1 inch long. Range the same.

American Holly
Ilex opaca

Leatherwood
Cyrilla racemiflora

Yaupon
I. vomitoria

Dahoon Holly
I. Cassine

Swamp Holly
I. decidua

James River Va.
J·R·C coll.

Swamp Holly
Ilex decidua

Another similar shrub or small tree, with light buff gray, smooth twigs.

The lustrous deep green leaves *deciduous*, obovate, long wedge-shaped at the base, rounded at the apex, and round-toothed, hairy on the midrib beneath, 1½–3 inches long. Flowers as in *Ilex opaca*, but the stems of the staminate, longer than those of the pistillate blossoms or those of the leaves.

Also in similar situations from southern Va. (the coast to the base of the Alleghany Mts.) south to western Fla., from southern Ill. to the Gulf, and through southwestern Mo. and Ark. to eastern Tex. (Colorado River).

Mountain Holly
Large-leaved
Holly
Ilex monticola

A beautiful shrub or small tree 8–35 feet high, with a trunk sometimes 10 inches in diameter. Bark light brown, smoothish, twigs dark gray.

The deciduous leaves large, 2½–4 inches long, elliptical or ovate, pointed, with sharp, shallow, long teeth, short-stemmed, and *smooth* throughout. Flowers as in *I. verticillata*, the staminate solitary. Fruit scarlet, berrylike, similar to the next.

In damp rich woods from the Catskill Mts. and Cattaraugus Co., N. Y., south through the mountains of Pa. (as far east as Northampton Co.) and the Alleghany Mts. to northern Ala. Only in the Carolinas, especially in the Great Smoky Mts., does it attain the proportions of a tree.

Ilex monticola var. *mollis* is the N. E. form with the leaves soft downy beneath. In the Taconic Mts. western Mass. also in Burgoon's Gap, Alleghany Mts. Pa. and south (in the mountains), merging into *Ilex Beadlei* of Ashe.[1]

Black Alder
Winterberry
Ilex verticillata

A beautiful shrub or small tree 6–22 feet high, with smooth, dull warm gray ascending stems and branches, the twigs warm pale gray.

The leaves early deciduous dark green, paler and fine-hairy on the veins beneath, elliptical, or obovate, sharply

---

[1] *Vide* Small, *Flora of the Southeastern United States*, pg. 733, ed. 2, 1913.

and abruptly pointed, sharp-toothed, sometimes indistinctly so. 1½–2½ inches long, turning black in autumn, hence the common name. The flowers small, inconspicuous and white. June–July. The beautiful fruit a brilliant orange scarlet berry about ¼ inch thick, in scattered clusters, persisting long after the leaves have fallen, through November–December.

The Black Aldar is common in swamps or on low grounds, from N. S. and Ont. to Wis. and Mo., and south to Fla. *Ilex verticillata forma chrysocarpa*, Robinson, is a form with yellow fruit. Rare. In Georgetown, Mass.

Ilex verticillata var. *tenuifolia* is a form with thinner, smoother leaves. The pistillate flowers more solitary. (*I. bronxensis*, Britton.) From N. S. to N. J. and through Ont. to Mich.

Ilex verticillata var. *cyclophylla*, Robinson, a form with small, nearly circular leaves, hairy on the veins beneath, clustered on the tips of the branchlets. Shores of Lake Erie.

Ilex verticillata var. *padifolia*, a form with the leaves like those of the type species but woolly on the whole under surface. Mass. to Minn. and south.

A shrub closely resembling *I. verticillata*, but the twigs always smooth, and slightly browner.

Smooth Winterberry
Ilex laevigata

The deciduous leaves generally narrowly elliptical, pointed at both ends, indistinctly round-toothed or toothless, 1–2 inches long, altogether smooth, turning light ocher yellow in autumn. The staminate flowers long-stemmed, generally solitary. May–June. The fruit slightly larger than *I. verticillata*, orange scarlet, ripening earlier.

On wet ground or in swamps, Me. and N. H. south through the mountains to Pa. N. C. and Ga.

Ilex laevigata forma *Herveyi*, Robinson, is an uncommon form with bright golden yellow berries, found at New Bedford, Lakeville (Plymouth Co.), and Andover, Mass.

HOLLY FAMILY. *Aquifoliaceae*

Inkberry
Ilex glabra

A beautiful small shrub 2–5 feet high, with ashen gray, more or less downy twigs, and light buff gray spreading branches.

The small leaves leathery, evergreen, narrowly elliptical or obovate, pointed at both ends, toothless excepting 2–3 indistinct, rounded teeth near the tip, deep green above, paler beneath, altogether smooth, 1–2 inches long, the edge rolled back especially after drying; staminate flowers similar to the foregoing, but 3–6 in a cluster. June–July. Fruit a lustrous black berry about ¼ inch in diameter.

On low sandy flats near the coast from southwest N. S. Cape Ann, Cape Cod, and Carver, Mass. to Fla. and La. The branches are often cut and sold for decorative purposes, as the lustrous black berries persist through the winter.

Shining
Inkberry
Ilex lucida

A much taller shrub 4–12 feet high, with smooth gray twigs. The leaves leathery, evergreen, obovate, abruptly sharp-pointed, toothless, or with very few widely separated indistinct sharp teeth, the edge rolled back, 1½–3 inches long, dark green, paler and smooth beneath. Flowers clustered at the bases of the leaves, the staminate mostly solitary. Fruit as in *I. glabra*.

In the Dismal Swamp, Va. and south along the coast to Fla. and La.

Mountain
Holly
Nemopanthus
mucronata

A slender, erect, gray-stemmed shrub 1–10 feet high, with many slender, mostly ascending branches. Bark on newer twigs greenish gray, on older branches ashen gray, smooth, sparingly marked with elongated brown dots.

The leaves deciduous, elliptical or long elliptical, thin, toothless, or occasionally very slightly toothed, light green, a trifle paler beneath, altogether smooth, and exceedingly slender-stemmed. Flowers very small, white, borne on long, slender stems, solitary or in small clusters at the bases of the leaves, with 4–5 narrow petals. May. Fruit berrylike (a drupe) light crimson red (not in any degree scarlet) without gloss, long-stemmed, about ⅓ inch in diameter. August–September.

Mountain Holly
Ilex monticola
Alleghany Mts.
N·C

Black
Alder
I. verticillata
M·A·D
coll.
Melvin Vill
N·H

Smooth
Winter-
-berry
I. laevigata

I. lucida

Inkberry
I. glabra
Falmouth. Mass. C·F·B coll.

Mountain   Holly
Nemopanthus mucronata

STAFF TREE FAMILY. *Celastraceae*

The Mountain Holly is found in damp rich woods, from Newf. south through the mountains to Va., and west to Ind. and Wisc., and northward. It is frequent throughout all the mountain regions and wooded hills of Me. N. H. and Vt., but rare near the coast.

STAFF TREE FAMILY. *Celastraceae.*

Shrubs with commonly opposite, fine-toothed leaves (in *Celastrus* alternate), and generally perfect, small flowers with 4–5 petals.

Burning Bush
Spindle Tree
Waahoo
Evonymus
atropurpureus

A slender shrub, sometimes a small tree 6–12 and occasionally 25 feet high when growing in an advantageous situation. Bark dark gray roughened with perpendicular ridges through vertical splitting, the branchlets often four-sided.

The leaves, short-stemmed, lusterless deep bluish green, scarcely paler beneath, elliptical, or ovate, pointed, very fine-toothed, and smooth, 2–4 inches long. Flowers with 4 rounded, spreading deep purple petals, with as many short stamens. Blooming in June. Fruit a deeply divided, small, smooth pod with 3–5 lobes, drooping on a long stem, light lusterless crimson red, the seeds within orange scarlet. Ripe in September.

The Burning Bush is commonly cultivated, and is indigenous from western N. Y. west through Mich. to Neb. and the upper Missouri River in Mont., and south to northern Fla. southern Ark. and Okla.

European
Spindle Tree
Evonymus
Europeus

A similar European species, 6–10 feet high, common in parks and gardens, with smaller leaves 1¼–2 inches long, similar to those of *E. atropurpureus*, squarish branchlets, and green new twigs. Flowers creamy white or greenish yellow, borne at the junction of the leaf with the branch, fewer in number than those of the preceding species, with 4 long, narrow petals. Fruit a similarly four-lobed, smooth, short pod, lusterless crimson red, splitting open and showing the cadmium orange-skinned, hard seed within. Not infrequently an escape from cultivation in the eastern States; introduced from Europe.

A small upright shrub 2–7 feet high, with brown gray bark and ash gray twigs slightly four-sided.

Strawberry Bush
Evonymus americanus

The leaves ovate or elliptical, pointed, similar to those of the other species, indistinctly round-toothed. Flowers solitary, greenish white, ½ inch broad with 5 rounded petals. June. Seed capsule covered with sharp tubercles, crimson red, seeds orange scarlet.

In moist woods from southern N. Y. to Fla., and west to Ill. and Tex.

A similar species, with a trailing habit, scarcely over 1 foot high, with long slender branches and prostrate rooting twigs.

Trailing Strawberry Bush
Evonymus obovatus

The leaves strongly obovate, scarcely pointed at the apex, wedge-shaped at the base, finely and indistinctly round-toothed, 1–2 inches long. Flowers greenish, ¼ inch broad, with 5 rounded petals. April–May. The seed capsule as in the foregoing species, roughly sharp-tuberculate.

On river banks, from Ont. to Pa. Ill. and Tenn.

A large shrub, with upright branches and gray white, squarish twigs, on the Pacific coast only.

Western Spindle Tree
Evonymus occidentalis

The leaves ovate, somewhat abruptly pointed, indistinctly or finely toothed, 2–3½ inches long. The purple flowers in groups of 1–3.

Distributed from Ore. and Nev. to southern Cal.

A low, evergreen shrub 6–12 inches high with very small, dull dark green linear leaves ½–1 inch long, and insignificant green, solitary (or few clustered) flowers. Blooming April–May. Fruit a tiny pod ¼ inch long. Described and illustrated in the *Field Book of American Wild Flowers,* pgs. 254, 257.

Pachistima Canbyi

In the mountains of Va. and W. Va.

BLADDER NUT FAMILY. *Stapnyleaceae*

Climbing Bittersweet
Celastrus scandens

A climbing shrub with a twining, woody, buff gray, smooth stem, and alternating light green, ovate, pointed, fine-toothed leaves, small greenish white flowers, and beautiful, berrylike orange and scarlet fruit, described and illustrated in the *Field Book of American Wild Flowers*, pg. 254.

BLADDER NUT FAMILY. *Staphyleaceae*

Shrubs or trees with opposite-growing commonly compound, fine-toothed leaves, and regular, perfect, small white flowers.

American Bladder Nut
Staphylea trifolia

A slender shrub 6–12 or rarely a tree 25 feet high, with ascending, curved, light warm gray stems conspicuously green-striped, the newer twigs light olive green. The compound leaves with 3 ovate, pointed, coarsely toothed leaflets, deep green above, slightly paler beneath, and altogether smooth, 1½–2 inches long. The small white flowers, with 5 erect obovate petals in drooping clusters at the bases of the leaves or terminal. May. Fruit a large, inflated, three-divisioned obovoid pod, opening at the apex, net veined, light brown, nearly 2 inches long, containing 1–4 hard seeds.

In moist thickets from western Que. and N. E. west to Ont. and Minn., and south to S. C. Mo. and Kan.

MAPLE FAMILY. *Aceraceae.*

Trees and shrubs with watery, sweet sap, and opposite-growing, commonly toothed leaves radiately lobed; the small, inconspicuous, often petalless flowers polygamous, or staminate and pistillate on different trees.

Striped Maple
Moosewood
Goosefoot Maple
Acer pennsylvanicum

A slender, small tree 15–30 feet high, often a mere shrub, with a somewhat smooth, ruddy brown or dull greenish trunk striped with white. Bark thin, on old trees dark brownish gray, on younger ones brown, or dark olive green, finely scored with longer or shorter white lines; the twigs smooth, olive green, sometimes red brown, often white-lined.

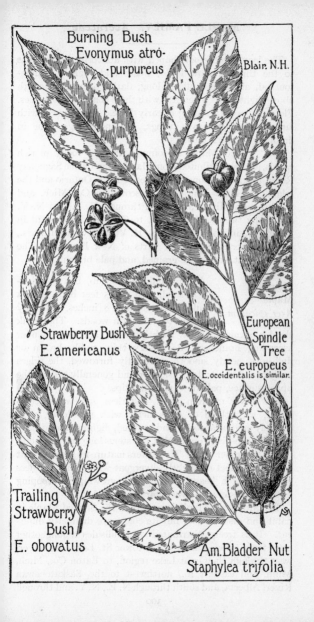

Burning Bush
Evonymus atro-
·purpureus

Blair. N.H.

Strawberry Bush
E. americanus

European
Spindle
Tree
E. europeus
E. occidentalis is similar.

Trailing
Strawberry
Bush
E. obovatus

Am. Bladder Nut
Staphylea trifolia

The leaves goosefoot-shaped with abruptly sharp points to the three shallow lobes, finely and sharply double-toothed, about 4–6 inches long, dark green and smooth above, lighter green beneath with three conspicuous nerves. Flowers green appearing in early June. Fruit green, with large, widely divergent wings, $\frac{3}{4}$–1 inch long; borne in drooping terminal clusters.

The Striped Maple is common in cool rocky or rich woods, and is distributed from Ha-Ha Bay on the Saguenay River, Que. west along the shores of Lake Ontario and the Islands of Lake Huron, to Roscommon Co. Mich. and northeastern Minn., and south through N. E. and N. Y. and along the Alleghany Mts. to Ga. It is abundant in the mountain woods of Me. N. H. Vt. and western Mass., but is rather rare in other parts of New England. The wood is light, soft, close-grained, and pale brown.

Mountain Maple
Acer spicatum

A commonly tall shrub, but occasionally a small tree 12–25 feet high, with a trunk diameter of 4–8 inches, generally confined to mountain woods. The trunk slender, straight, short, slightly rough, and with slender ascending branches. Bark very thin, ruddy brown or dull gray, nearly smooth or slightly furrowed, the ridges broken and short; twigs slender and generally red on the upper surface, pale downy on the tips.

The leaves medium green, lusterless, somewhat attenuated, with three or indistinctly with five lobes, very coarsely and sharply round-toothed, lighter and downy beneath, especially on the ribs, the stems long and distinctly red on the upper side. The flowers mature in June. Fruit with small erect or slightly divergent wings $\frac{3}{4}$ inch or less long, mostly a beautiful deep red, growing in drooping terminal clusters, but very variable in color.

The Mountain Maple is similar to the Striped Maple in habit and distribution, but its colors are distinctly different. It is freely distributed over hillsides among other trees from Newf. Lab. and the lower St. Lawrence River, west through the Great Lake region, to Eaton Co., Mich. Minn. and eastern Io., northwest to the Saskatchewan River, Alberta, and south through N. E., N. Y. and through

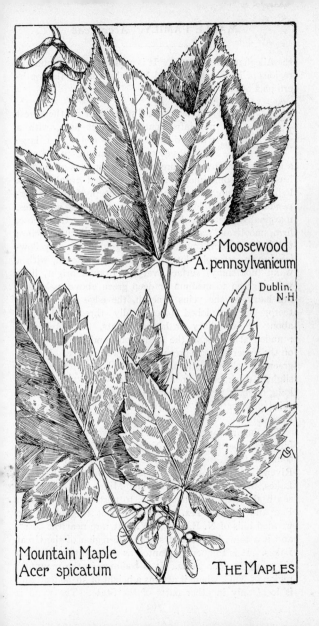

Moosewood
A. pennsylvanicum

Dublin.
N·H

Mountain Maple
Acer spicatum

THE MAPLES

the Alleghany Mts. to Ga. It is common in the mountain regions of Me. N. H. Vt. and Mass. but rare in the southern part of New England.

Sugar Maple
Rock Maple
Acer saccharum

A large tree 50–70 and in the forest not infrequently 110 feet high, with a trunk diameter of 5 feet. The large branches ascending, attaining in the open a symmetrical, ovoid figure with a continuous or more or less short, sometimes heavily buttressed trunk. Bark light brown gray, often ocher-tinged, deeply furrowed perpendicularly into long, coarse, shaggy flakes or plates, marginally curved backward, on very young trees close, firm, smooth and warm gray with buffish or whitish patches; the twigs slender, smooth, lustrous gold-ocher, or yellowish brown, strongly dotted. The leaves smooth, with a waxy (not shiny) surface, varying from a bright, light yellow green to medium or deep green above, pale, and fine-hairy on the veins beneath, the edge unbroken by teeth, but five-lobed (occasionally three-lobed) with about 12 subsidiary or lateral points, the notches all rounded at the base, the stems long and commonly red on the upper but pale green on the lower surface. Flowers greenish yellow, budding with the leaves. Fruit with slightly divergent or nearly parallel wings 1¼–1¾ inches long, in short terminal clusters; borne rhythmically every third year or so, at which time the leaves often appear three-lobed.

The Sugar Maple is common in rich woods and on rocky hillsides especially in the North; it is distributed from southern Newf. west along the St. Lawrence and Saguenay Rivers, Lake St. John and the northern shores of the Great Lakes, to the Lake of the Woods; Minn. Neb. Kan., and south along the Alleghany Mts. to northern Ga. western Fla. and eastern Tex. It is abundant throughout the wooded hills of N. E. and N. Y., but rare near the coast, and it attains its greatest size in the region of the Great Lakes. It is frequently planted as a shade tree on roadsides and in door yards. It is common in the mountain region of N. C. where it attains a height of 50–80 feet, and is local only in other parts of the State. The wood is

Sugar Maple
Acer
saccharum

Black
Sugar
Maple
A.
saccharum
var. nigrum

Silver
Maple
A. saccharinum

THE MAPLES

heavy, very hard, strong and close-grained, susceptible of a fine lustrous polish; it is pale buff white or palest brown buff, and weighs 43 lbs. to the cubic foot; abnormal conditions of growth produce the irregular and interrupted grain known as curled Maple and bird's eye Maple; it is used for cabinet-work, the interior finish and floors of buildings, turnery, ship-building, shoe-lasts, and very largely for fuel. In the manufacture of Maple sugar this tree stands supreme.[1]

Black Sugar Maple
Acer saccharum var. *nigrum*

A variety of the Sugar Maple, the dark green leaves of which are commonly *downy beneath*, and generally have three wide lobes (or five, two of which are not distinctly defined) mostly shorter than those of the type species, and without lateral points, the stipules (leafy formations at the base of leaf-stems) conspicuous. The leaves are variable—*emphatically so.* Wings of the fruit nearly parallel.

In rich soil. Not farther east in N. H. than the Connecticut River Valley, south at Pack Monadnock Mt. but from western Que. and Lake Champlain, Vt. (only occasional), and Franklin Co., Me. and west to Minn. eastern Kan. Mo. and southwestern Ark., and southwest through the Alleghany Mts. to northern Ala. and the Chickasaw River, Miss.

[1] The method employed in the making of sugar to-day is commonly by the use of an evaporator consisting of an indefinite length of partitioned trough through which the sap flows; about two hours are required to reach the point of complete evaporation. One hundred eight-quart bucketfuls of sap are boiled about sixteen hours in the production of syrup, and about twenty hours in that of sugar. More recent improvements of sap evaporators have reduced this time considerably. A gallon of sap yields approximately four ounces of sugar; a single tree is capable of yielding about five pounds of sugar, but everything depends upon the weather and the consequent run of sap. On a large estate near Stamford, N. Y., the output of sugar in a good season is five thousand pounds. *Vide Familiar Trees and their Leaves.* D. Appleton & Co., N. Y., p. 199.

The sugar-yielding property of the Maples was known to the Indians before the colonists landed in America. The Ottawa Tribe turned its sugar-making into a festive and ceremonious occasion, the first product of the early trees being sacrificed by the medicine-men to the Great Spirit. But in time the primitive methods of production by the Indians were slowly displaced by the scientific processes of the white man. To-day the sap is held at a temperature of 219° in the modern partitioned trough for the production of syrup which must weigh 11 lbs. net to the gallon, and at a temperature of 235° for what is called "80 test" sugar.

In the hill region of central New Hampshire the springtime period of the flow of sap varies a little, but it practically extends from the middle of March to the middle of April, expanding or contracting in accordance with the higher or lower temperature of different seasons. As a rule the tapping is now done with galvanized iron spiles which are inserted about half an inch into the wood beyond the bark. One and two spiles are respectively set in small and large trees, and on these are hung eight quart buckets which are emptied morning and evening. The spile is placed in a fresh section of the trunk each year, and although the south side of the tree promises the earliest and most profuse flow of sap, all sides are available and profitable for tapping. The Rock, Red, and White Maples are commonly tapped, and one species is as likely to yield as much sugar as the other, but it is said that the sugar of the White Maple, although light-colored, contains a certain amount of tannic acid and if used for sweetening tea will turn the latter dark. Indeed, a decoction of White Maple bark combined with copperas and sweet gum or molasses furnishes a blue purple dye and a fair substitute for ink.

The quantity of sugar made from sap is extremely variable, it ranges from 10 to 23 lbs. to the 100 gallons. South of the frost line and of Virginia the Maple does not yield sugar. About 35 million pounds are produced in the northeastern states in a good season.

**White Maple
Silver Maple
Soft Maple
*Acer sacchari-
num***

A large and ornamental tree with beautifully incised leaves, 40–50 and not infrequently 60 feet high, with a trunk diameter of 2–5 feet, dividing near the ground into several heavy spreading limbs. The leaves very light-colored beneath, turn upward in every passing breeze and give the foliage that broken, whitish color, which has distinguished the tree as a White or Silver Maple. Bark on younger trees, smooth, gray with a brown tinge, and on older trees ruddy brown, rough, and scaly, often flaking off and exposing the inner ruddy coloring; the branchlets drooping and with an upward tilt at the tip; the twigs green or reddish, similar to those of the Red Maple, but rank-odored when fresh and broken.

The leaves with five distinct lobes, the incisions often very deep and sharp at the base, the edge sharply double-toothed or triple-toothed, deep green above, silvery bluish green white beneath (downy when young); types vary from a shallow notched to a very deeply cut-lobed leaf. Flowers in dense clusters, stemless, from separate lateral buds, maturing much earlier than the leaves. Fruit woolly when young, large, with widely divergent wings, 1½–2½ inches long, ripening in early spring.

The White Maple is common in the rich, moist soil of river banks, or in lowland woods, and is often planted as an ornamental tree. It is distributed from the St. John's River, N. B., west to Ottawa (where it is rather infrequent), west again from Ottawa through Ont. to Mich. eastern Dak. Neb. Kan. (Blue River) and Okla., and south to Fla. and the Gulf States. It develops its greatest size in the Ohio basin, but is rare or absent on the immediate coastal plain throughout its range. The wood is moderately hard, strong, close-grained, easily worked, and a dull pale brown, the weight 34 lbs. to the cubic foot; it is used for the manufacture of furniture, and interior house-finish, and for fuel. Sugar is also made from the sap.

Red
Maple
Acer rubrum

Dublin. N.H.

Lancaster
Co. Pa.

Lake Okeechobee
Fla.

A. rubrum var. Drummondi

A. rubrum var. tridens

THE MAPLES

Red Maple
Swamp Maple
Water Maple

Acer rubrum

Well named the Red Maple; altogether red in spring, red on the twigs in summer, and brilliantly red-leaved in autumn.

A medium-sized tree 40–50, and sometimes in wet situations 75 feet high, with a trunk diameter of 2–4 feet. The branches heavy, mostly ascending, the figure ovoid, similar to that of the Sugar Maple. Bark smooth light brown gray on young trees, very dark gray brown, furrowed into long ridges and somewhat shaggy on old trees, the twigs slender, and a lighter or deeper lustrous red, odorless when bruised or broken (the twigs of the Silver Maple have a rank odor). The leaves remarkably red in the bud, fine-hairy especially on the veins beneath when young, broadly three-lobed (rarely five-lobed), the nerves of the lateral lobes distinctly curved, sharp-pointed, double-toothed or triple-toothed, either deep green or light green above, pale or whitish green beneath, smooth throughout, 3–4½ inches long, the long stems commonly bright red above, usually turning deep, rich red in autumn. Flowers deep red, occasionally ocher yellow, on very short stems, appearing in April long before the leaves. Fruit small, about an inch long, the wings diverging at an angle of about 85° smooth, in lateral, long-stemmed drooping clusters, ripening in spring.

The Red Maple is common in swamps, in low, wet woods or on the borders of streams, and is distributed from N. S. west through eastern Que. and western Ont. to the Lake of the Woods, the Daks. and Neb., and south to the Caloosa and Indian Rivers, Fla. and Trinity River, Tex. It is common throughout N. E. and N. Y. and often climbs to an altitude of 3000 feet in the mountains of N. H. and Vt. and on Mt. Katahdin in Me. The wood is heavy, weight 38 lbs. per cubic foot, close-grained, and light brown, ruddy-tinged at times; it is used in the manufacture of furniture—particularly chairs, for wooden ware and turnery, and for fuel. The Onondaga Indians of N. Y. call it "Ah-wah-hot-kwah"—the Red Flower.

A. rubrum var. *Drummondii.* A form with large, deep green almost leathery, firm leaves, permanently fine-hairy beneath, distributed from southern Ga. and Ala. (coastal plain) to Covington, southeastern Tenn. western La.

Ash-leaved Maple
Acer Negundo
Harvard Botanic Garden
Cambridge. Mass.

Sycamore
Maple
A. Pseudo-Platanus

southern Ark. and eastern Tex. *A. rubrum* var. *tridens.* Less common, with small broad leaves 2–3½ inches long, very slightly toothed below the lateral lobes, the middle lobe broadly triangular. A rare and local form distributed from Mass. to Fla. and westward to Mo. and Tex.

Ash-leaved Maple Box Elder *Acer Negundo* — A small-sized tree 30–50 feet high, with a trunk diameter of 1–2 feet, the irregular spreading branches stout, the trunk short and undulate-ridged. Bark light brown gray, with shallow, narrow furrows, and short, flat-topped ridges. Twigs light olive green. The leaves compound with 3–5 ovate, smooth (rarely slightly rough), veiny leaflets, irregularly and coarsely toothed, deep green or lighter olive green. Flowers staminate and pistillate on separate trees, small, green, developing before the leaves. April. Fruit borne in drooping clusters, with broad incurved wings 1⅓–1¾ inches long, diverging at an angle of about 60°.

The Box Elder is found on river banks and the margins of ponds and swamps; it is frequently planted as a shade tree, and thrives in a moist soil. It is distributed from Me. (locally), the Winooski River and the shores of Lake Champlain, Vt. west to Cayuga Lake, N. Y. and eastern Pa., and northwest to Winnepeg (Dog's Head Lake and along the southern branch of the Saskatchewan River, Alberta), and the eastern base of the Rocky Mts., and south to Mont. the Wasatch Mts., Utah, western Tex. N. Mex. eastern Ariz and Hernando Co. Fla. In Me. it is found in common cultivation along the St. John River and its tributaries; especially in the French villages; in N. H. it is occasional along the Connecticut River, abundant from Walpole to South Charlestown; in Conn. it is rare and local, possibly native along the Housatonic River from Oxford to Salisbury; it is an escape from cultivation at Putnam, Groton, Southington, Weatherfield, and Norwalk. The wood is light (27 lbs. to the cubic foot), soft, close-grained, and pale buff white; it is manufactured into furniture, the interior finish of houses, woodenware, cooperage, and paper pulp. The sap is occasionally made into Maple sugar.

Norway Maple
A. platanoides

Cambridge
Mass.

Lake Co. Cal.

California Maple
A. macrophylla

Foot of Mt. Shasta Cal.

Vine Maple
Acer circinatum

THE MAPLES

Sycamore Maple
Acer Pseudo-Platanus

A large Maple of Europe 50–60 and in favorable conditions in its native habitat 120 feet high, with a round head and wide-spreading limbs. Planted as a shade tree and for ornament in this country. Bark flaky, dark umber brown, with short, flat scales, the furrows shallow, the new twigs stout, smooth, lustrous yellow olive green, or light brown.

The large leaves with three (scarcely five) broad, rounded lobes, coarsely blunt-toothed, deep green above, paler beneath, smooth. Fruit with very broad incurved wings about 1¾ inches long, diverging at about a right angle. Commonly in cultivation as a shade tree in eastern cities. Wood similar to that of the Norway Maple, and used for the same purposes.

Norway Maple
Acer plata-noides

A European Maple cultivated as a shade tree in eastern cities, 45–60 feet high, reaching a height of fully 100 feet in its native habitat in northern Europe, similar in character to the Sugar Maple, with a rounded top and a broad figure. Bark dark brown, not at all similar to that of the Sugar Maple, much smoother and compact, the small, close, narrow furrows running together and forming short, incontinuous ridges.

The leaves, broad, five-lobed, almost exactly similar to those of the Sugar Maple; the young leaves when broken from the twigs show milky sap, a reliable point of distinction. Fruit extremely large, broad-winged; the wings quite 2 inches long, diverging at an angle of 140° almost opposite each other. The wood is heavy, hard, close-grained, and buff-white; it is used in Europe for joinery, wagon making, and interior house-finish.

Big-leaved Maple
Oregon Maple
California Maple
Acer macro-phyllum

A handsome Californian Maple in extensive cultivation, 30–60 and occasionally 90 feet high, with a trunk diameter of 1–4 feet. Bark brown gray with shallow confluent ridges broken into squarish plates. The large leaves cut into 5 narrow, deep lobes, undulate edged, scarcely toothed, 4–10 inches broad

Soapberry
Sapindus
Drummondi

Horse-
-chestnut
Aesculus
Hippocastanum

Flowers cream white, perfect and staminate in the same cluster. The fruit a very broad-winged samara, stiff hairy over the seed-enclosed base, the wings set at an angle of 60°. The Big-leaved Maple is generally found on river banks or on bottom-lands and is distributed through Wash. Ore. and the valleys of the Coast Range and Sierra Nevadas, south to San Diego Co. Cal.   Northward it extends to southern Alaska. The wood is ruddy brown with light sapwood, hard, close-grained and is used for tool handles, furniture, and interior finish.

The Vine Maple, *Acer circinatum*, a shrub or small tree 5–35 feet high, has more often a vinelike habit with a reclining trunk scarcely 5 inches in diameter. The leaves are palmately seven-lobed and sharp-toothed, 2–5 inches broad. In Ore. Wash. and northern Cal. and north to Alaska.

SOAPBERRY FAMILY. *Sapindaceae.*

Trees or shrubs with mostly radiately compound opposite or alternate leaves (in *Sapindus* pinnate and alternate) and showy, irregular commonly polygamous flowers in erect, terminal clusters.

Soapberry
Sapindus
Drummondi

A small tree of the Southwest, 20–40 rarely over 55 feet high, with a trunk diameter of 16 inches. Bark gray brown, smooth, or nearly so, when young, rough and scaly when old, the trunk often buttressed. The compound deep green leaves, with 9–19 commonly 15 asymmetrically lance-shaped leaflets, generally curved, sharp-pointed and toothless, smooth, at least when mature, 1½–3 inches long. Flowers white, tiny, scarcely ¼ inch wide, with 4–5 petals, in dense clusters 5–6 inches long. May–June. Fruit a dull white berry nearly ½ inch in diameter, prolate spherical, very saponaceous (often used as a substitute for soap), with 1–3 large seeds, commonly but one.

The Soapberry is common in the rich soil of bottom-lands, and is distributed from the Savannah River, Ga. south to Fla. (St. John's River on the east coast and Cedar Keys to Manatee River on the west coast) and Ala. (escaping from

cultivation near Mobile), and from western La. to southern
Ark. (Washita River), Tex. southern N. Mex. and Ariz.
and northern Mex. The wood is light buff brown, hard,
and tough, the weight 51 lbs to the cubic foot. It is used
for a variety of purposes, but possesses no especial com-
merical value. In Texas it is manufactured by virtue
of its tough and pliant character into cotton baskets.
Sapindus Saponaria is a similar species of southern Fla.
(Cape Sable, shores and islands of Caximbas Bay and Biscayne Bay, and Largo and Elliots Keys).

A symmetrical and beautiful tree indigenous in southern Europe and Asia,
(from the Himalaya Mts. to Greece),
but much planted in this country for
ornament, 40–80 feet high, with a trunk
Horse-chestnut
Aesculus
Hippo-
castanum
diameter of 1¼–3 feet, a much larger tree in the Old World
than in America. The stem usually divided into several
strongly ascending limbs at a point about 10 feet above
the ground, the general figure ovoid. Bark dull umber
brown, with flat, irregularly (scarcely perpendicularly) set
scales. The branches and twigs stout and coarse.

The compound dark green leaves commonly composed of
7 wedge-shaped, round-tipped, abruptly-pointed, coarsely
toothed leaflets radiately arranged. The showy white
flowers in terminal, erect clusters, five-petaled, spotted
with dull yellow and madder purple, blooming in June–
July. The fruit a smooth pod 1½ inches in diameter, with
scattered, rather soft spines, at first green, finally rusty
brown, containing a single large shining chestnut-red
nut, the meat aromatic, bitter narcotic, not edible; mature
in September.

The Horse-chestnut is a familiar ornamental shade tree
common in many American towns and cities where it has
become naturalised. The wood is light, soft, and close-
grained. It is in common use in Europe by wood carvers
and turners.

The Red-flowered Horse-chestnut, *Aesculus rubicunda*
is a hybrid between *A. Hippocastanum* and *A. Pavia*.

Ohio Buckeye
Fetid Buckeye
Aesculus glabra

This is an indigenous western Buckeye, not a tall tree, its maximum height being 50 feet, with a trunk diameter of 1½ feet. Bark gray brown, rough-scaly, scarcely perpendicularly seamed, and with a fetid odor, the limbs and branches wide-spreading.

The leaves are similar to those of the previous species, composed of 5–7, usually 5 elliptical taper-pointed leaflets, unevenly or doubly toothed. The flowers are light greenish yellow, with 4 vertically contracted petals; not showy, otherwise similar to those of the Horse-chestnut; blooming in April–May. The fruit is also similar to the Horse-chestnut, but the pod contains 2 nuts, is covered with spines when young, and appears warty when old.

The Ohio Buckeye is a common tree of woodlands and river banks in the middle west, and is distributed from the western slopes of the Alleghany Mts. in Pa. west to southern Io. central Kan. and Okla., and south to the Tennessee River Valley and the hills of northeastern Ala. and northern Ga. It is frequent along the banks of the Ohio River, western W. Va. The wood is soft, fine-grained, perishable, buff white, and weighs about 28 lbs. to the cubic foot. It is used for a variety of small wooden-ware articles, but is not commercially valuable.

Aesculus glabra var. *arguta*, is a form with 6–7 narrow, attenuated leaflets, which is reported from Io. Mo. Kan. and Tex.

Sweet Buckeye
Aesculus
octandra

The Sweet Buckeye is a larger tree, 50–60 and occasionally 90 feet high, with a trunk diameter of 3 feet. Bark dark brown, grayer with age, rough-scaly with an irregular trend, without a disagreeable odor; the branches small and rather pendulous. In its southern and southwestern limits it is reduced to a shrub about 6 feet high.

The leaves are similar to those of *A. glabra*, with 5–7 elliptical, taper-pointed, evenly sharp-toothed leaflets; beneath they are slightly downy on the ribs. The pale ocher yellow flowers with an elongated calyx, the lateral petals long (about ½ inch) and obtuse, otherwise similar

Ohio Buckeye
Aesculus glabra

Leaflet of
A. glabra
var. arguta

Smyth
Co. Va.

Sweet
Buckeye A. octandra

Leaflet of
A. Pavia

to those of *A. glabra*. Blooming in May. The fruit similar in most respects to that of the foregoing but with a large, *smooth* pod, not a spiny bur. 2–3 inches long.

The Sweet Buckeye is common in fertile soil or in rich woods, and is distributed from Allegheny Co. Pa. through the Alleghany Mts. south along the Savannah River to Augusta, Ga., southwest through the mountains of northeastern Ala., and west to southern Io. Okla. and western Tex. (the Cibolo River near Boerne). It reaches its finest development in the Alleghany Mts. of Tenn. and N. C.; in the latter State it is reduced to a shrub on the Piedmont plateau. In W. Va. it is a fair-sized tree in the mountain region, and in Pa. it is a large tree in frequent cultivation.

The wood is soft, tough, and strong, palest buff, and weighs 27 lbs. to the cubic foot. It does not endure in contact with the soil, and although it is used for a variety of purposes including interior house finish, it has no especial commercial value.

Aesculus octandra var. *hybrida* is a form with lighter brown bark, pale flesh pink or dull lilac flowers, and leaves which are persistently downy beneath. It is found from W. Va. southward and westward.

Red Buckeye   A shrub 4–10 or a small tree 24 feet high,
Aesculus   with brown gray bark, and compound
Pavia   leaves usually soft downy beneath but
nearly smooth on both sides when mature, the leaflets narrower but similar in other respects to those of *A. glabra*. The flowers are bright magenta red, but the stamens unlike those of the other species of *Aesculus* do not protrude beyond the corolla. Blooming in May. The fruit is smooth, smaller than that of the preceding species, but otherwise similar.

The Red Buckeye is found in rich alluvial soil in the fertile valleys of Va. W. Va. Ky. N. C. and Mo. and southward. The tree is cultivated in the northern States; it appears in rich woods along the banks of streams in W. Va., and in the Carolinas where it is common, its saponiferous bark is used as a substitute for soap.

BUCKTHORN FAMILY. *Rhamnaceae.*

Mostly shrubs, rarely small trees often with thorns, and commonly with alternate-growing, toothed leaves; flowers small, perfect or polygamous, with 4–5 petals, or sometimes petalless.

Alder-leaved Buckthorn
Rhamnus alnifolia

A low shrub 2–3 feet high, with ascending slender, gray brown, or gray stems, nearly smooth and quite thornless.

The deep green leaves elliptical, pointed at either end, sometimes slightly obovate, with fine, rounded teeth, and many curved, conspicuous veins, 1½–3½ inches long, the stems very short. Flowers small, petalless, inconspicuous green, usually solitary at the base of the leaf-stems, developing with the leaves. May. Fruit an early spherical, purple black berry, ¼ inch in diameter, with 3 grooved seeds. August.

Found in swamps from Newf. and N. B. west to B. C. and south to N. J. Pa. Ill. Neb. Mont. and Cal.

Buckthorn
Rhamnus cathartica

A European shrub in common cultivation, 6–16 feet high, the dark brown twigs commonly tipped with thorns. Bark sepia brown, rough, with confluent ridges. The small leaves ovate, or broadly elliptical, 1½–2 inches long. Flowers green. Fruit black, ⅓ inch in diameter. Naturalised in the eastern States. Described and illustrated in the *Field Book of American Wild Flowers*, enlarged edition, 1912, page 258.

Lance-leaved Buckthorn
Rhamnus lanceolata

A slender shrub 3–6 feet high, with ascending, smooth brown gray branches, without thorns.

The lusterless light olive green leaves ovate, elliptical or broadly lance-shaped, 1½–3 inches long, very finely and indistinctly dull-toothed, mostly sharp-pointed, downy on the veins beneath. Flowers yellow green, tiny, inconspicuous, mostly staminate and pistillate on different plants, developing with the leaves. May. Fruit purple black, ¼ inch in diameter, like the foregoing, with but two seeds. Found in damp or swampy ground or on gravelly river banks, from Pa. west to Io. Neb. and Mo., and south to Ala. and Tenn.

Carolina Buckthorn *Rhamnus caroliniana* — A tall shrub or small tree 10–34 feet high with ascending light brown branches, and (when young) fine hairy pale brown twigs. Bark umber brown, comparatively smooth. Thornless.

The large olive green leaves elliptical, pointed but not sharply so at the tip, very indistinctly fine-toothed, and smooth. Flowers inconspicuous green and tiny, with 5 petals, developing after the leaves. May–June. Fruit nearly spherical, slightly obovoid, $\frac{1}{3}$ inch in diameter, at first red, finally purple black, sweet, with 3 seeds. September. Common in swamps and moist lowlands from Long Island, N. Y. south to Fla., and west through the Ohio River Valley to eastern Kan. Neb. and Tex. Sometimes called Indian Cherry, and Yellow Buckthorn.

Alder Buckthorn *Rhamnus Frangula* — A shrub introduced from Europe 5–8 feet high, with spreading, thornless branches, the young twigs very fine-hairy.

The small leaves light olive green, elliptical or obovate, toothless or very obscurely round-toothed, conspicuously veined, smooth, $1\frac{1}{2}$–2 inches long. Flowers green, in tiny stemless clusters, perfect, with 5 petals. May–June. Fruit black, about $\frac{1}{4}$ inch in diameter, with 3 seeds. Found in swamps on Long Island, N. Y. and in northern N. J.

New Jersey Tea *Ceanothus americanus* — A shrub 1–4 feet high with dark red roots, brown stems, and yellow green twigs, the branchlets downy, the leaves, dull light green, ovate, acute-pointed, about 2 inches long. The fine white flowers in compact ovoid clusters. July. Distributed from central Me. to western Ont. and southward. Described and illustrated in the *Field Book of American Wild Flowers*, page 258.

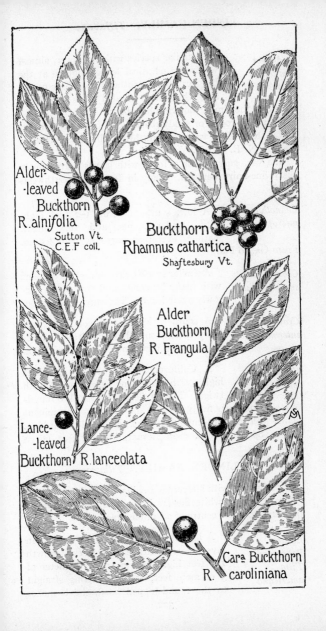

Alder-
-leaved
Buckthorn
R. alnifolia

Sutton Vt.
C.E.F coll.

Buckthorn
Rhamnus cathartica

Shaftesbury Vt.

Alder
Buckthorn
R. Frangula

Lance-
-leaved
Buckthorn R. lanceolata

Carə Buckthorn
R. caroliniana

Red-root
Ceanothus ovatus

A similar species with narrower, almost willowlike elliptical leaves, obtuse at the tip, very finely toothed, smooth or nearly so.   The almost parallel veins prominent beneath; the similar flowers blooming in May.

Found on rocky or sandy, barren soil from western Vt. and eastern Mass. west to Man. Minn. Ill. and southwest. Rare in N. E. and N. Y.

The var. *pubescens* is a form with leaves permanently rusty fine-hairy beneath.   Only in Iowa and southwestward.

Ceanothus microphyllus

A low, southern shrub 1–2 feet high, with slender stems, and very small, leathery, evergreen, narrowly ovate leaves. From Ga. to Fla.

Ceanothus serpyllifolius

A similar species, slender and decumbent with many branches, and very small narrowly ovate leaves. The same distribution.

Ceanothus intermedius

A southern shrub 1–3 feet high, fine-hairy throughout, the small leaves ovate-oblong.   On pine lands Ga. Ala. and Fla.

Ceanothus tomentosus

A Californian shrub about 3–4 feet high, with ascending gray or reddish twigs.   The tiny leaves elliptical to round-ovate, glandularly finely toothed and with three prominent veins.   Flowers in terminal clusters, small and bright blue. May.   Southern Cal. (San Bernardino and San Diego Cos.)

LINDEN FAMILY. *Tiliaceae.*

Mostly trees with alternate-growing, toothed leaves, and fragrant, cream white flowers in small drooping clusters pendent from the centre of a leaflike bract.

**Linden
Basswood**
Tilia americana

A large symmetrical tree 50–70 and in favorable conditions of forest growth 130 feet high, with a trunk diameter of 3 or more feet, the stem rising straight to the round-topped head, the branches

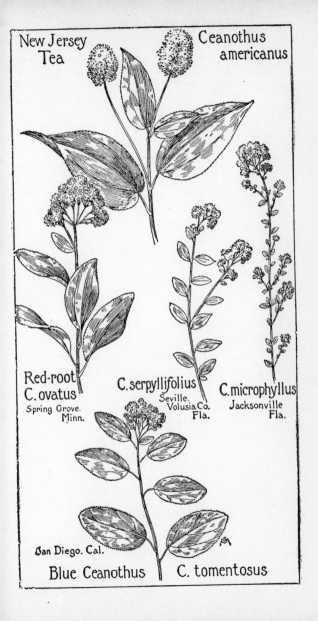

New Jersey
Tea

Ceanothus
americanus

Red-root
C. ovatus
Spring Grove.
Minn.

C. serpyllifolius
Seville.
Volusia Co.
Fla.

C. microphyllus
Jacksonville
Fla.

San Diego. Cal.

Blue Ceanothus

C. tomentosus

horizontal, slender, often drooping. Bark deep brownish gray, firm, scored perpendicularly with elongated fissures, the ridges confluent, narrow, flat-topped marked with transverse cracks; the twigs slender, smooth, ruddy brown, and often zig-zagged, slightly dotted.

The leaves perfectly heart-shaped, sharp-pointed, some-times oblique or asymmetrical, large, 4–7 inches long, coarsely double-toothed, prominently yellow-veined, light green above, scarcely paler beneath, smooth above or nearly so, hairy-tufted on the veins beneath with few white hairs scattered on the general surface, the stem about ⅓ of the length of the leaf. Flowers with 5 cream white petals and sepals, sweet-scented, a scale alternating with each petal; blooming in May–June. Fruit spherical, about the size of a pea, borne singly or few in a cluster on a common stalk merged half-way in a leaflike narrow wing or bract; often persistent on the tree until mid-winter.

The American Linden differs only slightly from the European species, *Tilia Europaea* which is cultivated in this country as a shade tree. The latter is smaller, tapers to a lesser or narrower rounded top, its leaves are smaller, and the flowers possess no petal-like scales attached to the stamens as in the American species.

The American tree is common in rich woods or fertile soil, and is distributed from N. B. west to the eastern shores of Lake Superior, the southern shores of Lake Winnipeg, the Assiniboine River (Man.) eastern Dak. and Neb. Kan. Okla. and eastern Tex., and south to Va. and along the mountains to Ga. In N. C. it is common in the mountain region, and rare in other parts of the State, its maxium height is 80 feet. It is common throughout N. E. and climbs to an altitude of 1200 feet in the hills. The wood is soft, straight-grained, light brown, and is easily worked; it is manufactured into general woodenware, furniture, carriages, and wood-pulp. Weight 28 lbs. per cubic foot. The tough inner bark is shredded and used for mat-fiber.

Downy Bass-wood
Tilia Michauxii

A more southern, smaller tree not more than 60 feet high, with smaller leaves, 2–3 inches long, thickly rusty fine-hairy and dull sage green beneath; the leaflike bract of the fruit is rounded at the base, not tapering as in *Tilia americana*. Fruit smaller, scarcely ¼ inch thick.

The Downy Basswood is usually found on the margins of swamps and streams, and is distributed from Conn. (where it is rare) and Long Island, N. Y. south to N. C. S. C. Ga. northern Fla. La. and Rio Blanco River, Tex. The range is imperfectly known.

White Basswood
Tilia heterophylla

The White Basswood is also a small southern species 40–60 feet high, distinguished by its larger heart-shaped, decidedly asymmetrical leaves which are 6–8 inches long, smooth, bright light green above, and grayish with shiny white, fine-downy hairs beneath. The leaflike bract of the fruit tapers at the base like that of *Tilia americana*, and the flowers appear earlier.

This species is found chiefly on limestone soil, and is distributed generally in mountain woods, from southern N. Y. (Westchester Co.), and the mountains of Pa. through the Alleghanies to Ga., and south to Lake Charm, Orange Co. central Fla. and the Tennessee River, Ala., westward it extends to southern Ind. and Ill. Ky. and to Nashville, Tenn. In N. C. it attains a height of but 40 feet, and is common only in the mountains, occurring very sparingly on the Piedmont plateau and along the coastal plain; but it is more abundant in the State than *T. americana*. The wood is not commercially distinguished from that of the other species. The weight is 26 lbs. to the cubic foot.

MALLOW FAMILY. *Malvaceae.*

Herbs and shrubs with alternate-growing, toothed, and in *Hibiscus* mostly lobed leaves, flowers large, commonly perfect with 5 petals.

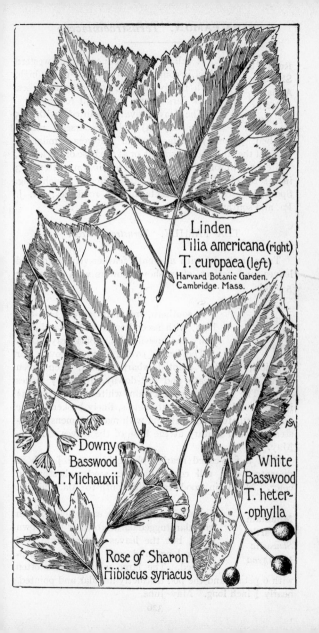

Linden
Tilia americana (right)
T. europaea (left)
Harvard Botanic Garden.
Cambridge. Mass.

Downy
Basswood
T. Michauxii

White
Basswood
T. heter-
ophylla

Rose of Sharon
Hibiscus syriacus

Rose of Sharon
Shrubby
Althaea
Hibiscus syriacus

A tall shrub introduced from western Asia, in common cultivation, 8–18 feet high, with nearly smooth, spreading branches. Bark dark brown, somewhat rough.

The leaves ovate, pointed, with 3–5 (commonly 3) lobes coarsely round-toothed, generally quite smooth. Flowers similar to those of the Holyhock, terminal, or at the base of the leaves, white or crimson pink with a deep crimson center, 2–3 inches broad. Fruit an ovoid capsule about ¾ inch long. Sparingly escaped in thickets and on roadsides, N. J. Pa. and southward.

TEA FAMILY. *Ternstroemiaceae.*

Trees or shrubs with alternate, feather-veined, toothed leaves, and perfect, often showy flowers with commonly 5 petals.

Stewartia
Malacho-dendron

A southern, mountain shrub 3–15 feet high, with ascending branches, and fine-hairy, tan brown twigs. Bark gray brown.

The leaves ovate, narrowly ovate, or elliptical, abruptly pointed, sharp-toothed, deep green above, paler beneath and soft-downy, about 3½ inches long. The large, lustrous cream white flowers are 3½ inches broad, with 5 obovate petals, finely broken on the edge (serrulate-crenulate), and with many stamens; short-stemmed and solitary at the base of the leaves. April–May.

Fruit a five-celled nearly spherical capsule ½ inch in diameter, each cell containing 1–2 seeds; chestnut in color. Mountain woods from Va. south to Ala. and Fla.

Mountain
Stewartia
Stewartia pentagyna

A similar shrub, the same height, with irregular, rugged dark brown or tan brown twigs, but the leaves larger, ovate, 5–6 inches long, and very obscurely sharp-toothed. The large white flowers often with 6 petals, and the pod distinctly angular and pointed, nearly ¾ inch long. May–June.

ROCKROSE FAMILY. *Cistaceae*

On the wooded slopes of the Alleghanies and along streams from N. C. and Ky. to Ga. Often cultivated in parks and gardens northward.

A southern, evergreen tree, 40–75 feet high, with a trunk diameter of 2 feet. Bark red brown, thick, in long, broad, strongly rounded, perpendicular ridges, the furrows, somewhat regular and shallow.

Loblolly Bay
Tan Bay
Gordonia
Lasianthus

The lustrous, leathery, dark evergreen leaves narrowly elliptical or obovate, slightly and very shallowly dull-toothed, acute-pointed, pale dull green beneath, 3–5 inches long. Flowers fragrant, showy white, solitary, 2½ inches broad, with 5 obovate petals, and many stamens. July. Fruit an ovoid, pointed capsule covered with fine silvery hairs, and with a long, thickened stem.

The Loblolly Bay is found in swamps and on hummocks along the coast from southern Va. south to Fla. (Capes Malabar and Romano), and west along the Gulf to La. It is most common and reaches its highest development in Ga. and eastern Fla. In N. C. it appears on the coastal plain and reaches a height of 50–70 feet. The wood is light brownish red, soft, close-grained, and neither strong nor durable, the weight is nearly 30 lbs to a cubic foot. It is sometimes used in cabinet work, and the bark is employed for tanning.

ROCKROSE FAMILY. *Cistaceae.*

Tufted shrubs and herbs, including *Hudsonia* with alternating, fine leaves crowded on ascending branches.

A low, tufted, diffusely branched shrub, with tiny scalelike leaves, scarcely ¼ inch long, gray green, very soft fine-hairy throughout. Flowers numerous, shining yellow, small, ⅓ inch broad, with 5 narrowly obovate petals. Seed capsule, oblong, tiny.

Heathlike
Hudsonia
Hudsonia
ericoides

Found on dry, sandy soil usually in pine barrens, from Newf. to N. C.

**Woolly
Hudsonia**
*Hudsonia
tomentosa*

A hoary little shrub, thickly branched, similar to the last, with tiny, oblong, scalelike, downy leaves. Flowers yellow, numerous, smaller than those of *H. ericoides*. On sandy beaches and pine lands from N. B. south to N. C., and west along the shores of the Great Lakes to Slave Lake and the Lake of the Woods; also on the shores of Lake Champlain (Burlington and Apple Tree bays). Described and illustrated in the *Field Book of American Wild Flowers*, page 274.

MEZEREUM FAMILY. *Thymelaeaceae.*

Shrubs with alternate-growing, toothless leaves, and perfect flowers borne in small clusters at the base of the leaves, but preceding the leaves.

**Leatherwood
Moosewood
Wicopy**
Dirca palustris

A peculiarly stocky shrub 2–5 feet high, with a thick, gnarled, light dull brown trunk, often inclined, about 5 inches thick and scarcely longer, diverging near the ground into many curved branches 1–1½ inches in diameter. The ascending, smooth, yellow green twigs are thickly clustered at the ends of the branches. Bark remarkably fibrous and strong, used by the Indians and others for thongs and cordage.

The dull light green leaves obovate or broadly elliptical, not pointed, toothless, smooth or nearly so, thin, 2–3 inches long, with extremely short stems. Flowers small, inconspicuous light ocher yellow, with 8 stamens, developing with the leaves or preceding them, tubular, about ¼ inch long, 3–4 in a cluster. Fruit an ovoid berry nearly ½ inch long, dull red.

Commonly in damp rich woods and thickets, N. B. west to Ont. and Minn., and south to Mo. and Fla. The wood is buff white, soft, brittle, and irregular-veined. The bark is used medicinally—as an emetic. *Dirca occidentalis* is a Californian species.

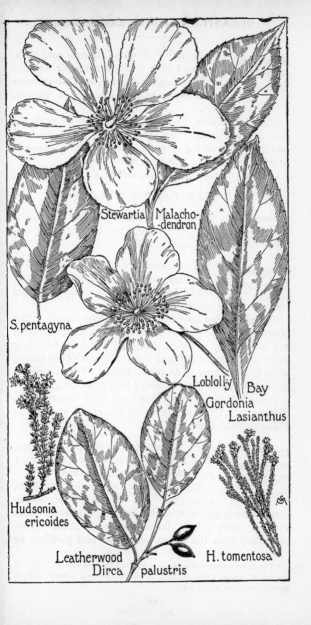

Stewartia Malacho-
-dendron

S. pentagyna

Loblolly Bay
Gordonia
Lasianthus

Hudsonia
ericoides

H. tomentosa

Leatherwood
Dirca palustris

Mezereum
Daphne
Mezereum

A native shrub of Europe and Asia, escaped from cultivation in this country, 1–4 feet high, with erect, light brown stems and nearly smooth squarish or angular, yellow ocher twigs.

The thin leaves broadly lance-shaped or narrowly obovate, 3–4 inches long, toothless. Flowers fragrant, small, tubular, with 4 spreading (lilaclike) lobes, magenta or white, not quite $\frac{1}{2}$ inch long, April–May.

Que. and Ont. south to Mass. and N. Y.

OLEASTER FAMILY. *Elaeagnaceae.*

Shrubs with toothless, alternate (*Elaeagnus*) or opposite (*Shepherdia*) leaves, and perfect or staminate and pistillate flowers on separate plants.

Silverberry
Elaeagnus
argentea

A tall shrub of the Northwest, 6–12 feet high, with ascending branches, and scurfy brown twigs eventually becoming silvery gray.

The green gray leaves elliptical or lance-shaped, rather blunt-tipped, silvery scurfy,[1] on both sides, short-stemmed, 1–4 inches long. Flowers tubular, $\frac{2}{3}$ inch long, with four ovate lobes, fragrant, borne 1–3 at the base of the leaves, silver gray without, pale yellow within. Fruit an ovoid, mealy berry, edible but insipid, $\frac{1}{3}$ inch long. August.

James Bay to Northwest Territory, Bonaventure River, Bonaventure, Que., and from the Isle of Orleans west to Minn. S. Dak. Utah, and B. C.

Canadian
Buffalo Berry
Shepherdia
canadensis

An ornamental shrub 3–7 feet high, with dark brown, rugged stems, and slender rust-colored scurfy-coated twigs.

The leaves ovate or elliptical, toothless, olive green and smooth above, densely silvery downy and rusty-scurfy beneath, 1–1$\frac{1}{2}$ inches long. Flowers green yellow, inconspicuous, in small spikes, expanding with the leaves, staminate and pistillate on

---

[1] The silvery gray color in this and the following species is due to the piling up of white cellular tissue in distinct, minute, radiate groups (examine under a glass).

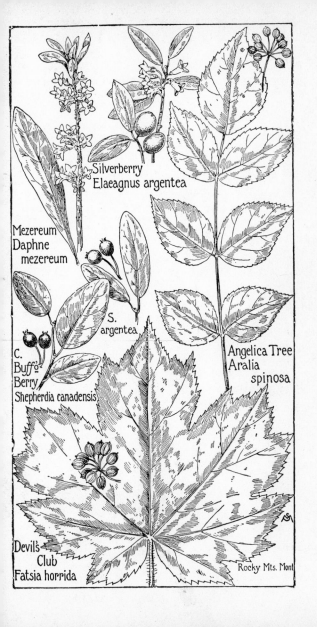

Silverberry
Elaeagnus argentea

Mezereum
Daphne
mezereum

S.
argentea

C.
Buff'o
Berry
Shepherdia canadensis

Angelica Tree
Aralia
spinosa

Devil's
Club
Fatsia horrida

Rocky Mts. Mont

separate bushes. Fruit an ovoid ruddy or yellowish berry about the size of a pea, insipid and nauseous. August. On the rocky banks of streams from Newf. west to B. C. and Alaska, and south to N. S. Me. Vt. northern N. Y. Mich. Wis. Utah, and along the Rocky Mts. to N. Mex.

A similar, western species 3–18 feet high, with scraggy, angularly set, light gray twigs, mostly sharp-pointed, frequently terminating in actual thorns, in late autumn studded with tiny bunches of silver gray buds.

Buffalo Berry
Shepherdia argentea

The leaves narrowly oblong, or elliptical, rounded at the tip, narrowed towards the base, toothless, densely silvery gray scurfy on both sides. Flowers as in the last, but the buds silvery. April–May. Fruit ovoid, dull scarlet, sour and edible, $\frac{1}{4}$ inch long. Minn. Wyo. Kan. Nev. Manitoba and westward. July–August. Also called Silver Leaf.

GINSENG FAMILY. *Araliaceae.*

A small family of herbs and a few shrubs or trees with mostly alternate-growing leaves and perfect, five-petalled flowers.

A shrub or tree 12–38 feet high, with a trunk diameter of 10 inches, the stem and branches of the shrub form covered with hard, slightly reflexed spines, twigs dark brown. In the tree form the trunk coarsely not deeply ridged.

Angelica Tree
Hercules' Club
Aralia spinosa

The large leaves *doubly* compound (2–4 feet long), with rather thick, broadly ovate, abruptly pointed, toothed leaflets, dark green above, very pale and usually smooth beneath, often with prickles on the midrib, about 1–3 inches long. Flowers white, in large, diffuse, compound, terminal clusters sometimes 20 or more inches long. July. Fruit an ovoid, at first dull blue but finally black berry $\frac{1}{8}$–$\frac{1}{2}$ inch in diameter, in spreading clusters. August.

In woods and along streams from southern N. Y. south to Fla. and Tex., and west to Ind. and Mo. Often planted for ornament.

Devil's Club
Fatsia
horrida

A tall western shrub 10–13 feet high, with stem, twigs and leaf-stems thickly beset with very slender prickles $\frac{1}{8}$–$\frac{1}{4}$ inch long.

The large leaves nearly round in outline, with about 7 (3–11) lobes of many points, sharply toothed, deep green above, lighter beneath and prickly on the ribs. Flowers greenish white in terminal clusters 4–12 inches long. Fruit $\frac{1}{2}$ inch long, scarlet. In rocky situations from Isle Royale, Lake Superior, west to Mon. Ore. and Cal., also in southern Alaska and Japan.

DOGWOOD FAMILY. *Cornaceae.*

Mostly shrubs or sometimes trees with commonly opposite, toothless leaves (*Cornus alternifolia* an exception to the rule), and polygamous, or staminate and pistillate flowers growing on separate plants.

Flowering
Dogwood
Cornus florida

A very beautiful, picturesque though common shrub or small tree 12–20 or sometimes 40 feet high, with a trunk diameter of about 14 inches. Bark sepia brown, round-checked or nearly square-checked, not perpendicularly scored; the branches with a generally straggling habit, frequently erect but most often irregularly divergent and spreading, the tips of the branchlets curved upward and terminated by the conspicuous large white four-bracted flowers, cream white or magenta pink-tinged. May–June. The ovoid fruit deep scarlet. Described and illustrated in the *Field Book of American Wild Flowers*, page 318.

Common in woodlands and distributed from Me. and Que. west to Minn. and south to Fla. and Tex. In N. C. it is common throughout the State and grows 12–20 feet high. The wood is heavy, hard, and strong; it is put to a variety of minor uses, but is of no especial value.

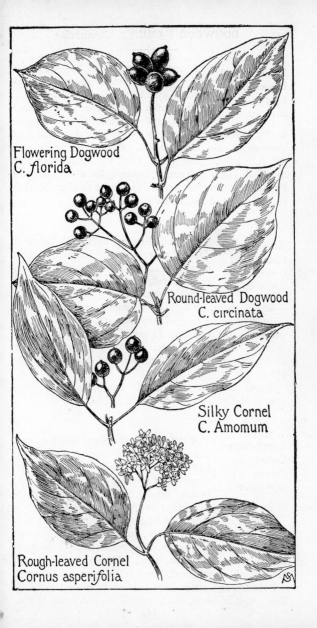

Flowering Dogwood
C. florida

Round-leaved Dogwood
C. circinata

Silky Cornel
C. Amomum

Rough-leaved Cornel
Cornus asperifolia

DOGWOOD FAMILY. *Cornaceae*

Round-leaved Dogwood
Cornus circinata

A smaller shrub 6–10 feet high with dull olive green branchlets, more or less covered with wartlike gray dots.

The leaves almost round, very broad-ovate, abruptly pointed, light green above, woolly beneath, toothless, the veins curved inward from the margin, 2–4 inches broad. Flowers white in open flatish clusters. June–July. Fruit a dull light gray blue, spherical, ⅓ inch in diameter, in nearly flat-topped clusters. Found in copses from eastern Que. west to Man. N. Dak. Ia. and Ill., and south to Va.

Silky Cornel Kinnikinnik
Cornus Amomum

A shrub 3–10 feet high, with lighter or darker ocher brown irregular stems, smooth and streaked, the newer branchlets maroon red, covered with gray (often rusty) silky hairs.

The large leaves light olive green, ovate or elliptical, pointed, gray or rusty-downy beneath, with converging veins, 3–4 inches long. Flowers like the foregoing, but in more compact clusters. June. Fruit also similar, a trifle larger, ¼ inch in diameter, and dull, leaden light blue.

Found on moist ground, river banks, etc., from Newf. west to N. Dak., and south to Fla. and La.

Rough-leaved Cornel
Cornus asperifolia

A tall shrub in the Northwest 4–15 or in the southern part of its range a tree 40–50 feet high, with an umber brown roughish trunk about 9 inches thick, and pale gray brown, slender, ascending branches, the twigs tan-color, somewhat rough-hairy.

The leaves elliptical or long-ovate, pointed, light olive green and rough-hairy above, paler and downy beneath, 2–5 inches long. Flowers cream white as in *C. circinata*, in flat clusters 2–3 inches broad. May–June. Fruit dull greenish white, spherical, ¼ inch in diameter, red-stemmed. Found in dry, sandy soil, from Ont. (north shore of Lake Erie), west to Minn. and eastern Kan., and south to Fla.

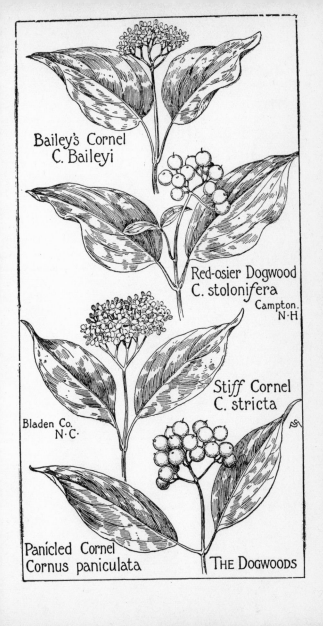

Bailey's Cornel
C. Baileyi

Red-osier Dogwood
C. stolonifera
Campton.
N·H

Stiff Cornel
C. stricta

Bladen Co.
N·C·

Panicled Cornel
Cornus paniculata

THE DOGWOODS

DOGWOOD FAMILY. *Cornaceae*

A very similar species, with soft-hairy not harsh-hairy branches, and ovate or commonly more narrowly elliptical leaves approaching lance-shape, *not* rough-hairy above, but covered with soft down beneath. The green white flowers with tiny short petals (in *C. asperifolia* they are longer). Fruit quite white. Found on sandy margins of lakes and rivers from western Pa. and southern Ont., west to Minn. and Man.

Bailey's Cornel
Cornus Baileyi

A rather low straggling shrub 2–6 and sometimes 9 feet high, with crimson maroon red shoots and branches, which propagates by subterranean shoots forming broad clumps or thickets on the borders of low meadows. Bark on the larger stems near the ground smooth, brownish tan-color; the newer shoots and branchlets intense Venetian red, brilliant in sunshine but maroon in subdued light, sprinkled with few or many little wartlike grayish dots, in winter showing the red-color at a great distance.

Red-osier Dogwood
Cornus stolonifera

Leaves light yellow olive green above, pale whitish green beneath, very slightly fine-hairy on both sides (under a glass), strongly ribbed, the veins converging toward the tip of the leaf, ovate, pointed, toothless, with red stems about ½ inch long. Flowers in small flat clusters of not many dull yellow white blossoms with 4 petals, and as many prominent stamens. Blooming in June. Fruit small dull white or leaden gray berries, black-dotted, the size of small peas, in small slender ruddy-stemmed clusters. Ripe in August.

The Red-osier Dogwood is common in wet or sandy lowlands and along water courses from Newf. northwest to the Mackenzie River, Can., and south to Washington, D. C. the Great Lake region, Ia. Neb. and N. Mex.

A southern shrub 6–16 feet high, with light brown or gray stems and maroon branchlets.

Stiff Cornel
Cornus stricta

The leaves ovate, narrowly ovate, or elliptical, pointed at both ends, light olive green, scarcely paler beneath, altogether smooth. Flowers white, in flat clusters, much as in *C. circinata*. Fruit also similar, dull pale, leaden blue.

Common in swamps and wet margins of streams, from Va. west to Mo. and southward.

Cornus paniculata
A similar, lower shrub 4–8 feet high, with smooth, light gray brown, ascending stems, and thickly divergent irregular branches.

The leaves similar to the foregoing, light olive green, paler beneath but not downy. Flowers white in somewhat dome-shaped clusters. Fruit about the size of a small pea, greenish or leaden white, in close, small bunches, on crimson pink stems.

Common in thickets and on the margins of streams from central Me. west to Ont. and Minn., and south to N. C.

Alternate-leaved Dogwood
Cornus alternifolia
A shrub or sometimes a tree 6–25 feet high, with a trunk occasionally 9 inches thick, the umber brown bark roughly scored. The shrub form with slender stems and smooth olive green branches, often streaked with white.

The leaves are alternate-growing, an exception to the opposed leaf of this genus; they are mostly crowded at the tips of the branches, and are light green, smooth above, pale and slightly fine hairy beneath, ovate, sharp-pointed, and narrowed at the base. Flowers white, in broad, flat clusters. Blooming in May–June. Fruit about the size of a pea, dark leaden or cadet blue, the branching stems crimson red.

In damp thickets or copses, from eastern Que. west to western Ont. Minn. and Ia., and south to Ga. and Ala.

Tupelo. Sour or Black Gum Pepperidge
Nyssa sylvatica
Commonly a small tree 20–50 but occasionally in the South 100 feet high with a trunk diameter of 4 feet. The stems ascending continuously to the crown, the branches slender and nearly horizontal. Bark brown gray lighter or sometimes blackened, smoothish, or rough with an indistinct per-

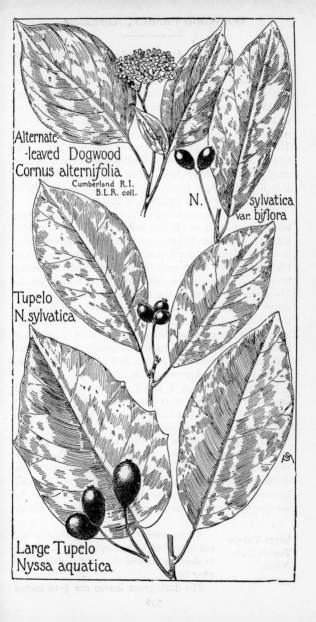

Alternate-
-leaved Dogwood
Cornus alternifolia
Cumberland R.I.
B.L.R. coll.

N. sylvatica
var. biflora

Tupelo
N. sylvatica

Large Tupelo
Nyssa aquatica

pendicular trend, the furrows and ridges on older trees deeply scored and confluent.

The leaves a lustrous dark olive green, lighter and smooth beneath, 2–4 inches long, ovate or obovate, toothless or with few obscure teeth, the surface often undulating with a marginal fullness, the tip abruptly pointed; they turn a brilliant maroon brown in autumn. The inconspicuous green flowers are staminate and pistillate on different trees, with 5 small petals or none, in very small clusters. May–June. The fruit ovoid, berrylike, ½ inch long, purple black, on long stalks, commonly in pairs (rarely one or several), ripe in September.

The Tupelo is found along water courses on rich alluvial land or in swamps, and is distributed from Waterville, Me. (on the Kennebec River), west through southern Ont. to central Mich. and southeastern Mo., and south to central Fla. (Kissimmee River and Tampa Bay), and the Brazos River, Tex. It is not a common tree in N. E., it is rare in Me. scarcely frequent in the Merrimac Valley, rare on the shores of Squam and Winnepesaukee Lakes, and absent in the White Mts. N. H., only occasional in Vt., and less than common in the more southerly States. In N. C. where it has an average height of 55 feet it occurs on the coastal plain and the Piedmont plateau, and climbs to an elevation of 3000 feet in the mountains.

The pale buff wood is heavy, rather soft, tough and fine-grained, the weight 41 lbs. to the cubic foot. It is used for the hubs of wheels, ox-yokes, fruit boxes, etc., but has no especial commercial value.

N. sylvatica var. *biflora* is a form with smaller, narrower leaves, elliptical or obovate and obtuse. The flowers are twin-clustered. The distinctively strong diagnostic point in this variety separating it from the species is the flat and furrowed stone of the commonly twin-clustered fruit. In the type species the stone is ovoid and very slightly ridged.

Large Tupelo **Tupelo Gum** *Nyssa* *aquatica*	A tree similar to the foregoing species, not taller, but with a larger leaf. Confined to deep swamps of the coastal plain, or of river basins.

The dark green leaves are 4–10 inches

---

long, slender-stemmed, elliptical or ovate, and rarely slightly scolloped at the base, with very few angular teeth (commonly 5), pale and downy beneath when young, and often persistently so. Flowering in March–April. The comparatively large pistillate, yellowish green flower is solitary. The single, dark violet blue, ellipsoidal berry is about an inch long; the stone is longitudinally ridged.

The Large Tupelo is distributed from southern Va. south along the coast to northern Fla. and along the Gulf to the Nueces River, Tex., westward it extends through western Ky. and Tenn. southern Ill. (the lower Wabash River), southeastern Mo. and Ark. It attains its greatest development in the Cypress swamps of western La. and southeastern Tex. In N. C. it is confined to the coastal plain, where it grows along with the Cypress in impenetrable swamps to a height of 80 feet, with a swollen butt sometimes 11 feet in diameter.

The wood is light (29 lbs. to the cubic foot), soft, close-grained but not strong, and light brown in color; it is used for wooden-ware, broom handles, and turnery, and has no especial economic value.

HEATH FAMILY. *Ericaceae.*

Shrubs and herbs with commonly alternate, toothed or toothless leaves, and perfect regular flowers with 4–5 corolla-lobes, or petals.

A fragrant-flowered shrub 3–10 feet high, the ascending slender stems with dull dark brown bark, the twigs when young covered with a minute gray hairiness.

**White Alder
Sweet Pepper-
bush**
*Clethra
alnifolia*

The deep green leaves, paler beneath, strongly obovate with a wedge-shaped base, gothic-arch pointed at the tip, sharply toothed above the middle, smooth, straight veined, 1–3 inches long. Flowers small with a spicy odor, white or pale pink, with five petals and a long pistil, in slender, terminal clusters 3–5 inches long. July–August. Fruit a spherical, three-divisioned capsule ⅛ inch in diameter.

In wet situations, often in large patches, occasionally in moist woods; from Me. south along the coast to Fla.

The var. *tomentosa* has similar but slightly larger leaves, extremely velvety downy on the under side.

Mountain Sweet Pepperbush
Clethra acuminata

An inland and similar species, often a small tree 12 feet high, with smooth, slender, ruddy tan-colored stem and branches, the deep green leaves ovate or elliptical, rarely slightly obovate, sharp-pointed, thin, very finely sharp-toothed, 3–6 inches long. The similar slender flower clusters inclined or drooping, the tassels of the seed-capsules persisting into the winter.

Found in mountain woods from Va. and W. Va. south to Ga. Climbing to an altitude of 4500 feet in the mountains of N. C.

Labrador Tea
Ledum groenlandicum

A northern, evergreen shrub 1–3½ feet high, with slender light brown ascending stems, and extremely velvety hairy twigs.
The small evergreen, leathery leaves narrowly oblong or linear, dark green above, light rusty brown woolly beneath, the toothless margin curled back, 1–2 inches long. The small white flowers ⅓ inch broad, with 5 petals, in terminal clusters, of about 12 or more blossoms, the stems velvety-hairy. May–June. Fruit an ellipsoidal capsule ¼ inch long, in nodding clusters; opening from the base upward.

Found in bogs and moist thickets, on the margins of ponds in high altitudes and on mountain slopes, from Greenland south to Conn. N. J. and Pa., and west to Mich. Wis. and Minn. The leaves are astringent and have been used as a substitute for tea.

Narrow-leaved Labrador Tea
Ledum palustre

A lower, similar species of the extreme North, about 8–20 inches high, with narrow, linear, blunt leaves reflexed on the margin and similarly brown-woolly beneath, ¾–1¼ inches long. Flowers similar, a trifle smaller. Capsule ellipsoid-ovoid.

Sweet
Pepperbush
C. alnifolia

Mountain
Sweet Pepperbush

Clethra
acuminata

Labrador
Tea
Ledum groenlandicum

Narrow-leaved

Labrador
Tea
L. palustre

In cold bogs, Arctic regions and from Newf. west to Alaska, also in Siberia and northern Europe.

Smooth Azalea
Rhododendron arborescens

A shrub 6–18 feet high, with smooth, irregular gray brown branches.

The lustrous light green leaves obovate or narrowly so, obtuse-pointed, the edge toothless, fringed with tiny hairs, very pale beneath, 2–3½ inches long. Flowers funnel-shaped, with five lobes, very fragrant, pale or rose pink with five prominent, exserted pink red stamens, somewhat clammy, 1½ inches broad; in bloom after the leaves unfold. June. Fruit capsule ellipsoidal, about ⅝ inch long, glandular hairy. In mountain woods from southern Pa. south to N. C.

Clammy Azalea
White Swamp Honeysuckle
Rhododendron viscosum

A similar but lower shrub, 4–8 feet high, with hairy light brown branches and twigs.

The narrowly obovate leaves similar, the flowers white or pale pink, but the sticky-hairy tube much longer than the spreading lobes; 5 stamens. June–July.

In swamps, generally near the coast, from Me. south to Fla. and Tex., and inland to O. and Ark. Described and illustrated in the *Field Book of American Wild Flowers*, page 334.

The var. *glaucum* has lighter green leaves, very whitish beneath, and occasionally stiff-hairy. The var. *nitidum* is a dwarf form with reverse lance-shaped leaves green on either side; both varieties extend from N. E. to Va.

Pinxter Flower
Rhododendron nudiflorum

A common shrub 2–6 feet high, the obovate or narrowly obovate leaves, yellow green, slightly hairy beneath, the tubular flowers flesh-color, pale pink (deep ruddy pink at the base) occasionally magenta, fragrant, expanding before the leaves. April–May.

In rocky woods or swamps from Me. west to Ill. and south to Fla. and Tex. It ascends to 3000 feet among the mountains of Va. and N. C. Described and illustrated in the *Field Book of American Wild Flowers*, page 336.

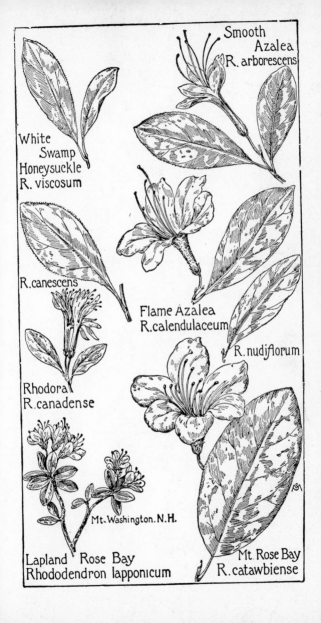

Smooth
Azalea
R. arborescens

White
Swamp
Honeysuckle
R. viscosum

R. canescens

Flame Azalea
R. calendulaceum

R. nudiflorum

Rhodora
R. canadense

Mt. Washington. N.H.

Lapland Rose Bay
Rhododendron lapponicum

Mt. Rose Bay
R. catawbiense

A similar shrub 4–15 feet high. The leaves ovate, elliptical, or rarely obovate, very fine-hairy beneath, and the edge bristly-hairy. Flowers pale pink or white, similar to the preceding. April–May.

Mountain Azalea
Rhododendron canescens

In mountain woods and on gravelly river banks from N. H. Mass. the Catskill and Shawangunk Mts. N. Y. and the Pocono plateau Pa., and south through the Alleghany Mountains to Fla., and to La. Often suspiciously near *R. nudiflorum* in some of its forms.

A shrub with obovate or sometimes ovate leaves, and showy light orange yellow or flame-colored flowers, scarcely fragrant, not sticky, the hairy tube *shorter* than the lobes, appearing with the leaves. May.

Flame Azalea
Rhododendron calendulaceum

Woodlands from southern N. Y. and the mountains of Pa. south to Ga. Many varieties in common cultivation. Described and illustrated in the *Field Book of American Wild Flowers*, pages 335 and 336.

A low shrub 1–3 feet high. The narrowly elliptical leaves obtuse at the tip, toothless, 1–2 inches long, light green. The light magenta flowers scarcely tubular, very narrow-lobed, with 10 stamens, in terminal clusters preceding the leaves.

Rhodora
Rhododendron canadense

Common on moist hillsides and in swamps from Newf. south to N. J., and west to Que. central N. Y. and Pa. Described and illustrated in the *Field Book of American Wild Flowers*, pages 335 and 336.

The three following species belonging to the division EURHODODENDRON have leathery evergreen leaves, and the flowers have 10 stamens.

A tall straggling shrub or a small tree 7–40 feet high, with a trunk diameter of about one foot. Bark smooth, gray brown, and slightly scaly.

Great Laurel Rose Bay
Rhododendron maximum

The lustrous evergreen, oblong-elliptical or slightly obovate leaves 4–8 inches long, with curled-back edge, often rusty beneath, spreading or drooping. Flowers in large terminal clusters, pale pink spotted with orange, greenish in the upper part of the throat. June–July. Fruit a red-brown capsule ½ inch long.

Moist woods and along streams (never on limestone soil) from N. S. Me. Que. Ont., and the northern shores of Lake Erie, to O., and south (plentifully) through the Alleghany Mts. to Ga. Wood hard, strong, and light brown, the weight 4c lbs. to the cubic foot. Often employed for tool handles and in turnery. Described and illustrated in the *Field Book of American Wild Flowers*, page 338.

Mountain Rose Bay *Rhododendron catawbiense*	A similar species 3–18 feet high, with leathery, distinctly elliptical leaves, shorter than those of *R. maximum*, and lilac or light purple flowers 2–2¼ inches broad. May–June.

In the high Alleghanies from Va. and W. Va. south to Ga. and DeKalb Co. Ala. on Lookout Mt. range and on Little River. Described in the *Field Book of American Wild Flowers*, page 338.

Lapland Rose Bay *Rhododendron lapponicum*	A dwarf species 4–12 inches high, growing in broad, tufted masses among the rocks of Alpine mountain summits. The tiny elliptical leaves ⅓–⅔ inch long, dark green, with a rolled-back edge.

Flowers small light purple, with 5–10 stamens. Summits of the higher mountains of N. E. and N. Y., and in the Arctic region. Described in the *Field Book of American Wild Flowers*, page 338.

Smooth Menziesia *Menziesia glabella*	A shrub 2–6 feet high, with irregular straggling branches, the gray brown twigs commonly with thin, slightly scaly bark nearly or quite smooth.

The small obovate leaves, thin, mostly obtuse, smooth, light green above, pale beneath, ¾–1½ inches long. Flowers tiny, ⅙ inch long, bell-shaped, greenish, magenta-stained, about 2–5 in a terminal, spreading

Rose Bay
Rhododendron
maximum

Alleghany   Menziesia
Menziesia pilosa

Smooth Menziesia
M. glabella

Welch Mt.
Thornton. N·H

Sand
Myrtle
Leiophyllum buxifolium

Alpine
Azalea
Loiseleuria procumbens

cluster. May–June. Fruit capsule obovoid, erect.
Found from Minnesota Point, Lake Superior, west to Ore.
and B. C.

**Alleghany
Menziesia**
*Menziesia
pilosa*

A similar species, the twigs of which are
more or less rusty red, chaffy-scaly, and
covered with bristly hairs.

The leaves elliptical or slightly obovate,[1]
conspicuously tipped with a tiny glandular
point, rough-hairy above, pale and chaffy on the veins
beneath. Flowers similar 3–6 in a cluster, with slender
glandular stems, drooping. May–June. Capsule similar,
set with glandular bristles.

In woodlands of the Alleghany Mts. from Pa. south
to Ga.

Sand Myrtle
*Leiophyllum
buxifolium*

A low spreading shrub 6–20 inches high,
with scragged stem and branches, and
rough, dull sepia brown bark; the foliage
similar to that of English box.

The leaves crowded, narrowly ovate, lustrous dark
green, the margin slightly curled back, $\frac{1}{4}$–$\frac{1}{2}$ inch long.
Flowers tiny white with purple anthers and 5 petals.
April–June. Fruit a tiny ovoid, pointed capsule. In
sandy pine barrens from N. J. south to Fla. (The same or
a related species on the higher mountains of N. C. Britton
and Brown.)

Alpine Azalea
*Loiseleuria
procumbens*

A similarly much-branched, spreading,
matted, dwarf shrub of Alpine summits,
the branches 2–4 inches long.

The minutely small leaves evergreen,
$\frac{1}{8}$–$\frac{1}{2}$ inch long, crowded, mostly opposite, dark green above,
paler, and the midrib prominent beneath. Flowers tiny,
deep crimson pink or white, bell-shaped with 5 lobes, 2–5
in a terminal cluster.

On the summits of the higher White Mts. (south to
Welch Mt.) N. H., Mt. Albert, Que., in humus on the bay
of Fundy, N. S. and from Newf. and Lab. north to the
Arctic regions and Alaska.

[1] It is extremely improbable that the genus *Menziesia* under any
conditions produces an *ovate* leaf.

A most beautiful evergreen shrub and (in the South) a tree 4–38 or more feet high, with a trunk diameter of 20 inches; it attains its greatest proportions in the woodlands of the southern Alleghany Mts. The trunk is irregular, the bark dark ruddy brown furrowed into narrow ridges separating into elongated scales, the branches rigid and spreading.

Mountain Laurel Calico Bush Spoonwood *Kalmia latifolia*

The leaves, crowded at the tips of the branches, are mostly alternating, elliptical or obovate, pointed, thick, leathery, toothless, deep lustrous green above, a trifle paler beneath, 2–5 inches long, drooping. Flowers waxy white pink-tinged, bowl-shaped, with 5 lobes, conventional, nearly an inch broad, in large showy terminal clusters. May–June. Fruit capsule small, oblate-spheroidal.

In sandy or rocky soil, often forming dense thickets, distributed from N. B. to Ont. the northern shores of Lake Erie (local in the northerly part of its range), south to western Fla. mostly along the Alleghany Mts. western Ky. Ind. Fla. Ark. (Red River), and La. In N. C. it is abundant in the mountain region, and is cut in large quantities at Cranberry and Elk Park, Mitchel Co. It is also sparingly distributed over the Piedmont plateau and the coastal plain. The wood is heavy (44 pounds to the cubic foot), very hard, strong, brittle, close-grained and pale brown in color. It takes a good polish and is used for tool handles, turned articles, and fuel. Described and illustrated in the *Field Book of American Wild Flowers*, page 332.

A low shrub 1–3 feet high, with straight ascending stem, and elliptical, commonly dull-tipped, thin, leathery leaves mostly opposite, deep green above, paler beneath, 1–2 inches long, drooping. Flowers similar to those of the preceding species, but miniature, $\frac{1}{4}$–$\frac{1}{3}$ inch broad. June–July. Capsule with a persisting style.

Sheep Laurel Lambkill *Kalmia angustifolia*

In moist soil from Lab. and Newf. southwest to Ont., and south to Ga. and Mich. Described also in the *Field Book of American Wild Flowers*, page 334.

**Southern
Sheep Laurel
*Kalmia
carolina*** A species similar to the foregoing, with tan or buff brown stems, and similar, usually larger leaves $1\frac{1}{2}$–$2\frac{1}{2}$ inches long, very pale and exceedingly velvety soft beneath. Flowers, pink and pink magenta, the calyx fine-hairy, *not* glandular. Generally in open woodlands, from the region of the Dismal Swamp, Va. to N. C.

**Pale Laurel
Swamp Laurel
*Kalmia
polifolia*** A spreading, scragged shrub 6–22 inches high, often with ascending branches; smooth.

The small, narrowly elliptical or almost linear, opposite-growing leaves dark green above, white green with a bloom beneath, the edge rolled back, nearly or quite stemless. Flowers in terminal clusters, crimson pink or magenta, comparatively large, $\frac{1}{2}$–$\frac{5}{8}$ inch broad, with threadlike stems.

Generally in bogs or on shores of cold ponds at a considerable altitude, from Newf. and Lab. to Alaska, and south to Conn. N. J. Pa. Mich. Minn. and Cal. Also in Greenland and boreal Europe and Asia. Described and illustrated in the *Field Book of American Wild Flowers*, page 334.

**Hairy Laurel
*Kalmia
hirsuta*** A low southern shrub 8–20 inches high, with ascending rough-hairy branches and tiny narrowly elliptical, hairy leaves $\frac{1}{4}$–$\frac{1}{2}$ inch long, with a rolled-back margin. Flowers solitary, crimson pink or magenta, $\frac{1}{3}$–$\frac{1}{2}$ inch broad May–August. Fruit capsule with long leafy calyx segments. In wet sandy barrens or swamps from Va. to Fla

This Kalmia has distinctly bristly-hairy leaves and branches when young, later the leaves become quite smooth. The flowers are not closely-clustered but scattered, or solitary at the bases of the leaf-stems.

Although a few of the Kalmias develop magenta-tinged flowers, most of the species are inclined toward a perfectly pure pink which fades to an almost pure white. It is apparent, therefore, that the original flower-colors were decidedly deep-toned.

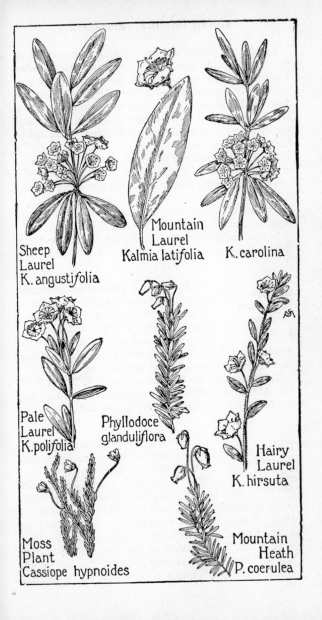

Sheep
Laurel
K. angustifolia

Mountain
Laurel
Kalmia latifolia

K. carolina

Pale
Laurel
K. polifolia

Phyllodoce
glanduliflora

Hairy
Laurel
K. hirsuta

Moss
Plant
Cassiope hypnoides

Mountain
Heath
P. coerulea

The flowers, never blue but turning a pale violet in drying, reasonably account for the inapt title *caerulea*. The fruit is borne erect with the five-pointed calyx persistent. This species occurs in the cool regions of northern America, Europe, and Asia. The flowers resembles those of *Leucothoe* but are borne solitary or few in a cluster; also the dissimilar anthers are attached at their *backs* not at their bases as in *Leucothoe*.

Usually found in stony situations on the alpine summits of the mountains of Me. and N. H. Mt. Albert, Que. and through Newf. and Lab., to the Arctic regions and Alaska.

Phyllodoce glanduliflora is a similar western species slightly taller, with light yellow ovoid flowers.

In the Rocky Mts. the Cœur d'Alene Mts. and the Selkirk Range, Can., etc., and northwest to Alaska.

Cassiope
Moss Plant
Cassiope
hypnoides

A tufted and procumbent evergreen alpine shrub 1-4 inches high; mosslike.

The tiny leaves linear, needle-shaped, curved, densely crowded and appressed on the branches, deep olive green. Flowers white or rose pink, bell-shaped, with 5 deep lobes, nodding. June–July. Capsule spherical, and nodding.

The summits of the high mountains of N. E. and N. Y. Mt. Albert, Que. cliffs of Lake Superior, Newf. Lab. and the Arctic regions; also in boreal Europe and Asia.

Downy
Leucothoe
Leucothoe
axillaris

A southern, evergreen shrub 3-6 feet high, with light brown, ascending branches, the twigs very fine-hairy.

The large deep green leaves paler beneath, elliptical, pointed, finely, sometimes sparingly toothed, over the upper half, 2-6 inches long. Flowers white, in dense spikes about 2 inches long, at the base of the leaves, the corolla nearly cylindrical, tiny, $\frac{1}{4}$ inch long, toothed at the edge, with persistent bracts. April. Fruit capsule globular. On low ground and in moist woods near the coast from Va. to Ala. and Fla.

A straggling shrub of the Gulf States, from Ga. to Miss. The leaves are broadly ovate, or elliptical, 2–3 inches long, similarly toothed. Flowers similar.

Leucothoe platyphylla

A similar species with large, broad lance-shaped, *very* sharp-pointed leaves, sharp spiny-toothed, 3–6 inches long, the stems longer. Flower spikes sometimes over 3 inches long, the corolla often pinkish, unpleasantly odored. May. Fruit oblate-spheroidal, ⅛ inch broad, in thick clusters. Beside streams mostly in the mountains from Va. to Tenn. and Ga.

Catesby's Leucothoe *Leucothoe Catesbaei*

In the following two species the leaves are *deciduous*.

A wide-branched species with (sometimes narrowly) elliptical or ovate leaves 2–4 inches long, toothed, downy on the veins beneath. The flower spikes crowded, often branching, the corolla white, the anthers awned (under the glass). April. On mountain sides Va. to Ga. and Ala.

Mountain Leucothoe *Leucothoe recurva*

A similar shrub with erect branches and elliptical or broadly lance-shaped (rarely ovate or obovate) leaves, finely, rather indistinctly dull-toothed, 1½–3 inches long. The flower spikes often over 3 inches long, the corolla about ¼ inch long, pink or white, the anthers long-awned. Fruit capsule spherical. May–June. In swamps and moist thickets beside rivers, from Mass. south to Fla. and La. near the coast.

Swamp Leucothoe *Leucothoe racemosa*

Also similar, 3–6 feet tall, with similar leaves not quite as long. Flower clusters *very* long, 4–7 inches. In swamps from Va. to Fla.

Leucothoe elongata

A beautiful low shrub 2–12 inches high, with a creeping habit, stems ascending, with few if any branches. Formerly confused with the next species.

Moorwort Wild Rosemary *Andromeda Polifolia*

The small leaves linear, toothless, with strongly reflexed margin, olive green above, very pale beneath, or often light green, abruptly pointed, $\frac{3}{4}$–$1\frac{1}{4}$ inches long. Flowers in small terminal clusters, broadly ovoid, slightly five-angulate, constricted at the opening, $\frac{1}{3}$ inch long dainty crimson pink and white, nodding. The fruit capsule pear-shaped, $\frac{1}{8}$ inch long, on erect stems.

In cold bogs throughout the Arctic regions, south to the Adirondack Mts. N. Y. Priest Lake, Ida., Lake Huron, James Bay, Can., and northwest to the Mackenzie River and Alaska.

Bog Rosemary
Andromeda
glaucophylla
A similar species, the leaves larger, sometimes 2 inches long, white beneath with a *very fine hairiness*. Branchlets smooth with a slight bloom. The similar flowers white, crimson pink-stained, on stouter *curved*, short stems. Fruit capsule oblate-spheroidal in 5 divisions (resembling a pumpkin or turban), the stems curving mostly downward.

In bogs, and on lake shores and river banks from Lab., west to Man., and south to N. J. Pa. and Minn. Also on Mts. Washington and Lafayette in N. H.

Mountain
Fetter Bush
Andromeda
floribunda
A shrub 2–4 feet high, with spreading or ascending, leafy branches, the twigs set with appressed stiff hairs.
The olive green leaves, lustrous, leathery, rigid, elliptical, acute-pointed at the tip, more rounded at the base or broadly lance-shaped, toothless, slightly lighter beneath and glandular dotted, $1\frac{3}{4}$–$2\frac{1}{3}$ inches long. Flowers white in crowded, slender terminal clusters, similar to those of *A. Polifolia*. May. Capsule ovoid. Moist mountain slopes from Va. to Ga.

The earlier name for the following three species was *Andromeda* to which they are similar and closely allied.

Fetter Bush
Lyonia nitida
A shrub 2–5 feet high, with slender, erect, leafy branches, quite smooth and with a slight bloom, sharply triangular in section.
The elliptical, obovate, or very rarely ovate[1] pointed, lustrous leathery, evergreen leaves with a revolute (curled

[1] The ovate leaf in *Lyonia* is almost non-existent.

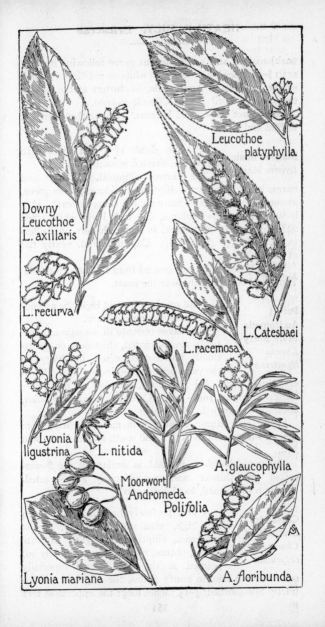

Leucothoe
platyphylla

Downy
Leucothoe
L. axillaris

L. recurva

L. Catesbaei

L. racemosa

Lyonia
ligustrina

L. nitida

A. glaucophylla

Moorwort
Andromeda
Polifolia

Lyonia mariana

A. floribunda

back) margin and a conspicuous nerve following it; they are $1\frac{1}{2}$–3 inches long. Flowers white or red-tinged, ovoid, similar to those of Andromeda, in clusters at the base of the leaves. April–May. Capsule globose.

In low wet woods and barrens, from southeastern Va. to Fla. and La.

Stagger Bush
Lyonia mariana

An erect shrub $1\frac{1}{2}$–4 feet high, with ascending, slender, smooth branches. The leaves elliptical, broadly and narrowly so, or obovate-elliptical, deciduous, olive green, smooth above, slightly hairy on the veins beneath, $1\frac{1}{2}$–3 inches long. Flowers large, $\frac{1}{3}$–$\frac{1}{2}$ inch long, white often suffused slightly with pink, in small clusters on leafless twigs, nodding. May–July. Capsule ovoid, nearly flat at the tip, erect.

In sandy soil or on low ground from R. I. south to Fla. Tenn. and Ark., mostly near the coast.

Privet
Andromeda
Male Berry
Lyonia ligustrina

A tall species 2–10 feet high, the ascending branches minutely hairy. The leaves obovate or sometimes elliptical, acute-pointed, toothless or indistinctly fine-toothed, often fine-hairy on the veins beneath, 1–3 inches long. Flowers white, small, $\frac{1}{6}$–$\frac{1}{4}$ inch long, crowded on commonly leafless twigs. June–July. Capsule nearly globular, obtusely five-angled. September.

Found on swampy ground or in moist thickets, from central Me. to central N. Y., and south to Fla. Tenn. and Ark.

The var. *foliosiflora*, Fernald, is similar but the flower-spikes are thinner and conspicuously leafy-bracted. Common southward, local northward.

Cassandra
Leatherleaf
Chamaedaphne calyculata

A low, profusely branching shrub 2–4 feet high, with small, leathery, almost evergreen, elliptical or slightly obovate leaves, obtuse, never (unless minutely so) pointed at the tip, covered especially beneath with minute scurfy scales, the edge very indistinctly fine-toothed, $\frac{1}{2}$–$1\frac{1}{2}$ inches long; the uppermost *very* small. Flowers white, similar to those of Andromeda, at the base of the upper tiny leaves, in one-sided clusters. April–May. Fruit capsule oblate spheroidal.

In bogs from Newf. and Lab. west to B. C., and south to southern N. J. Ga. Ill. Mich. Wis. and Minn.

A small tree 20–60 feet high, with a trunk diameter of 20 inches. The trunk straight with gray brown bark, rather smooth above, furrowed below into short, broken, rounded ridges, the branches spreading and pendulous; foliage acid, hence the popular name.

Sorrel-tree
Sour-wood
Oxydendrum
arboreum

The deep green leaves are elliptical pointed, or broadly lance-shaped, sharply fine-toothed, smooth, very slightly paler beneath, 4–7 inches long. The white flowers are borne in branching, one-sided, loose, drooping clusters or spikes 7–8 inches long, and are similar to those of Andromeda; $\frac{1}{4}$ inch long. June–July. Delicious clear honey is collected by the bees from the flowers. The capsule is narrowly ovoid, tipped with the persistent style.

The Sorrel-tree is found in rich woods from Pa., Westmoreland Co., west to Ind., and south mostly along the Alleghany Mts. to central Tenn. southern Ala. (eastern shores of Mobile Bay), western Fla. and western La. It attains its highest development in eastern Tenn. In N. C. on the eastern slopes of the Blue Ridge it reaches a height of 50–60 feet, but is a mere shrub on the coastal plain. The wood is heavy (46 lbs. to the cubic foot), hard and close-grained, light brown in color, the sapwood slightly lighter. It takes a fine polish and is used for tool handles, turned articles, and bearings of machinery.

A small straggling shrub 5–15 inches high, introduced from Europe, with ascending branches and evergreen foliage.

Heather
Calluna vulgaris

The gray green leaves are minute, scarcely $\frac{1}{12}$ inch long, crowded and overlapping on the branches. The delicate magenta pink or sometimes white flowers $\frac{1}{8}$ inch long, somewhat bell-shaped, the 4 conspicuous sepals carrying the color; in terminal one-sided spikes. July–September. Capsule slightly four-sided, minute.

Sandy or rocky soil on the coast, very local, from Newf. Nantucket, Mass. R. I. etc. to N. J. The Scottish Heather *Erica cineria* has one station on Nantucket, Mass.; it is similar, with the larger linear leaves growing in groups of three. The similar magenta flowers have a longer corolla ¼ inch long, exceeding the calyx. *Erica Tetralix* is similar; it is also on Nantucket,[1] and is in cultivation in Biltmore N. C., the leaves are borne in groups of four. Both Heaths are from Europe.

The following five species are called HUCKLEBERRIES.

Box Huckleberry
Gaylussacia brachycera

A low shrub 8–16 inches high, with commonly erect branches more or less angular in section, light brown.

The leaves normally elliptical, occasionally slightly ovate, rather indistinctly and shallowly dull-toothed, the edge curled back, deep lustrous olive green above, paler beneath, smooth, thick, evergreen, ½–1 inch long. Flowers in small clusters white or suffused with magenta pink, narrow bell-shaped, five-toothed, ⅙ inch long. May. Berry a drupe, cadet blue, *bloomy* (not light blue), with 10 *seedlike nutlets*, each containing a single seed. This is the distinguishing character of *Gaylussacia* in contradistinction to that of *Vaccinium* in which the berry is many-seeded not nutlet-seeded. To distinguish the two genera on a basis of fruit-color is impracticable.

In dry woods on hillsides from Pa. (Perry Co.), south to Del. (shores of Indian River, Sussex Co.) and Va., and through the mountains of eastern Tenn.

Dwarf Huckleberry
Gaylussacia dumosa

A similar but common species, 1–2 rarely 5 feet high, the branches mostly leafless below, and the younger ones distinctly fine-hairy and glandular.

The leaves variable, elliptic-obovate, narrowly obovate or reverse-lance-shaped, toothless and bristle-tipped, not so thick as those of the foregoing species,

[1] These Heaths were adventiously introduced on Nantucket Island along with the planting of the so-called Henry Coffin Pines in 1875-1877; see page 12 under *Pinus sylvestris*.

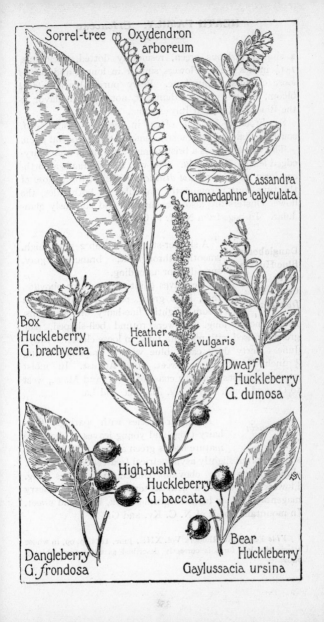

Sorrel-tree　Oxydendron
arboreum

Cassandra
Chamaedaphne calyculata

Box
Huckleberry
G. brachycera

Heather
Calluna vulgaris

Dwarf
Huckleberry
G. dumosa

High-bush
Huckleberry
G. baccata

Bear
Huckleberry
Gaylussacia ursina

Dangleberry
G. frondosa

a similar lustrous green, resinously dotted, deciduous, 1-1½ inches long. Flowers similar in longer and rather loose clusters. May–June. Berry purple black *without* bloom, about ⅓ inch in diameter, not equal in flavor to the Blueberry, ripe in July–August.

Sandy or rocky soil, often in swamps, from Newf. south to Fla. and La., mostly confined to the coastal plain.

The var. *hirtella* is a bristly-hairy form, with even hairy-edged leaves; Va. to Fla. The var. *Bigeloviana* is a northern form with leaves *not distinctly* different from those of the type, but permanently glandular on both sides, the flower clusters are also permanently and copiously glandular. In bogs from Newf. to Conn.[1]

Dangleberry Blue Huckleberry

Gaylussacia frondosa

A slender-stemmed shrub 2–5 feet high, smooth throughout, branches gray, spreading or ascending.

The leaves elliptic-obovate or obovate, thin, light green, paler beneath with a bloom, slightly fine-hairy on the veins, 1½-2½ inches long. Flowers rotund bell-shaped, pale green suffused with magenta pink, in loose clusters. May–June. Berry dark cadet blue with a grapelike bloom, ⅓ inch in diameter; sweet. July–August. In moist woods or copses from the coast of N. H. and Mass., west to O., and south to Va. Ky. Ala. Fla. and La.

Gaylussacia ursina

A similar species with sparingly fine-hairy twigs and young leaves. The large mature leaves green above, paler beneath, smooth, often slightly asymmetrical (scarcely rhomboidal). elliptic-obovate or obovate pointed, 2–4 inches long. Flowers similar, often with a terra-cotta tinge. Berry magenta black or lustrous purple black, large and sweet. In mountain woods of N. C. Ky. and Ga.

[1] *Vide* Fernald in Rhodora Vol. XIII., June, 1811, p. 99, in whose article the leaf form is correctly described as elliptic, or oblong-obovate.

HEATH FAMILY. *Ericaceae*

An erect shrub with many stiff gray brown branches, 1–3 feet high, the young twigs fine-hairy.

High-bush Huckleberry Black Huckleberry *Gaylussacia baccata*

The leaves similar in form to the last species, mostly elliptical pointed or elliptic-obovate, *never* normally oval, toothless, extremely clammy-resinous (including the flower clusters) when young, green on both sides and smooth, 1–2 inches long. Flower-clusters one-sided, the bracts ruddy, the corolla ovoid or nearly cylindrical, small, green suffused with crimson or crimson pink. May–June. Berry black, or purplish black, rarely with a slight bluish or a magentaish bloom, or even white, about ¼ inch in diameter, sweet, but the seeds (properly nutlets) large. July–August.

In rocky woods and thickets from Newf. west to Manitoba and Wis. and south to Ky. and Ga.

A tall shrub 7–15 or in the southern part of its range a small tree 30 feet high, with a trunk diameter of 8 inches, the branches irregular and contorted, the trunk short, the gray brown bark thin and scaly, the twigs light brown and smooth.

Farkleberry Tree Huckleberry *Vaccinium arboreum*

The thin leathery leaves obovate or elliptical, deep lustrous green above, dull and sometimes slightly fine-hairy beneath, quite evergreen in the South, very veiny, toothless (the margin slightly rolled back), or very obscurely fine-toothed, the tips often bristle-pointed, ¾–2¼ inches long. Flowers white, bell-shaped and pendent, in leafy-bracted clusters, the corolla five-lobed, ¼ inch long. Fruit a spherical black berry, persistent, dry, sweet, edible, but poor and insipid, ¼ inch in diameter.

In sandy soil, on moist bottom-lands, on the margins of streams and ponds, and often in the woods among taller trees, from southern Ill. and N. C., south to Fla. Ky. eastern Okla. and Tex. It is often draped (in Florida) with the long, stringy grayish moss called *Tillandsia*. The wood is ruddy brown, hard, close-grained, and heavy

(47 lbs. per cubic foot), it is used for tool handles, etc., and the bark is useful for tanning leather.

**Deerberry
Squaw
Huckleberry
*Vaccinium
stamineum***
A shrub 1–6 feet high, with spreading, light brown, slightly fine-hairy branches. The leaves elliptical or obovate, whitish but smooth beneath, 1–3 inches long. Flowers numerous in graceful leafy, bracted clusters, similar to the foregoing but yellowish green or magenta-stained with a bloom when mature, the stamens and style protruding. Berry nearly spherical, dull green or yellow, sour, not edible. In dry woods or thickets from central Mass. to southern Ont. and Minn., and south to Fla. Ky. and La.

Vaccinium melanocarpum is a similar species, the young twigs and the calyx of which are minutely *white fine-hairy*. The berry a shining dark purple; edible. In woods N. C. west to Mo. and southward.

Vaccinium neglectum is also similar but the branchlets are smooth, and the leaves elliptical (mostly narrowly so) or a trifle obovate, slightly whitish and smooth beneath. Flowers white or pink magenta, the fruit like that of *V. stamineum*.

Dry woodlands from N. J. (Cranberry Lake, Sussex Co.) and Va. to Kan., south to Fla. and La.

The following *Vacciniums* are called BLUEBERRIES.

**Evergreen
Blueberry
*Vaccinium
Myrsinites***
cadet blue.
A low southern shrub 8–22 inches high; the tiny leaves obovate, wedge-shaped at the base, or nearly elliptical, mostly smooth beneath, and indistinctly toothed, $\frac{1}{4}$–$\frac{3}{4}$ inch long. Berry globular, dark

On sandy soil from Va. to Fla. and La.

**Southern
Huckleberry
or Blueberry
*Vaccinium
virgatum***
A shrub 3–11 feet high, with slender green branches and fine-hairy green twigs. The leaves elliptical or obovate, pointed, tipped with a tiny bristle, pale with a slight bloom beneath, toothless or nearly so, 1–1$\frac{3}{4}$ inches long. Flowers white suffused with pink,

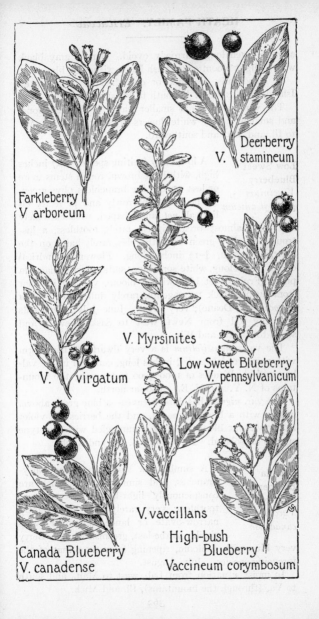

Deerberry
V. stamineum

Farkleberry
V arboreum

V. Myrsinites

V. virgatum

Low Sweet Blueberry
V. pennsylvanicum

V. vaccillans

Canada Blueberry
V. canadense

High-bush
Blueberry
Vaccineum corymbosum

about $\frac{1}{3}$ inch long, narrowly ovoid. Berries gray black with a slight bloom or purplish black without a bloom.

In woodlands, swamps, or dry thickets from Staten Island, N. Y. and N. J., south to Fla. and La.

The var. *tenellum* has smaller leaves $\frac{1}{2}$–$1\frac{1}{4}$ inches long, and smaller, nearly white flowers in closer clusters. Va to Ill. and Mo., and southward.

Low Sweet Blueberry *Vaccinium pennsylvanicum* — A low, early fruiting species 8–27 inches high, with light brown, rough stems more or less warty; the branchlets olive green. The leaves narrowly and perfectly elliptical, *not* lance-shaped, with extremely fine teeth almost bristle-tipped, rarely toothless, a lustrous dark olive green on both sides, rarely hairy on the midrib beneath, $\frac{3}{4}$–$1\frac{1}{2}$ inches long. Flowers cylindrical ovoid, $\frac{1}{4}$ inch long, white sometimes suffused with magenta pink. Fruit cadet blue with a bloom, varying in color from purple black to magenta, rarely dull white (*forma leucocarpum*, Deane); very sweet. June–July. Dry hills or rocky soil from Newf. west to Saskatchewan, and south to Va. Ill. and Wis.

The var. *angustifolium* is a very dwarf northern form with narrower leaves $\frac{1}{3}$–$\frac{3}{4}$ inches long, common in the valleys and at altitudes of 1000–4000 feet among the mountains of N. Y. and N. E. Also far north.

The var. *nigrum* has darker leaves—a blue green above, lighter with a bloom beneath, and the berries are violet black without bloom. Often commingled with the type species or isolated. N. B. to N. J. Pa. and Mich.

Canada Blueberry Sour-top *Vaccinium canadense* — A similar low shrub with fine hairy-branches, and similar leaves which are conspicuously light-hairy beneath, and toothless; very rarely they are slightly narrow-ovate or lance-shaped. Flowers similar to the last, greenish white. Berry very blue with a bloom, ripening later than that of the foregoing species. July–August.

In moist situation from Lab. west to Man., and south to Va. (through the mountains), Ill. and Mich.

A low shrub 6–40 inches high, with
yellow green branches, smooth throughout.
The flowering branches 2–3 inches long
are mostly without leaves in the fruiting
season.

Late Blueberry
*Vaccinium
vacillans*

The leaves broadly elliptical or slightly obovate, bright
green above, with a slight bloom beneath, toothless, 1–1¾
inches long. Flowers greenish yellow or white tinged
with pale magenta. Berry cadet blue with a bloom,
very sweet, ripening later than that of *V. pennsylvanicum.*
July–August. On dry ground from N. E. west to Mich.
and southward.

The var. *crinitum* is a form with fine-hairy twigs and
mostly small, similar leaves, fine-hairy beneath especially
on the veins. Rutland, Vt. Niagara Falls, N. Y. and Ont.,
south to Va. and Tenn., west to Mo. (St. Louis Co.).

A tall species 3–13 feet high, with
spreading branches, and elliptical (narrow
or broader), pointed leaves, light green
and smooth above, paler and smooth or
very slightly hairy on the veins beneath,

**High-bush
Blueberry**
*Vaccinium
corymbosum*

toothless, 1½–3 inches long. Flowers white or suffused
with magenta pink, narrowly ovoid, nearly ½ inch long.
Berry purple black with a bloom, slightly acid. In swamps,
on wet meadows and in thickets, etc. from Me. west to
Minn., and south to Fla. and La.

The var. *amoenum* is a form with broadly elliptical (almost
ovate) or typically elliptical leaves, the edge finely toothed
or toothless and fringed with fine hairs. The same range.

The var. *pallidum* is a form with hairy-margined leaves
much whitened on the under side. Similar range.

This species is similar, but the leaves
are downy beneath and unfold later than
the flowers. Berry lustrous violet black
without a bloom. Swamps and moist
woodlands, from southern Me. to N. C.
and Ont. Flowering a week or so earlier than *V. corymbosum.*

**Black
Blueberry**
*Vaccinium
atrococcum*

The following four species are called BILBERRIES.

Bog Bilberry
Vaccinium uliginosum
A stocky little shrub 4–20 inches high, with rough and gnarled stems, and tiny olive green, obovate, thickish leaves, smooth on both sides, paler beneath, toothless, $\frac{1}{4}$–$\frac{5}{8}$ inch long. Flowers very small, white suffused with pink, ellipsoidal, often four-lobed, with 8 stamens; single or very few in a cluster. Berry blue black with a bloom, sweet, $\frac{1}{4}$ inch in diameter. July–August.

Throughout the Arctic regions, south to Newf. Lab. Me. Washington Co. (barrens), the summits of high mountains in N. E. and N. Y., Lake Superior, Mich. and Alaska.

Dwarf Bilberry
Vaccinium caespitosum
Somewhat similar, not over 11 inches high, nearly or quite smooth throughout, the leaves similar but larger, wedge-shaped at the base, *fine-toothed*, $\frac{1}{3}$–$1\frac{1}{4}$ inches long.

Flowers similar, often a deeper pink, with a five-lobed corolla and 10 stamens. Berry cadet blue; sweet. August Rocky ground from Lab. to Alaska, and south to Me. N. H. Vt. and N. Y. (mostly on mountain summits), west to northern Mich. and Wis., south in the Rocky Mts. to Col. and to northern Cal.

Vaccinium membranaceum
An erect western shrub 1–5 feet high, the branchlets distinctly angulate in section, practically smooth throughout. The thin, bright green leaves mostly elliptical, commonly slightly ovate, very rarely (or abnormally) obovate, indistinctly fine-toothed, $\frac{3}{4}$–2 inches long. Flowers greenish suffused with magenta pink, broadly ovoid, almost globular, $\frac{1}{5}$ inch in diameter. Berry large, blue black, rather sour. July–August. In moist woods from Mich. (Lake Superior), to Ore. and B. C.

Vaccinium ovalifolium
A similar northern shrub, more straggling in habit, with very slender, angulate branchlets, and distinctly ovate or elliptical, thin leaves, toothless or very nearly so, pale with a bloom beneath. Flowers similar but ovoid. Berry

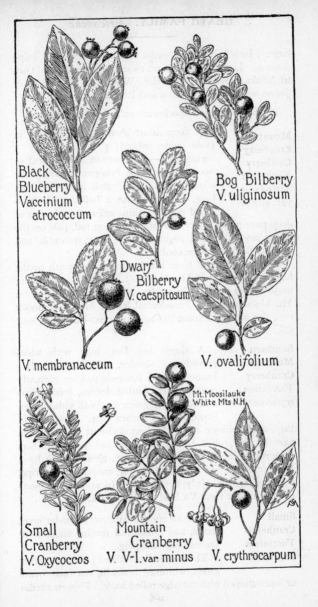

Black
Blueberry
Vaccinium
atrococcum

Bog Bilberry
V. uliginosum

Dwarf
Bilberry
V. caespitosum

V. membranaceum

V. ovalifolium

Mt. Moosilauke
White Mts N.H.

Small
Cranberry
V. Oxycoccos

Mountain
Cranberry
V. V-I. var. minus

V. erythrocarpum

large, $\frac{1}{3}$ inch in diameter, cadet blue with a bloom. July-August. Low woodlands and mountain slopes, from Que. to Alaska, and south to Mich. Wash. and Ore. Also in Japan according to Britton and Brown.

The following four species are called CRANBERRIES.

Mountain Cranberry Cowberry
Vaccinium Vitis-Idaea var. *minus*

A very dwarf shrub, tiny, growing in close mats, about 3 inches—rarely 7 inches high—with very small elliptical or obovate, leathery evergreen leaves, the edge toothless and rolled back, $\frac{1}{4}$–$\frac{5}{8}$ inch long. Flowers with a bell-shaped, four-lobed corolla, white suffused with rose or deep pure pink. Berry globular, crimson red, pale on the under side, acid and slightly bitter, very palatable and delicate-flavored when cooked.

On dry stony soil from the Arctic regions south to the higher mountains of Me. N. H. Vt. and N. Y., ascending to 5000 feet in the White Mts. N. H., very common on Mt. Moosilauke the Presidential Range Mt. Monadnock etc., also along the coast to Cape Ann and Danvers Essex Co., Mass.

Southern Mountain Cranberry
Vaccinium erythrocarpum

A shrub 1–5 feet high with wide-spreading, slender, slightly angulate branches, and lance-shaped or narrowly ovate, sharp-pointed leaves, *bristly fine-toothed*, thin, green on both sides, paler beneath, 1–1$\frac{1}{2}$ inches long. Flowers solitary, deep crimson pink, the four divisions of the corolla narrow, and rolled back, the elongated yellow anthers compressed into a narrow erect cone, about $\frac{1}{2}$ inch long. Berry crimson red turning dark dull magenta when ripe, acid and insipid. July–September. In woodlands among the mountains from Va. and W. Va. to Ga.

Small Cranberry
Vaccinium Oxycoccos

A small species with very slender erect stems, and horizontal rooting stems 6–16 inches long; creeping.

The leaves tiny—about $\frac{1}{4}$ inch long, olive green, whitened beneath, narrowly ovate or lance-shaped with the edge rolled back. Flowers similar to the foregoing, small, about ⅓ inch long, the corolla lobes a pure red pink or rose pink. Berry crimson red, acid, spherical, about ⅓ inch in diameter. August–September.

In cold mossy bogs from the Arctic regions and Newf. to Alaska, and south to N. E., N. Y., N. J., N. C. Mich. and B. C. Largely in the mountains. Also in Europe and Asia.

The common cranberry of the markets, in wide cultivation. Stems similar to those of the foregoing species but stouter; the leaves, flowers, and fruit also larger; the leaves absolutely elliptical, or slightly	**Large Cranberry** *Vaccinium macrocarpon*

varying toward ovate or obovate. Fruit ripe in September–October.

In bogs from Newf. Me. Mass. (Cape Cod), and N. J. west to Ont. Mich. and Ark., and south to Va. and W. Va

SAPODILLA FAMILY. *Sapotaceae.*

Trees or shrubs commonly with milky sap, and with toothless, alternate leaves, and small, perfect, regular (in *Bumelia* five-parted) flowers.

A shrub or small tree 10–35 feet high, often with a trunk diameter of 6 inches. The bark rough and with short, firm confluent ridges, warm brown gray, the twigs thorny.	**Southern Buckthorn** *Bumelia lycioides*

The leaves elliptical, broadly lance-shaped or very narrowly obovate, pointed, toothless, slightly leathery, olive green and smooth, 1½–4 inches long. Flowers small, white, ⅛ inch broad, in dense globular clusters at the base of the leaves. Fruit black, cherrylike, ovoid, over ⅓ inch long.

In moist thickets and on lowlands from Va. south to Fla. (Mosquito Inlet and Caloosa River), and west to southern Ill. Mo. Ark. and Tex. (Rio Concho River). The wood is hard, heavy (46 lbs. to the cubic foot), and buffish brown.

SAPODILLA FAMILY. *Sapotaceae*

Woolly Bumelia
Shittimwood
False
Buckthorn
Bumelia
lanuginosa

A similar shrub or tree 10–60 feet high, sometimes with a trunk diameter of 3 feet, the bark similar, in a network of strong, confluent ridges, branches armed with stout thorns sometimes over an inch long.

The leaves *leathery*, olive green and smooth above, densely fine-hairy and rusty tan-color beneath, strongly, often attenuately obovate, the tip very obtuse, the base wedge-shaped. Flowers in smaller clusters of 6–22 blossoms. Berry similar.

In similar situations from southern Ga. and northern Fla. through Ala. (Tennessee River Valley to the coastal plain), and from southern Ill. and Mo. southwestward through Ark. and Tex. to Mex.

EBONY FAMILY. *Ebenaceae*

Persimmon
Diospyros
virginiana

A slender southern tree with wide-spreading branches, commonly 40–60 but under very favorable conditions 110 feet high, with a trunk diameter of 2 or more feet. Bark sepia brown or grayish brown, somewhat corky, deeply scored or furrowed into coarse *rectangular plates*, with a scarcely perceptible perpendicular trend, the limbs ascending, the branches rather slender.

The lustrous deep green leaves paler and a trifle downy beneath when young, are 2–5 inches long, thick, smooth, ovate or long-ovate pointed at the tip, and smooth on both sides when old. The ribs are strongly incurved and irregular. The greenish yellow flowers are small, somewhat bell-shaped and four-lobed, they are staminate and pistillate, the former with about 16 stamens, the latter with an abortive 8, the pistillate flower, the larger—about ½ inch long and solitary, the staminate flowers in small clusters. Each kind is usually borne on a separate tree, and sometimes flowers occur which are perfect.

The pistillate-flowered tree bears fruit abundantly in alternating years, or sometimes annually. The fruit is plumlike, oblate-spheroidal, with the withered, thick calyx at the base, 1–1½ inches broad, at first green, finally ocher orange, often ruddy cheeked, sweet and edible especially after frost although this partially destroys the flavor. The

Southern
Buckthorn
Bumelia lycioides

Large
Cranberry
Vaccinium
macrocarpon

Flower of
D. kaki

Shittimwood
B. lanuginosa

Leaves bright
yellow olive
green.

Persimmon Diospyros virginiana

Horse
Sugar
Symplocos
tinctoria

fully ripened fruit tastes not unlike a date, the unripe fruit is excessively astringent with tannic acid.

The Persimmon is common in fields and open woods, and is distributed from New Haven (Light-house Point), Conn. Long Island, N. Y. northern N. J. and eastern Pa. south to Biscayne Bay and Caloosa River, Fla., and west of the Alleghanies from southern O. to Ala. thence west to south-western Io. southern Mo. eastern Kan. (Franklin, Anderson, Bourbon, Crawford, and Cherokee Cos.), Okla. and the Colorado River, Tex. It is common throughout N. C. except among the high, mountainous, western counties. It reaches its highest development in the lower Ohio basin.

The wood is heavy (50 lbs. to the cubic foot), hard, strong, close-grained, the heartwood deep brown to nearly sepia brown. It takes a fine polish, and is used for shoe-lasts, shuttles, bench screws, mallets, and wagon shafts. A decoction from the fruit is also used medicinally.

The Japanese Persimmon, *Diospyros kaki*, one of the principal fruit trees of Japan, has been for many years planted in the South, where it flourishes most satisfactorily. It has large, shining, leathery leaves, and luscious golden yellow fruit which measures about 2 inches in length, and is often seen in the Eastern markets.

STORAX FAMILY. *Styracaceae.*

Shrubs or trees with alternate-growing leaves and perfect, regular flowers, the corolla formed of 4–8 petals united at the base.

Sweet Leaf Horse Sugar
Symplocos tinctoria

A southern shrub or occasionally a small tree 10–38 feet high, with a trunk diameter of 10 inches. Bark *smooth*, light gray brown, shallowly seamed with widely separated short fissures when old.

The leaves thin leathery, elliptical (or narrowly so) or obovate, indistinctly or remotely round-toothed, yellow green above, *pale* and fine-hairy beneath, 3–5½ inches long, drooping at the tips of the branchlets. Flowers pale creamy yellow, delicately fragrant, in small, close clusters at the bases of the leaves, ⅓–½ inch broad, with a five-lobed corolla and numerous stamens; developing with the leaves.

April. Fruit a nutlike, elliptical drupe $\frac{1}{3}$ inch long, with one seed.

Rich woods and thickets from Del. to Fla. and La. Wood soft, brittle, pale red brown, the weight 34 lbs. per cubic foot. The sweet-tasting leaves are relished by cattle and they yield a yellow dye.

A beautiful small tree, often a tall shrub, 18–45 feet high, reaching its greatest development on the slopes of the southern Alleghany Mts., in N. C. and Tenn., where it occasionally reaches a height of 90 feet, with a trunk diameter of 3 feet. Trunk straight, the bark ruddy brown, broken into short conspicuously confluent ridges, the stout branches smooth, striped with shallow, tan-colored fissures.

Snowdrop Silver-bell Tree *Halesia carolina Mohrodendron carolinum* **Britton**

The leaves thin, elliptical or slightly obovate, pointed, finely toothed, deep green above, paler and slightly downy beneath, 2–6 inches long. The beautiful snow white flowers (appearing with the leaves) are four-petaled and bell-shaped, $\frac{1}{2}-\frac{7}{8}$ inches long, borne in slender drooping clusters. Fruit elongated ellipsoidal, four-winged, about $1\frac{1}{4}$ inches long, with a bony nut.

The Snowdrop Tree is found on the banks of streams in rich soil from W. Va. (in the mountains), south to central Fla., and from Ala. (Lauderdale, Cullman, and Talladega Cos.), Miss. Ark. and western La. to eastern Tex. The wood is soft, close-grained, light brown, and weighs 35 lbs. to the cubic foot. It has no commercial value.

A southern shrub 3–12 feet high, with smooth or nearly smooth ascending branches.

Storax *Styrax grandifolia*

The elliptical or obovate, abruptly pointed leaves deep green and smooth above, white-velvety beneath, with few remote teeth or none, 2–6 inches long. The showy white flowers with 5 narrow, mostly recurved, soft-downy lobes and 10 closely grouped yellow stamens, about $\frac{5}{8}$ inch long, commonly in long, loose clusters; drooping. Fruit an obovoid capsule $\frac{1}{3}$ inch long. In woods, southern Va. to Fla.

Downy Storax
Styrax pulveru-lenta

A shrub 1–4 feet high, similar to the preceding, but the elliptical or obovate leaves slightly downy above and scaly or scurfy fine-hairy beneath. The fragrant white flowers similar but larger, about $\frac{1}{2}$ inch long, 1–3 in a cluster at the base of the leaves, or terminal. Capsule globular. In moist pine-barrens, southern Va. to Fla. and Tex.

Smooth Storax
Styrax americana

A southern shrub 3–9 feet high, with smooth ascending branches.

The leaves deep green above, paler beneath, smooth, broadly elliptical or obovate, pointed, and remotely toothed or quite toothless, 1–3 inches long. The fragrant, showy flowers white with 5 narrow, spreading petals, about $\frac{2}{3}$ inch long, with ten yellow stamens, usually solitary (or 3–4 in a cluster) at the base of the leaves. Fruit globular, leathery, brown, about $\frac{1}{4}$ inch in diameter.

On the banks of streams or in moist thickets (often in Cypress swamps) from Va. to Fla. and west to Ill. Ark. Mo. and La., in the Mississippi Valley.

OLIVE FAMILY. *Oleaceae*

Trees or shrubs with opposite simple or compound, toothed or toothless leaves, and perfect polygamous, or dioecious, (*i. e.*, staminate and pistillate on different plants) flowers in commonly terminal clusters, usually with a four-petaled corolla.

White Ash
Fraxinus americana

A large and valuable timber tree 60–75 and occasionally 120 feet high in woodlands of the Ohio and Mississippi Valleys, with a trunk diameter of 4–6 feet. In isolation it is broadly ovate, with large, ascending limbs and branches, the lower branches often drooping. In the forest the stem is tall and very straight. Bark dark gray or gray brown, deeply and somewhat conventionally furrowed into short, perpendicular channels and strongly confluent, narrow ridges. The twigs stout, smooth, brittle, brown gray, the newer ones greenish gray.

Downy
Storax
S. pul-
-verulenta

Silver-bell
Tree
Halesia carolina

Storax
S. grandifolia

Biltmore Ash
F. Biltmoreana

Smooth
Storax
Styrax
americana

White
Ash
Fraxinus americana

Blair. N.H

The leaves compound, 8–12 inches long, with 5–9 usually 7 leaflets, irregularly and sparingly dull-toothed, lusterless light green above, paler or silvery green beneath, smooth except on the veins which converge toward the margin of the leaf, the stems slender, grooved, and greenish white; leaflet stems about $\frac{3}{8}$ inch long. Flowers green, without petals, the small calyx with four divisions. The tree is dioecious, *i.e.*, staminate and pistillate flowers are borne on different individuals. Blooming in late May.

Fruit in clusters, winged, 1–2 commonly $1\frac{1}{2}$ inches long, bluntly lance-shaped, the seed portion circular in section, about $\frac{3}{8}$ inch long; persisting on the bare branches until midwinter.

The White Ash is common in rich, moist, cool woods, in fields, or on river banks; it is distributed from Newf. and N. S. west to Ont. northern Minn. eastern Neb. Kan. Okla, and Trinity River Tex., and south to northern Fla. It is common throughout N. E. but scattered, seldom covering large areas except in Me. Its leaves unfold late in spring, turn yellow in the early autumn, and blacken and fall with an early severe frost. It is common throughout N. C. and reaches an average height of 70 feet.

The wood is heavy, very strong, tough, close but not fine-grained, and brown or paler brown. It is used in the manufacture of agricultural instruments, wagons and carriages, furniture, oars, and in the interior finish of buildings. Weight 41 lbs. to the cubic foot. Next to the oak it is commercially the most valuable of all American timber trees, growing rapidly under favorable conditions and attaining a height of 45 feet in thirty years under all ordinary circumstances.

Biltmore Ash
Fraxinus biltmoreana
A species with a limited range through the Appalachian mountain region, with characters similar to those of the White Ash except where otherwise specified. It is the common species about Asheville, N. C. Bark dark gray brown, the branchlets very fine-hairy.

Leaves with 7–9 narrow, lance-shaped, toothless, sharp-pointed leaflets, deep green above, much paler and slightly fine-hairy beneath, the stems also covered with fine hairs, in this respect quite different from the characteristically smooth White Ash.

Fruit winged, narrowly oblong very slightly if at all narrowed at the rounded or scolloped tip, the seed portion short and thick, $\frac{3}{8}-\frac{1}{2}$ inch long, $\frac{3}{16}$ inch thick.

The Biltmore Ash is found in rich woods and on river banks from the foothills of Pa. south through the mountains to Ga. and Ala. and to central Tenn.

A medium-sized tree 30–50 and occasionally 70 feet high, with a trunk diameter of 2–3 feet, closely resembling the White Ash but distinguished from it by the velvety downiness of its branchlets and twigs, and the light terra-cotta red under surface of the bark on the branches.

Red Ash
Brown Ash
River Ash
Fraxinus
pennsylvanica

The trunk like that of the White Ash but often with flatter-faced, confluent ridges and slightly shallower furrows.

The leaflets like those of the White Ash, taper-pointed, almost toothless, or indistinctly toothed, the stems and the pale green surface beneath covered more or less with downy hairs. Fruit 1–2$\frac{3}{4}$ inches long, the seed portion $\frac{9}{16}-\frac{3}{4}$ inch long, round in section, gradually spreading or flattening into the narrow, more or less blunt or broad-tipped wing; a characteristically narrow-fruited form.

The Red Ash is found in low, moist, rich soil on river banks or the margins of swamps and ponds from N. B. west to Man. the Black Hills, Dak. eastern Neb. northeastern and eastern Kan. and Mo., and south to northern Fla. and the mountain region of northern Ala. and western Tenn. It is infrequent in Me. and southern N. H., but common along the shores of Lake Champlain and its tributary streams in Vt., scattered in Mass. and R. I., and quite frequent in Conn.

The wood is heavy, hard, strong, coarse-grained, and light brown, of less value commercially than the closer-grained White Ash but is used for much the same purposes.

Green Ash
Fraxinus pennsylvanica var. *lanceolata*

A widely distributed variety of the Red Ash, differing from the typical species in its entire smoothness of leaf and twig.

Leaflets quite smooth, or very slightly downy at the angles of the ribs beneath, bright green on either side, a trifle lighter underneath, wedge-shaped or narrowed at the base, toothed nearer the tip, narrower than those of the Red Ash, and more sharply toothed.

The Green Ash is found on the margins of streams and in moist lowlands, and is distributed from the eastern shores of Lake Champlain, Vt. south among the mountains to northern Fla., and west to the Saskatchewan River, Alberta, and the eastern foothills of the Rocky Mts. the Wasatch Mts. Utah, the Pinalino mountain range of Ariz. and to the Colorado River, eastern Tex. It is most abundant in the Mississippi basin. East of the Mississippi River the red and green ashes grow side by side and retain their individual characters, but in the West they are connected by intermediate forms.

Pumpkin Ash
Fraxinus profunda

A tall, slender tree 60–120 feet high, with a trunk diameter of 3–4 feet. The branches spreading forming a narrow-topped tree, the slender branchlets velvety-hairy. Bark brown gray, shallowly seamed and scored into short, thickish, scales, with a scarcely distinct perpendicular trend, the trunk *strongly swollen* at the base which is often submerged in prolonged spring floods; the popular name is attributed to this peculiarity.

The 7–9 leaflets rather broadly lance-shaped or narrowly ovate, with a tapering point, quite toothless or with few obscure teeth, light green above, paler beneath and fine-hairy especially on the ribs, the long stem covered with velvety hairs. Fruit similar to that of the Red Ash, but linear-oblong or narrowly oblong, rounded or notched at the tip, and $2\frac{1}{2}$ inches long, the seed portion gradually merged into the wing.

The Pumpkin Ash is found in river swamps or on the wet margins of ponds, and is distributed from western N. Y.

Red Ash F. pennsylvanica

Green Ash
F. penn. var.
lanceolata

Water
Ash
F. caroliniana

Pumpkin Ash
F. profunda

Blue Ash
Fraxinus quadrangulata

west to New Madrid Co. southern Mo., to Varner, Ark., and south to Fla.

Water Ash
Fraxinus caroliniana

A tree of very modest size, 25–40 feet high, with a trunk diameter of 10 inches, often the companion of the Bald Cypress in the impenetrable river swamps of the South, its slender branches forming a narrow crown. Bark light brown gray, furrowed irregularly and incontinuously into thin plates, the branchlets smooth or slightly fine-hairy.

Leaves with 5–7 ovate or long-ovate, slightly toothed leaflets, pointed at either end, short-stalked, deep green above, paler beneath with a slight down along the ribs. Flowering in March. Fruit with a very broad elliptical wing, sometimes with three wings, the seed portion elongated and narrow.

The Water Ash is common in river swamps and the wet coastal regions of the south, and is distributed from southern Va. south to Cape Canaveral and the Caloosa River, Fla., and along the Gulf region through Tuscaloosa, Baldwin, Clark, and Mobile Cos. Ala. to the Sabine River, Tex., and northward through western La. to southwestern Ark.

The wood is light (23 lbs. to the cubic foot) soft, and bitter to the taste. It has no commercial value.

Blue Ash
Fraxinus quadrangulata

A large and valuable timber tree of the western and southwestern States 60–70 and sometimes 120 feet high, with a trunk diameter of about 30 inches. Its distinguishing character is its four-sided twigs—at least the younger twigs are square in section. Bark light brownish gray, deeply broken perpendicularly but not continuously into thin scales, the young, vigorous, rather coarse branchlets becoming round with age.

The leaves are compound 8–12 inches long, with from 7–11 (commonly 7) taper-pointed, narrowly ovate leaflets, sharply toothed, short-stalked (stalk ⅛ inch long), deep yellow green above, slightly paler beneath with a very slight downy-hairiness along the ribs; they turn a dull pale yellow in autumn. Fruit broad-winged, blunt-tipped, somewhat slightly notched, 1–2 inches long, often over ½ inch wide, generally twisted one quarter of the way around on the axis.

The Blue Ash is found mostly in moist woods on rich limestone hills, and is distributed from Mich. Ill. and Ia. south to Sumner and Cherokee Cos. southeastern Kan., Jackson and Madison Cos. Ala., and to northeastern Ark. The range is imperfectly known. A blue dye is extracted from the inner bark by steeping it in hot water.

The wood is hard, durable, rather close-grained, and brownish yellow; it is extensively used for carriage making, for agricultural instruments and for the interior finish of houses. Weight 47 lbs. to the cubic foot.

A tall, slender tree, 50–60 and occasion- **Black Ash**
ally 90 feet high, with a trunk diameter of **Hoop Ash**
1–2 feet, and with a continuous dark gray *Fraxinus nigra*
stem and slim, almost horizontal branches.
It is essentially a tree of swamps, seldom found in the open. Bark ash g ay, lighter or darker, with a buffish tinge, the scaly surface in irregular perpendicular ridges, the furrows shallow, the scales smoothish and soft beneath; the twigs smooth, stout, and light gray.

The compound leaves 12–16 inches long, composed of 7–11 broad lance-shaped, sharp-pointed leaflets, distinctly but irregularly toothed, deep green above (deeper colored than the White Ash), paler beneath, and beset over the whitish ribs with rusty fine hairs, especially when young. Flowers and fruit appearing in late May in northern N. H., and in April in the southerly part of its range. Fruit narrowly oblong, blunt at both ends, the broad wing distinctly notched at the tip and entirely surrounding the flattened seed portion.

The Black Ash is common in wet woods, swamps, and on river banks, and is distributed from Newf. west along the north shores of the Gulf of St. Lawrence to Lake Winnipeg, Man. southern Ill. central Mo. and northwestern Ark., and south to Newcastle Co. Del. and the mountains of Va. It is common in Me. and frequent in the southern White Mt. region of N. H., it is also common in Vt. and western Mass., but rather rare in R. I. and only occasional in Conn.

The wood is heavy, not very hard, tough, coarse-grained, and durable, easily separable into thin layers, and remarkably pliable, the color is light brown with buffish sapwood; it is largely used for the interior finish of houses, for barrels, hoops, and baskets, and occasionally for cabinet work. Weight 40 lbs. to the cubic foot.

Lilac
Syringa
vulgaris

The common lilac, a shrub about 8 feet high, is not infrequently found as an escape from cultivation beside roads and in the vicinity of old dwellings.

The leaves are smooth, absolutely without gloss, dull blue green, ovate, pointed, broad at the base, and toothless. Flowers white as well as lilac. Introduced from Europe.

Swamp Privet
Adelia
acuminata

A shrub or small tree of the middle West 5-10 or rarely 25 feet high, with trunk diameter of 10 inches, the branches smooth and somewhat spiny, the bark dull brown, smooth or slightly roughened without seams.

The leaves commonly elliptical, conspicuously narrowed and pointed at both ends, sometimes narrowly obovate, nearly toothless or indistinctly dull-toothed, thin, 1½-3 inches long, with slender stems, opposite-growing or in terminal groups. The staminate and pistillate green yellow flowers in inconspicuous small clusters. Fruit a berrylike wrinkled drupe, ellipsoidal, ½ inch long, dull purplish blue.

The Swamp Privet is found on swamp land or along river banks, and is distributed from southwestern Ind. and southern Ill. south to Ga., and southwest to Mo. Ark. and Tex. The wood is similar to that of the next species.

Fringe-tree.
Old Man's
Beard
Chionanthus
virginica

A beautiful shrub, or in the South a tree 8-18 and occasionally 35 feet high, with a trunk diameter of 8 inches. When isolated forming a round-topped figure with rather stout irregular branches.
Bark dark umber brown, nearly smooth above, deeply scored below into narrow, short. confluent ridges.

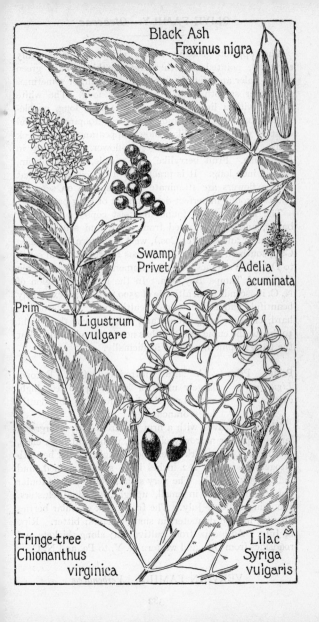

Black Ash
Fraxinus nigra

Swamp
Privet

Adelia
acuminata

Prim

Ligustrum
vulgare

Fringe-tree
Chionanthus
virginica

Lilac
Syriga
vulgaris

OLIVE FAMILY. *Oleaceae*

The opposite-growing leaves elliptical (occasionally obovate), pointed at either end, toothless, dark green above, paler and slightly fine-hairy beneath, or sometimes altogether smooth, about 3–5 inches long. The white flowers with 4 linear petals nearly 1 inch long, purple-dotted at the base within, in loose, drooping, graceful clusters with a fringelike, snowy appearance, the Greek name *chio-anthos* meaning Snow-flower. Blooming in May–June. Fruit berrylike, dull purple, with a bloom, oval, ½ inch long. It is practically a dioecious tree, that is, the flowers are staminate and pistillate on separate plants through imperfect development of their parts.

The Fringe-tree is found in moist copses or on river banks, and is distributed from N. J. and southern Pa. (Lancaster and Chester Cos.), west to eastern Kan. (Allen Co.), southern Ark. and the Brazos River Tex., and south to Del. W. Va. (Jackson and Summers Cos.), Ky. (Warren Co.), and Tampa Bay, Fla. In the mountain region of N. C. it ascends to an altitude of 2500 feet. It is extremely beautiful, and is in common cultivation. The wood is hard, close-grained, strong, and light brown; the weight 40 lbs. to the cubic foot. It has no commercial value, but the bark is sometimes used medicinally.

Privet. Prim
Ligustrum
vulgare
A shrub introduced from Europe, largely used for hedges, 4–10 feet high, with long, slender spreading, abundantly leafy branches.

The small leaves with a firm texture, nearly evergreen, lance-shaped or narrowly elliptical, pointed at both ends, toothless, lustrous dark green above, slightly paler beneath altogether smooth, 1–2 inches long, short-stemmed, and indistinctly veined. The very small, white, short-tubular flowers four-lobed, in small, upright, terminal clusters. Blooming in June–July. The fruit black globular berries about ⅓ inch in diameter, in small clusters; bitter. Ripe in July. An escape from cultivation; along thickets and roadsides from Ont. and western N. Y. to Pa. and N. C.

VERVAIN FAMILY. *Verbenaceæ*

FIGWORT FAMILY. *Scrophulariaceae*

A southern shrub 2–5 feet high, with spreading branches, and rough or scurfy fine-hairy twigs especially when young.

French Mulberry *Callicarpa americana*

The large leaves ovate, tapering to both ends, pointed at the tip, and very lightly round-toothed two-thirds of the way toward the base, 3–6 inches long, dark green above, very white woolly beneath. The small blue lavender flowers with a four-lobed corolla and as many very prominent stamens, in small clusters at the foot of the leaf stem. May–July. The fruit berrylike, deep violet blue, about ⅛ inch in diameter, beautiful and conspicuous in early autumn.

The French Mulberry is found on rich alluvial soil o. in moist thickets, and is distributed from Va. to Fla. Ala Ark. Mo. and Tex.

Callicarpa purpurea is a similar species introduced fron Asia. It has elliptical leaves, smooth beneath, and magenta pink flowers. August. An escape to swamps near Wilmington, Del.

FIGWORT FAMILY. *Scrophulariaceae.*

An extensive family of herbs including only the tree *Paulownia* in our range, with opposite, toothless leaves, and perfect flowers having 4 stamens in pairs of unequal length.

A medium-sized and very beautiful tree similar in leaf and flower to the Catalpa, introduced into this country from China and Japan, and named for

Paulownia *Paulownia tomentosa*

Anna Paulowna, a Russian princess, daughter of Czar Paul I. It grows 50–70 feet high, with a short, massive trunk often 3 feet in diameter. Bark a light brownish gray, thin, scored into shal'ow, confluent ridges, the branches coarse and wide-spreading, forming a round-topped open head.

The large leaves broad-ovate or heart-shaped, 6–12 inches long, light green and smooth above, lighter green and fine gray-hairy beneath, toothless, the long stems also downy. The handsome, large, extremely fragrant light violet flowers similar to those of the Catalpa, in terminal, erect, pyramidal clusters, their stems densely downy, the tubular corolla five-lobed, downy outside; they are rather ephemeral, and unfold with the leaves. May. Fruit an ovoid, leathery capsule resembling a bishop's mitre, 2 inches long, filled with tiny winged seeds.

Escaped from cultivation in southern N. Y. N. J. and the southern States, hardy as far north as New York City, common in parks and gardens.

BIGNONIA FAMILY. *Bignoniaceae.*

Trees or shrubs with mainly opposite, toothless leaves, and showy flowers with tubular corolla upon which the stamens are inserted; it includes the genus *Tecoma* (Trumpet Flower) a climber, with compound leaves.

Catawba Tree
Cigar Tree
Hardy Catalpa
Catalpa
speciosa

A large tree, 50–70 and in the Ohio basin 110 or more feet high, with a trunk diameter of 2–4 feet. A smaller tree in East, the stem continuing almost to the rounded apex of its rather symmetrical figure, the slender branches spreading horizontally. Bark thick, light brown gray, strongly scored with irregular perpendicular furrows of considerable length, the scaly ridges flat-topped; the branchlets coarse, smooth, and ruddy or light brown, the newer twigs thick, and greenish brown.

The leaves large, 5–7 inches long, heart-shaped with a prolonged sharp point, toothless, smooth and light green above, scarcely paler beneath covered with velvety fine-hairs, the ribs prominent, the stem long, sometimes purple-tinged, and also covered with fine hairs. Flowers conspicuous, showy, bell-shaped with 5 dull cream white corolla lobes two of which are larger than the others, lightly purple madder-spotted, with 2 or 4 fertile stamens, the others rudimentary; blooming in May–June. Fruit a long, curved, cylindrical, cigarlike or beanlike capsule, light brown, 8–18 inches long, the numerous ragged-winged seeds fringed with whitish hairs; persisting on the tree through the winter in loose clusters which swing and rattle in the wind.

French Mulberry
Callicarpa
americana
C. purpurea similar

Button-
-bush
Cephal-
-anthus
occiden-
-talis

C. speciosa
similar

Common
Catalpa
Catalpa bignonoides

Paulownia tomentosa

The Catalpa is found on rich bottom-lands and along the margins of streams in the middle West from the Vermillion River southern Ill. and Ind., south to western Ky. and Tenn. southeastern Mo. and northeastern Ark. Elsewhere it is in cultivation or is an escape, as in southern Ark. western La. eastern Tex., and to a very limited extent in the northeastern States.

The wood is light (26 lbs. to the cubic foot), soft, weak, pale brown, and durable; it has no economic value.

Common Catalpa
Catalpa bignonioides

A similar southern and less hardy species commonly much smaller than Catalpa speciosa, and with thinner, irregular, scaly bark without a perpendicular trend, and with wide-spreading lower branches. Its maximum height is about 60 feet.

The leaves are similar to those of C. speciosa, but disagreeably scented, heartshaped or rarely three-lobed, and densely downy beneath. Flowers with a smaller more thickly madder brown-spotted, yellow-throated corolla 1–1¾ inches long, with the lower lobes of the expanded lip *not* scolloped. Blooming in June–July. Fruit similar, the seed wings gray and *narrowly* fringed.

The Common Catalpa is naturalized from Penn. to southern N. Y. and is indigenous only in southwestern Ga. western Fla. central Ala. and Miss. and eastern La. It is a common tree of lawns, parks, and gardens and has become locally spontaneous in the north.

The wood is similar to that of the foregoing species; its weight is 29 lbs. to the cubic foot.

MADDER FAMILY. *Rubiaceae.*

A mostly herbaceous Family including the shrub *Cephalanthus*, with opposite-growing, toothless leaves and white flowers in crowded clusters.

Buttonbush
Cephalanthus occidentalis

A shrub 3–18 but commonly 5 feet high with ascending, widely branched stems. Bark smooth, brown gray.

The leaves ovate, pointed, rounded or narrowed at the base, toothless, 3–5 inches long, slender stemmed, deep green above, strongly veined and paler beneath, and altogether smooth; they grow oppositely or in groups of three. The flowers are dull white, in a dense spherical head about 1 inch in diameter, tubular, $\frac{1}{3}$ inch long, with 4 short, spreading lobes, and a long, protruding style, the latter in large numbers appearing pinlike on the flower-ball. Blooming in June–August. The fruit crowded, small, dry and hard, reverse pyramidal with 2–4 cells, each with one seed.

The Buttonbush is common in swamps and on low moist ground, and is distributed from southwestern N. B. west to western Ont. Cal. Ariz. and Tex., and south to Fla. The Var. pubescens has soft-hairy branchlets and the under surface of the leaves or rarely the whole leaf is also fine-hairy. From Ill. south to Ga. La. and Tex.

HONEYSUCKLE FAMILY. *Caprifoliaceae.*

Mostly shrubs, or vines with opposite-growing commonly toothless, simple leaves (in *Sambucus* they are compound) and thickly clustered *small*, or else funnel-shaped flowers with a five-lobed corolla.

An upright shrub 2–4 feet high, with slender brown ocher stems and smooth or somewhat scaly bark.

Bush Honey-suckle
Diervilla
Lonicera

The leaves ovate or elliptical, sharp-pointed, finely and irregularly toothed, smooth, 2–5 inches long. Flowers honey yellow, about $\frac{3}{4}$ inch long, funnel-shaped with 5 lobes and stamens, slender-stemmed, commonly 3 in a cluster. Fruit narrowly ellipsoidal with an elongated slender beak, dark brown, $\frac{3}{4}$ inch long over all. A common shrub of dry or rocky woodlands or in hillside woods from Newf. west to Man. Mich. Wis., and south mostly through the mountains to Ga. Described and illustrated in the *Field Book of American Wild Flowers*, page 452.

Mountain Fly-Honeysuckle
Lonicera caerulea var. *villosa*

A small, erect shrub 1–3 feet high, with light umber brown, upright stems, with shredded bark.

The leaves elliptical or oblong, rarely slightly ovate, toothless, light green above, paler beneath, conspicuously net-veined, 1–2½ inches long. Flowers pale honey yellow, five-lobed, honeysucklelike, about ⅔ inch long, in pairs at the base of the leaves; eventually the two ovaries become united and form a single cadet blue or gray black berry, ⅓ inch in diameter, ovoid-spherical, with 2 eyes; edible. Common on low ground and in bogs from Newf. west to Alaska, and south to Pa. Mich. Wis. Minn., and the northern mountains of Cal. Also on the summits of the Presidential Range of the White Mts. Mt. Katahdin Me., etc.

Lonicera Morrowi

A Japanese species commonly cultivated and locally established in eastern Mass. Salem, etc., with grayish stems, long ovate, roughish leaves paler and velvety beneath, a trifle heart-shaped at the base; the flowers white or cream-colored, the fruit scarlet (rarely orange yellow).

Tartarian Bush Honeysuckle
Lonicera tartarica

A native of Asia, in common cultivation and often an escape on rocky banks etc., from Me. to Ont. N. Y. N. J. and Ky. A smooth, branching shrub, bushy, 5–9 feet high, with thin smooth, ovate leaves, heart-shaped at the base, toothless, dull light green, 1–2¾ inches long. The irregularly five-lobed flowers white and rose pink, about ¾ inch long, in groups of two. May–June. Fruit two red berries united at the base or quite separate.

American Fly-Honeysuckle
Lonicera canadensis

A straggling, nearly upright shrub 3–5 feet high, with smooth light brown branchlets.

The leaves ovate, often heart-shaped at the base, nearly or quite smooth, 1–2 inches long. Flowers greenish yellow, Naples yellow

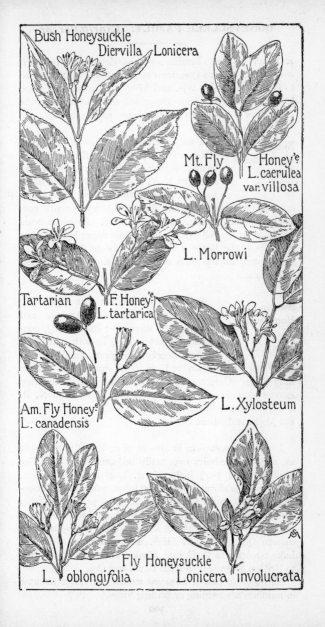

Bush Honeysuckle
Diervilla Lonicera

Mt. Fly Honey'e
L. caerulea var. villosa

L. Morrowi

Tartarian
F. Honey'e
L. tartarica

L. Xylosteum

Am. Fly Honey'e
L. canadensis

Fly Honeysuckle
L. oblongifolia
Lonicera involucrata

or honey yellow. Berries separate, deep red. In moist woods from eastern Que. west to Saskatchewan, and south to Conn. Pa. Mich. Wis. and Minn. It ascends to 2000 feet in the Catskill Mts. Described and illustrated in the *Field Book of American Wild Flowers*, page 450.

European Fly Honeysuckle
Lonicera Xylosteum

A native species of Europe and Asia, often an escape from cultivation and locally established in southern N. E. southern N. Y. and N. J. An erect shrub 3–6 feet high, with elliptical or obovate light green leaves pale and very fine-hairy beneath particularly when young, 1–3 inches long. Flowers cream white, or cream yellow, two-lipped, the upper lip shallowly four-lobed, the lower a single lobe; borne in pairs on a single stem at the base of the leaves. Berries scarlet. May–June.

Swamp Fly Honeysuckle
Lonicera oblongifolia

A similar species 2–5 feet high, with ascending light brown branches, and oblong-ovate leaves 1–2 inches long, conspicuously net-veined, smooth when old. Flowers deeply two-lipped, similar to the last. Berries crimson red, in pairs sometimes united. May–June. Common in swamps or wet woodlands often associated with the Larch and Arbor Vitae, from N. B. and Que. west to Man., and south to Me. Vt. N. Y. western Pa. Mich. and Minn.

Lonicera involucrata is also similar, but the branches are slightly fine-hairy eventually becoming smooth. The similar leaves 1–2¾ inches long, long-ovate or oblong. Flowers funnel-formed with short lobes, pale yellow, sticky-hairy, small, about ½ inch long, in pairs proceeding from 4 conspicuous, broad, leafy bracts. June–July. In moist woods and on the banks of streams from northern N. B. eastern Que. Ont. and Mich. west along the shores of Lake Superior to B. C. and Alaska, and south (according to Britton & Brown) to Ariz. Utah, and Cal.

All other species of *Lonicera* within our range about 8 in number, are twining or trailing vines.

HONEYSUCKLE FAMILY. *Caprifoliaceæ*

An erect shrub 2–5 feet high, with madder purple or brown stems. The ovate leaves dull gray green, toothless, 1–1½ inches long. Flowers very small, with 5 lobes, white suffused with pink. Fruit small, dull red. In cultivation in the East, and indigenous in N. Y. N. J. and Pa., west to the Daks., and south to Ga. and Tex. Described and illustrated in *Field Book of American Wild Flowers*, pages 448–449.

Coral-berry
Indian Currant
Symphoricarpos orbiculatus

A western shrub much stockier than the foregoing, 2–4 feet high, with larger, similar leaves 1–3 inches long, broadly ovate, toothless or sometimes with few slightly undulate or rounded teeth. Flowers in small, nodding, dense terminal or leaf-axil clusters, the corolla bell-shaped, white suffused with pink, ¼ inch long, five-lobed. June–July. Fruit a globular white berry about ⅓ inch in diameter, in small clusters. Generally on rocky woodlands from northern Mich. and Ill. west to Ken. the Rocky Mts. Col. and B. C.

Wolfberry
Symphoricarpos occidentalis

A shrub 1–3 feet high, with light brown, upright stems slenderer than the last. The dull blue green leaves long elliptical or ovate, blunt-tipped, soft-hairy beneath, toothless 1–1½ inches long. Flowers bell-shaped, very small, white suffused with pink, 1–2 at the tips of the branchlets, or in small clusters at the base of the leaves. June–July. Fruit a white berry in compact clusters. On dry limestone ridges and banks from Que. west to Alaska, and south to western Mass. central Pa. Mich. Mont. Ida. and Cal. Formerly confused with the two following varieties:

Wild Snowberry
Symphoricarpos racemosus

A low, western shrub with more or less fine-hairy leaves which are extremely white beneath. Shores of Lake Superior and Lake Winnipeg, and in the mountains from Alberta to Ore. and Cal.

S. racemosus var. *pauciflorus*

Garden Snowberry
S. racemosus
var. *laevigatus*
Fernald

A taller shrub 3–5 feet high, with larger leaves smooth beneath. The flowers in thicker clusters, the larger white berries in compact clusters. Saguenay Co. Que. west to Wash., and south through the Alleghany Mts. to Va. Commonly cultivated and a frequent escape to roadsides.

Wayfaring Tree
Viburnum Lantana

A native shrub of Europe and Asia, in cultivation in this country and occasionally as an escape; 8–12 feet high, with ascending or inclined dark brown stems, and spreading branches.

The dark green, ovate or narrowly ovate leaves sometimes heart-shaped at the base, coarsely or finely regular-toothed, grayish fine-hairy on both sides, much paler beneath, prominently veined, 2–4 inches long. Flowers white, five-lobed, ¼ inch broad, in dome-shaped clusters. June–July. The fruit a coral red, ovate berry in flat clusters. Generally on roadsides in southern N. E. etc.

Wayfaring Tree
Hobble Bush
Witch Hobble
Viburnum alnifolium

A very straggling, irregular shrub of woodlands commonly 5 rarely 9 feet high; the supple branches often drooping to the ground and taking root, forming loops which may trip up a careless wayfarer; hence the common names. Bark a dull madder purple or brown, smooth, the branches spreading horizontally, the young twigs scurfy-hairy.

The large leaves heart-shaped, finely and irregularly toothed, veiny, light green and finely downy above when young, smooth when old, but very rusty-downy beneath especially on the prominent veins, 4–8 inches long, with rusty-hairy stems about 1 inch long; turning maroon red in late summer and the fall. Flowers with 5 rounded white or sometimes pinkish lobes, in large flat clusters. The fruit ovoid, bright scarlet or coral red, berrylike, tipped with the brown dot of the withered calyx, ⅓ inch long, in flat, straggling clusters, finally turning dull dark purple.

The Hobble Bush is common in cool, damp woods, and is distributed from N. B. west through Ont. to Mich., and

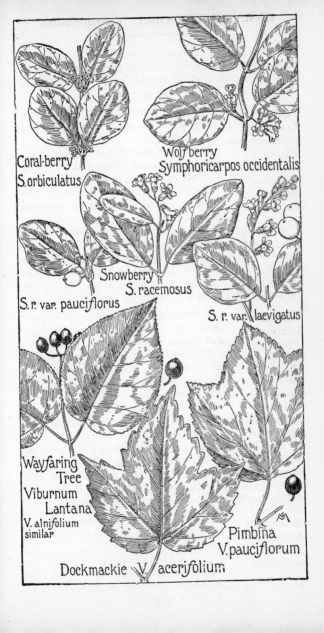

Coral-berry
S. orbiculatus

Wolf-berry
Symphoricarpos occidentalis

Snowberry
S. racemosus

S. r. var. pauciflorus

S. r. var. laevigatus

Wayfaring
Tree
Viburnum
Lantana
V. alnifolium
similar

Pimbina
V. pauciflorum

Dockmackie V. acerifolium

south to Pa. and through the mountains to N. C. It climbs in the White and Green Mts. to an altitude of 3000 feet. Described and illustrated in the *Field Book of American Wild Flowers* pages 446-449.

Pimbina
Cramp-bark
Cranberry Tree
Highbush
Cranberry
Viburnum
Opulus var.
americanum

A smooth-stemmed shrub with ascending gray brown or buff branches 3-14 feet high.

The leaves maplelike, commonly three-lobed, sometimes five-lobed, coarsely toothed, light green, nearly smooth. The white flowers in 3-4 inch broad, flat-domed clusters, the outermost blossoms neutral, with five large rounded lobes.

Fruit broadly ovoid, a beautiful, bright, translucent scarlet red, $\frac{1}{3}$ inch long, very acid, and sometimes used as a substitute for cranberries. In damp woods and along streams from Newf. and eastern Que. west to B. C., and south to N. J. Pa. Wis. Mich. and northeastern Iowa. An extract from the bark is used as a specific for rheumatism.

Squashberry
Pimbina
Viburnum
pauciflorum

A northern, low, irregular and scraggy shrub 2-5 feet high, with smooth, light dull brown, wide-spreading branches.

The light green leaves very variable in form, ovate, narrowly ovate, occasionally heart-shaped at the base, sometimes with but one lateral lobe, commonly with 3 shallow lobes above the middle, smooth or very slightly fine-hairy beneath on the veins, $1\frac{1}{4}$-3 inches broad. Flowers white, all perfect, small, scarcely $\frac{1}{4}$ inch in diameter, the clusters small, about 1 inch broad. June-July. Fruit bright translucent scarlet, similar to that of the foregoing species. In cool mountain woods from Newf. and Lab. west to Alaska, and south to Me. N. H. Vt. and Pa. Also in the Rocky Mts. to Col. and Wash. (according to Britton & Brown).

Dockmackie
Arrow-wood
Viburnum
acerifolium

A shrub 3-5 feet high, with smooth, warm gray or dull brown ascending stem and branches.

The leaves maplelike, shallowly or deeply three-lobed coarsely toothed, light green above, paler beneath, fine-hairy on both sides, more velvety beneath, nearly smooth when old, 2–4 inches broad; upper leaves sometimes not lobed. Flowers white, all perfect, $\frac{1}{4}$ inch broad, with prominent stamens, clusters broadly flat-domed, not very large. Fruit slaty, dark violet blue, broadly ovoid, about the size of a pea, with a nipplelike tip. On dry ground or in rocky mountain woodlands from N. B. west to Minn. Ont., and south to Ky. Ga. and Ala.

A low, straggling shrub 2–5 feet high, with slender, warm gray or light dull brown stem and branches, the latter numerous, the twigs tan-colored.

Downy Arrow-wood
Viburnum pubescens

The small, light yellow green leaves smooth above, densely velvety downy and pale sage green beneath, broadly or narrowly ovate, pointed, very coarsely toothed (not more than 9 teeth on a side), $1\frac{1}{2}$–$2\frac{1}{2}$ inches long. Flowers white, all perfect, in rather small loose clusters, $1\frac{1}{2}$–$2\frac{1}{2}$ inches broad. May–June. Fruit purple black about $\frac{1}{3}$ inch long. On rocky river banks and in woods from western Que. and western Vt., west to Ont. and Man., and south mostly through the Alleghany Mts. to Ga. and to Ill. Iowa and Wyo.

A much taller shrub 8–12 feet high, with slender stems and warm ashen gray, or dark slate gray, thin, scaly, separating bark often with raised dots.

Soft-leaved Arrow-wood
Viburnum molle[1]

The leaves conventionally coarse-toothed, commonly round-ovate, heart-shaped at the base, rather abruptly pointed, similar to *V. dentatum* but the teeth not so sharp, deep green above, paler and soft hairy especially on the veins beneath, 2–4 inches broad. Flowers in terminal, medium-sized clusters, white, with 4–7 lobes. Fruit less juicy than that of the preceding species, ellipsoidal, the pit deeply grooved. Rocky woods etc., Ky. (and probably O. according to Gray's *Manual*, 7th ed.), Ind. (Putnam Co.), Ia. and Mo. (Benton, Swan, and Taney Cos.)

[1] The *Viburnum Demetrionis* of Deane and Robinson. *Vide* Gray's *Manual*.

Viburnum	A similar shrub 6–10 feet high, with
venosum	dark gray brown bark *not* peeling off as
	in *V. molle*, the ocher-colored branchlets

covered with a gray fine-hairiness.

The leaves like those of the foregoing species in color, etc., elliptical or ovate, sometimes round-ovate, the many veins prominent. Flowers similar, the clusters $1\frac{3}{4}$–$2\frac{1}{4}$ inches broad. June–July. Fruit $\frac{1}{3}$ inch long, nearly spherical. Dry soil, Martha's Vineyard and Nantucket, Mass. to Pa. and Del. The var. *Canbyi*, Rehder, has leaves which are a trifle larger and whitish smooth beneath; the flowers in broader (about 3 inch) clusters. Pa. and Del. to the mountains of Va.

| *Viburnum* | Also similar, the stem dark brown, the |
| *scabrellum* | branches ruddy brown. |

The leaves very variable, ovate, rarely elliptical or obovate, infrequently round-ovate, coarsely and not so sharply toothed, sometimes round-toothed, with fewer teeth and veins, 2–4 inches long. Flowers a trifle larger; fruit slate blue, in similar clusters. May–June. In woods and on the banks of streams of the coastal plain from Pa. south to Ky. Fla. and Tex.

Arrow-wood	A familiar, slender shrub 3–8 or some-
Viburnum	times 15 feet high, with blackish sepia
dentatum	brown or ashen brown bark, the smooth
	new twigs or shoots often straight and

arrowlike.

The deep green leaves broadly ovate or round-ovate, coarsely and regularly sharp-toothed, the many veins beneath prominent and straight, with tiny tufts of hairs at the axils, 2–3 inches long. Fruit slate blue becoming nearly black, ovoid-spherical, about $\frac{1}{4}$ inch long.

Common in moist situations and in thickets from N. E. west to western N. Y. and southern Ont. Mich. and Minn., and south, especially through the mountains, to northern Ga.

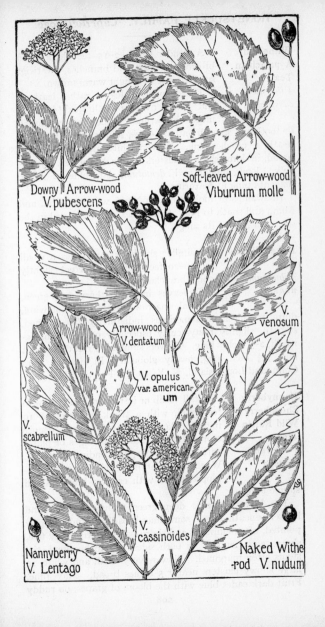

Downy Arrow-wood
V. pubescens

Soft-leaved Arrow-wood
Viburnum molle

V. venosum

Arrow-wood
V. dentatum

V. opulus
var. american-
um

V.
scabrellum

V.
cassinoides

Nannyberry
V. Lentago

Naked Withe
-rod V. nudum

HONEYSUCKLE FAMILY. *Caprifoliaceae*

Withe-rod
Appalachian
Tea
Viburnum
cassinoides

A slender shrub 2–15 feet high, with brown gray stem and branches, the twigs somewhat scurfy, light warm brown.

The deep green leaves rather leathery and thick, ovate or elliptical, pointed, rather obtuse, finely or indistinctly toothed or toothless, smooth on both sides, scurfy on the veins beneath, 1–3 inches long. Flowers white, all perfect, $\frac{1}{5}$ inch broad, in dome-shaped clusters 2–4 inches across. June–July. Fruit similar to *V. dentatum*, slate blue or rarely magenta pink at maturity.

In swamps or moist thickets Newf. west to Minn. and Man., and south to Fla. Sometimes quite arboreal in the southern part of its range.

Naked Withe-rod
Viburnum
nudum

A similar shrub or sometimes a small tree 10–20 feet high, with erect slightly scurfy branches.

The leaves similar, leathery, deep green, elliptical, narrow-elliptical, or obovate, quite toothless or sometimes indistinctly fine-toothed, smooth, slightly rusty-scurfy especially on the veins beneath, 2–5 inches long. Flowers similar. Fruit dark cadet blue $\frac{1}{4}$–$\frac{1}{3}$ inch long, nearly globular. In swamps from Conn. and Long Island, N. Y. to Ky. Fla. and Tex.

Nannyberry
Sheepberry
Wild Raisin
Tree
Viburnum
Lentago

A tall shrub or infrequently a tree 9–30 feet high, with a trunk diameter of 10 inches. Bark sepia brown, scaly, deeply scored, broken into small ridges or plates with a scarcely perpendicular trend. When in isolation developing a round-topped figure with crooked branches and supple twigs.

The leaves lustrous deep green above, yellower and lighter beneath, ovate, sometimes broadly so and abruptly pointed, often elliptical and sharp-pointed, with very fine, sharp teeth, smooth on both sides, 2–4 inches long, the stems often margined. Flowers very small and white, in large showy clusters nearly 5 inches broad. May–June. Fruit dark cadet blue with the bloom of grapes, on ruddy stems, ovoid with a nipplelike tip, $\frac{1}{3}$–$\frac{2}{3}$ inch in diameter, edible and sweet, ripe in September.

Common in woods and on the banks of streams from James Bay and Riviere du Loup, Que. west to Man., and south to N. J., along the Alleghany Mts. to Ga., and to southern Ind. southern Mo. and eastern Neb. The wood is yellow brown, hard, close-grained, and heavy, the weight nearly 46 lbs. to the cubic foot; it possesses a disagreeable, rancid odor, more unpleasant than that of the fresh Cypress.

An erect bushy shrub or sometimes a tree 10–28 feet high, with a trunk diameter of 10 inches. Bark gray brown, rough with short, narrow, rounded ridges broken laterally into small sections; it is sometimes used as a tonic and for other medicinal properties which it possesses.

Black Haw
Stag-bush
Viburnum
prunifolium

The deep green leaves are broadly elliptical or obovate, finely and sharply toothed, the under surface smooth, 1–2$\frac{3}{4}$ inches long, the stems only slightly if at all margined. Flowers similar to the last, with 3–5 lobes, in clusters 2–4 inches broad. May–June. Fruit ovoid or ellipsoidal, dark cadet blue, on red stems, edible but insipidly sweet.

On dry ground from Conn. (Fairfield Co.) and N. Y. (lower Hudson River), west to Mich. Kan. and Okla., and south to northern Ga.

The var. globosum is a form with smaller globular fruit.

A similar species often 20 feet high, with the under surface of the larger leaves rusty fine-hairy, 2–3$\frac{1}{2}$ inches long; the leaf stems distinctly wing-margined. The similar flowers blooming in April–May.

Southern Black
Haw
Viburnum
rufidulum

In woods and thickets from Va. south to Fla., and west to Ill. Kan. and Tex.

A southern shrub 2–8 feet high, with upright stems and strong-scented foliage.

Small Viburnum
Viburnum
obovatum

The very small leaves obovate or narrowly so, wedge-shaped at the base, obtuse or rounded and obscurely dull-toothed toward the tip, but mostly toothless, $\frac{1}{2}$–$1\frac{1}{2}$ inches long. Flower clusters 1–2 inches broad. April–May. Fruit ovoid with a prominent nipple, purplish black, $\frac{1}{3}$ inch long. In swamps and beside streams from Va. south to Fla. near the coast.

Elder
Sambucus canadensis
A tall shrub with scarcely woody, smooth, pithy, dark maroon or green stems 3–13 or commonly 7 feet high, the branches swollen at the joints, rank-odored when bruised, the bark warty.

Leaves compound with 5–11, usually 7 ovate, acute-pointed, finely-toothed, dark green leaflets, paler and smooth or mostly so beneath, also rank-odored when crushed. Flowers cream white in broad, rather flat clusters, numerous, small, with 5 prominent stamens. Blooming in June–July. Fruit black purple berries in broad, heavy clusters, bitter to taste, used medicinally. and in the making of elder-berry wine.

The Elder is common on rich, moist lowlands, mostly in thickets, and is distributed from N. S. to Fla., and westward to Man. eastern Kan. Ariz. and Tex. It ascends to an altitude of 3500 feet in the Alleghany Mts.

Red-berried Elder
Sambucus racemosa
A similar shrub 2–11 feet high, with gray stems, and persistently fine-hairy twigs and leaves. The scarlet red (rarely white) berries in a pyramidal, compact cluster about 3 inches high. Distributed from Newf. and N. B. west to B. C. Mich. Io. Col. and Cal., and south to Ga. *S. racemosa* var. *laciniata* is a western form with the leaflets divided into linear, lance-shaped sections, found on the shores of Lake Superior and also in Pa. Described and illustrated in the *Field Book of American Wild Flowers*, page 446.

COMPOSITE FAMILY. *Compositae.*

A mostly herbaceous family, the following shrubs with alternating leaves, and staminate and pistillate flowers on different plants.

Black Haw
Viburnum
prunifolium

Small
Viburnum
V. obovatum

V. rufidulum

S.
racemosa
var. laciniata

S. racemosa

Elder
Sambucus canadensis

COMPOSITE FAMILY. *Compositae*

Groundsel Tree
Baccharis halimifolia

A compact shrub 3–12 feet high, with light gray brown stems, the lower bark with shallow, perpendicular seams, otherwise smooth, the branchlets angular in section, a trifle scurfy.

The dark sage green leaves obovate, wedge-shaped at the base, coarsely and few-toothed, the upper leaves mostly toothless, 1–3 inches long. Flowers white or yellowish, tubular, in a compound head, the staminate slender and five-lobed, the pistillate extremely slender, with bright white hairlike bristles extending far beyond the leafy bracts of the involucre. September. Fruit a single, small, ribbed achene in clusters.

Common in salt marshes and along sea beaches from Mass. to Fla. and Tex. The pistillate plant is a conspicuous object in Autumn by reason of its profuse white-haired flowers.

Baccharis glomeruliflora

A similar species, with brighter green leaves, and larger flower-heads devoid (or nearly so) of stems, set close at the base of the leaves. Southern Va. (?) and N. C. south to Fla. Also in the Bermudas.

Baccharis salicina

A similar western, much-branched shrub with sage green foliage, similar to that of the foregoing species. Bark gray brown. Flowers small. May–July. Western Kan. and eastern Col. to Tex.

Marsh Elder
Iva frutescens

A partly herbaceous and shrubby plant woody at the base, 3–11 feet high, with a light brown, slightly fine-hairy stem.

The leaves narrowly elliptical or slightly ovate, pointed, coarsely toothed, the upper ones lance-shaped and sparingly toothed or nearly toothless, deep green, smooth or often fine-hairy, 3–4 inches long. Flowers whitish green in leafy, terminal, broad spirelike clusters, small, in drooping heads. Fruit a small achene in clusters.

On sea beaches and along salt marshes from N. C.

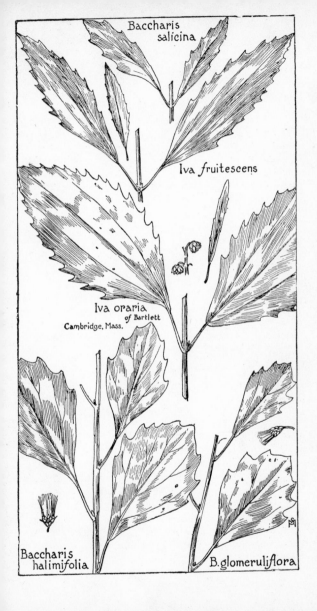

Baccharis
salicina

Iva fruitescens

Iva oraria
of Bartlett
Cambridge, Mass.

Baccharis
halimifolia

B. glomeruliflora

south to Fla. and Tex. (Galveston). Possibly also on Maxwell's Point, Gunpowder River, Md.

A similar but absolutely distinct species $1\frac{2}{3}$–$3\frac{1}{3}$ feet high, with many branches growing from a single woody stem.

Northern Marsh Elder
Iva oraria
Bartlett

The leaves much broader, mostly ovate, sharply toothed, growing oppositely, rough-hairy on both sides; the uppermost leaves entirely toothless. The flower-heads and the achenes quite $\frac{1}{3}$ larger, the latter about $\frac{1}{6}$ inch long. Formerly confused with the foregoing species. Salt marshes from N. H. to N. J. (Pa. ?) Md. and Del.

THE DISTRIBUTION OF TREES AND TREELIKE SHRUBS THROUGH THE UNITED STATES

These maps give a *generally* correct idea of the areas occupied by American trees. Absolute accuracy in the plotting of these areas is an impossibility as the distribution of species in minute detail is not fully known at the present time, but the plotting implicitly follows the published data of botanical experts with only such minor changes and extensions as were required to bring it up to date.

It becomes evident by a diligent examination of the maps that many species occupy almost identical areas, that some overlap each other more or less, and that others slightly project beyond or fall short of the boundaries of species very similarly distributed. It seemed wisest, therefore, in many cases to show these differences on the same map where it was possible to do so without confusion.

It will be readily understood that the distribution of a given species is entirely dependent upon certain conditions of climate, temperature, and soil, consequently maps of geology, altitude, temperature, and soils are furnished for purposes of comparative study.

These maps again are based upon those issued by expert authorities in the United States Signal Service, the Department of Agriculture (Dr. George Nelson Coffee, Bulletin No. 85), and the Geological Survey (Bailey Willis and George W. Stose. Professional Paper No 71), and still others are drawn from sketches and data collected by the author.

1. 1. *Monterey Pine*, pg. 20.
   2. *Western Wh. Pine*, pg. 16.
   3. *White Pine*, pg. 2, also *Hemlock*, pg. 40, west to Minn only, southward including Del.
   4. *Bald Cypress*, pg. 44.

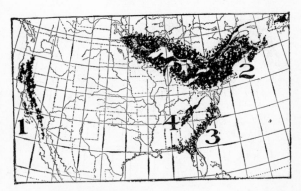

2. 1. *Sugar Pine*, pg. 17.
   2. *Red Pine*, pg. 13, also *Arbor Vitae*, pg. 50, not incl. Newf. but through the mts., incl. No. 4 to N. C. and Tenn.
   3. *Pond Pine*, pg. 6.
   4. *Carolina Hemlock*, pg. 41.

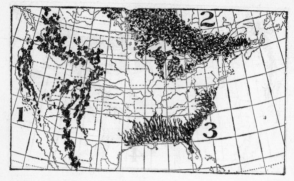

3. 1. *W. Yellow Pine,* pg. 18.
   2. *N. Scrub Pine,* pg. 9.
   3. *Loblolly Pine,* pg. 4.

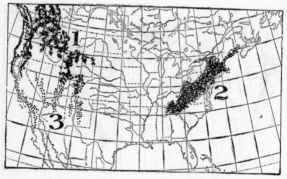

4. 1. *Lodgepole Pine,* pg. 18, including all of No. 3.
   2. *Pitch Pine,* pg. 5.
   3. *White Fir,* pg. 36, lapping slightly with No. **1.**

5. 1. *Digger Pine*, pg. 20.
2. *Table Mt. Pine*, pg. 6.
3. *Georgia Pine*, pg. 14.
4. *Utah Juniper*. pg. 56.

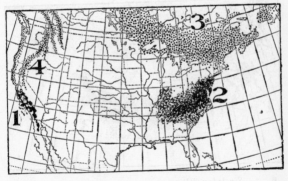

6. 1. *Coulter's Pine*, pg. 20.
2. *Jersey Pine*, pg. 8.
3. *Dwarf Juniper*, pg. 52.
4. *Pacific Yew*, pg. 57, south to Monterey.

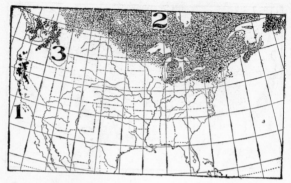

7. 1. *Knobcone Pine*, pg. 21.
2. *Black Larch*, pg. 21.
3. *Western Larch*, pg. 24.

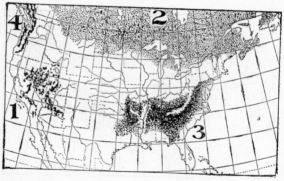

8. 1. *Single-leaved Pine*, pg. 17.
2. *White Spruce*, pg. 24.
3. *Yellow Pine*, pg. 10.
4. *Silver Fir*, pg. 37.

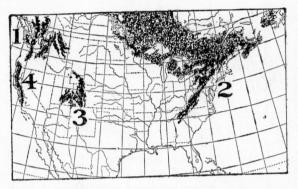

9. 1. *Alpine Larch*, pg. 24.
   2. *Red Spruce*, pg. 25.
   3. *Blue Spruce* pg. 30.
   4. *Redwood*, pg. 46.

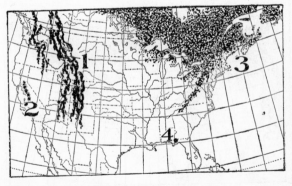

10. 1. *Engelmann Spruce*, pg. 29.
    2. *Cal. Big Tree*, pg. 45.
    3. *Black Spruce*, pg. 28, also *American Yew*, pg. 57, incl. Ia.
       but not N. C.
    4. *Florida Yew*, pg. 58.

11. 1. *Red Fir*, pg. 38.
      2. *Alpine Fir*, pg. 34.
      3. *Fraser Fir*, pg. 34.
      4. *Coast Wh. Cedar*, pg. 48.

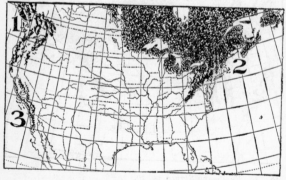

12. 1. *Grand Fir*, pg. 36.
      2. *Balsam Fir*, pg. 32.
      3. *California Juniper*, pg. 56.

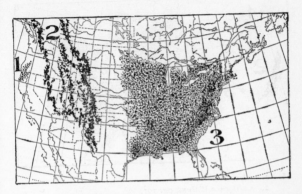

13. 1. *Weeping Spruce*, pg. 29.
2. *Rocky Mt. Red Cedar*, pg. 54, also *Douglas Spruce*, pg. 38.
3. *Red Cedar*, pg. 53.

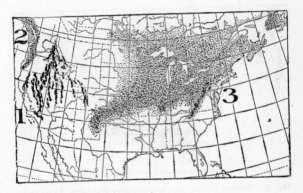

14. 1. *Western Juniper*, pg. 56.
2. *Yellow Cypress*, pg. 49.
3. *Common Juniper*, pg. 52.

15. 1. *Black Willow*, pg. 61.
2. *California Walnut*, pg. 101.
3. *Knowlton's Hornbeam*, pg. 112.
4. *Western Birch*, pg. 122.

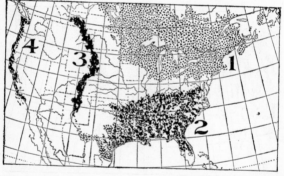

16. 1. *Shining Willow*, pg. 62, also *Pussy Willow* pg. 72 south to Del. and Ill. to limit of No. 2, not incl. Newf. eastward.
2. *Ward's Willow*, pg. 61.
3. *Lance-leaved Cottonwood*, pg. 90.
4. *Cal. Wax Myrtle*, pg. 96.

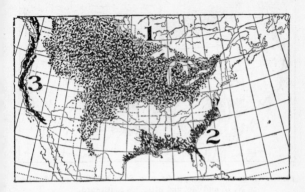

17.   1. *Peach-leaved Willow*, pg. 62.
      2. *Wax Myrtle*, pg. 93.
      3. *Red Alder*, pg. 128.

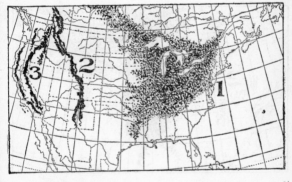

18.   1. *Sand Bar Willow*, pg. 68.
      2. *Mountain Alder*, pg. 129, incl. all but Cal. coast range of
          No. 3.
      3. *White Alder*, pg. 128, from Ida. southwest through Cal.

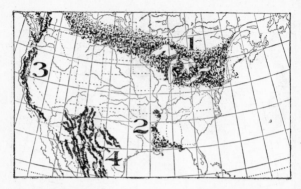

19. 1. *Autumn Willow*, pg. 64, also *Smooth Willow*, pg. 68, east
   to N. B. and Me. and little less southward.
2. *Corkwood*, pg. 97.
3. *Black Cottonwood*, pg. 92.
4. *Mexican Walnut*, pg. 101.

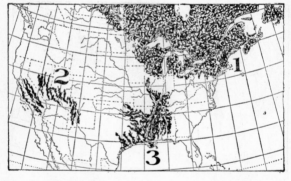

20. 1. *Balsam Willow*, pg. 70, not south of lat. 44°, also *Long-
   beaked Willow*, pg. 76.
2. *Fremont Cottonwood*, pg. 92.
3. *Pecan*, pg. 101.

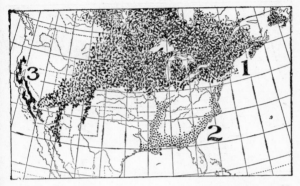

1. *Am. Poplar*, pg. 84.
2. *Swamp Cottonwood*, pg. 86, also *Water Hickory*, pg. 105, northeast only to Va., south half-way into Fla. and eastern Tex.
3. *Cal. Laurel*, pg. 186.

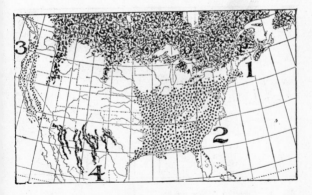

1. *Balsam Poplar*, pg. 88.
2. *Mockernut*, pg. 104.
3. *Western Chinquapin*, pg. 134.
4. *Morus celtidifolia*, pg. 170.

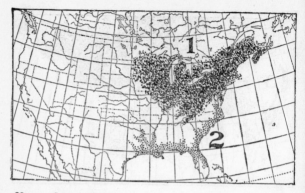

23. 1. *Large-toothed Aspen*, pg. 86, also *Butternut*, pg. 97, southwest to northeastern Ark., west to Dak.
    2. *Red Bay*, pg. 184.

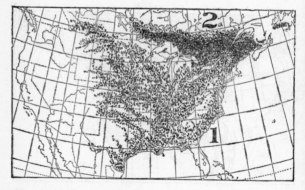

24. 1. *Carolina Poplar*, pg. 89.
    2. *Downy Green Alder*, pg. 125, lapping in N. Y. with No. 1. Extreme northern boundary unknown.

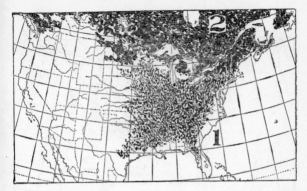

25. 1. *Black Walnut*, pg. 98, also *Bitternut*, pg. 108, northward to s. Me. w. Que. and Lake Huron.
    2. *Canoe Birch*, pg. 121, lapping with No. 1 in Long Island and Pa.

26. 1. *Shellbark Hickory*, pg. 102, also *Pignut Hickory*, pg. 106, s. Me. to s. Ont. only in northeast, south to e. central Fla., also *Small-fruited Hickory*, pg. 105, the upper half only, limitations from Md. to Mo. in the south, and from Mich. to Mo. in northwest.
    2. *Cedar Elm*, pg. 164, lapping with No. 1 through Ark. to Miss.

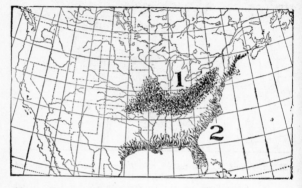

27. 1. *Big Shellbark*, pg. 104.
    2. *Smooth Alder*, pg. 126.

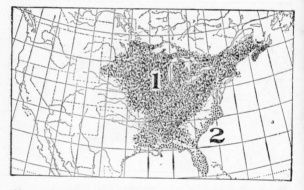

28. 1. *Am. Hop Hornbeam*, pg. 110, also *Am. Hornbeam*, pg. 112,
       south half-way into Fla.
    2. *Swamp Bay*, pg. 184.

29. 1. *Black or Sweet Birch*, pg. 113.
    2. *Water Oak*, pg. 154, also *Willow Oak*, pg. 158, northeast
    to Long Island and west only to extreme e. Tex.

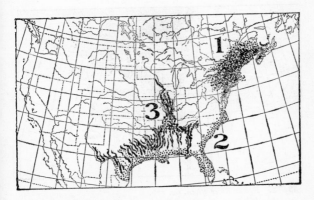

30. 1. *Gray-Birch*, pg. 117.
    2. *Live Oak*, pg. 145.
    3. *Texan Red Oak*, pg. 150, lapping westward with No. 2.

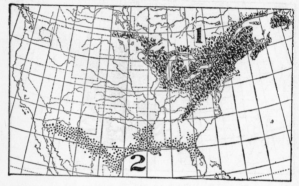

31. 1. *Yellow Birch*, pg. 114.
 2. *Soapberry*, 314.

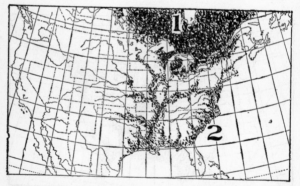

32. 1. *Red or River Birch*, pg. 116.
 2. *White Birch*, pg. 118, also *Betula alba*, pg. 120, more widely distributed east and west, Newf. to B. C.

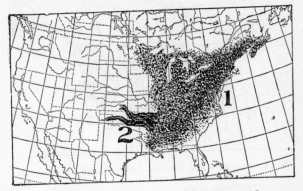

33. 1. *Am. Beech*, pg. 129. doubtfully south to Fla. and La.
2. *Osage Orange*, pg. 168, naturalized in some of the Atlantic
States.

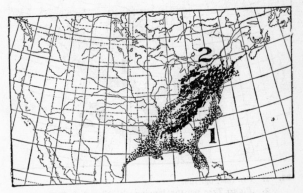

34. 1. *Carolina Beech*, pg. 130, distribution imperfectly known.
2. *Chestnut*, pg. 132.

35. 1. *Scarlet Oak*, pg. 149, also *Laurel Oak*, pg. 157, east only to Pa., northwest s. Mich. to Neb., southwest to n. Ark. and south to Ala.

2. *Spanish Oak*, lapping slightly with No. 1 in s. Ill. and Ind. pg. 153.

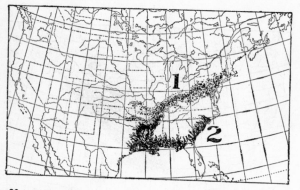

36. 1. *Pin Oak*, pg. 148.

2. *Planer Tree*, pg. 165, lapping with No. 1 in s. Ill. and cen. Ky.

37. 1. *Speckled Alder*, pg. 125.
    2. *Post Oak*, pg. 136, lapping with No. 1 in e. Mass. and Long Island, also *Overcup Oak*, pg. 138, also *Basket Oak*, pg. 141, westward only to s. w. Ind. and s. e. Mo.

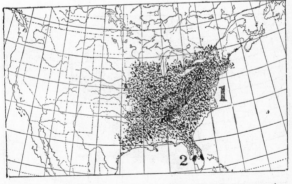

28. 1. *White Oak*, pg. 134, also *Swamp Wh. Oak*, pg. 140, the upper half only, south from Md. to n. Ga. not including La. Tex. Minn. and Wis., also *Red Oak*, pg. 146, north to N. S. and north shores of Lake Huron, south mostly through the mts. to Fla. and to Tex.
    2. *Pond Apple*, pg. 181, restricted areas on east and west coasts of Fla.

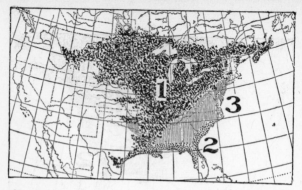

39. 1. *Bur Oak*, pg. 138.
    2. *Great-flowered Magnolia*, pg. 172, lapping with No. 1 in La. Ark. and Tex.
    3. *Liquidambar*, pg. 193, lapping with No. 1 from Conn. to e. Okla. and including all of No. 2.

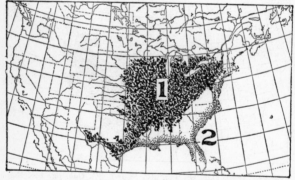

40. 1. *Chinquapin Oak*, pg. 142, also *Cork Elm*, pg. 162, northeast to e. Que. and n. w. N. H., northwest to s. Wis., south to cen. Tenn. and s. e. Mo., also *Red Mulberry*, pg. 169, w. Mass. to the Daks., and south including white area and No. 2.
    2. *Small Magnolia*, pg. 173.

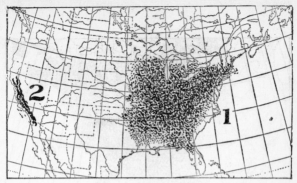

41. 1. *Black Oak*, pg. 152, also *Black Jack Oak*, pg. 156, north
only from Long Island to s. Minn., south to cen. Fla. and
s. Tex., also *Slippery Elm*, pg. 160, north to Quebec City
and N. Dak., south to w. Fla. and s. Tex., also *Papaw*,
pg. 18, east only to w. N. Y., and e. Pa., northwest to e.
Ia., also *Sassafras*, pg. 185, northwest to e. Ia., southwest
to mid. Tex., east on coastal plain, also *Sycamore*, pg. 194,
southwest to mid. Tex.
   2. *California Sycamore*, pg. 196.

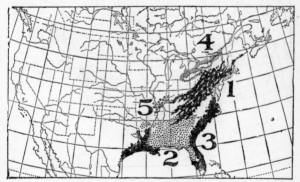

42. 1 *Chestnut Oak*, pg. 144, also *Cucumber Tree*, pg. 173, east
only to N. Y., west from s. Ont. to southwestern Ark. and
s. Ala., also *Umbrella Tree*, pg. 176, north only to s. Pa.,
east to coast of N. C., west to s. Ark.
   2. *Great-leaved Magnolia*, pg. 174, lapping with No. 1 in Ky.
and N. C.
   3. *Red Bay*, pg. 184, along the Gulf across No. 2, also *Swamp
Bay*, pg. 184, from Va. to Miss. only.
   4. *Crataegus suborbiculata*, pg. 218.
   5. *Crataegus fecunda*, pg. 214.

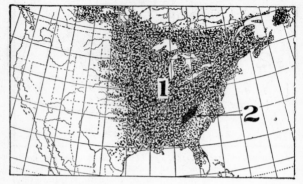

43. 1. *Am. Elm*, pg. 161.
     2. *Crataegus aprica*, pg. 224.

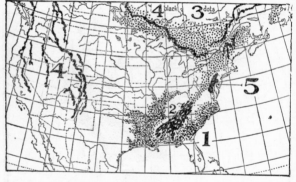

44. 1. *Wahoo Elm*, pg. 162.
     2. *Ear-leaved Umbrella Tree*, pg. 176 (in black white-dotted)
     3. *Am. Mountain Ash*, pg. 201 (in dots).
     4. *Elder-leaved Mt. Ash*, pg. 202, on mt. ranges at **high alti-**
        tudes including northern limits of No. 3.
     5. *Crataegus Canbyi*, pg. 214.

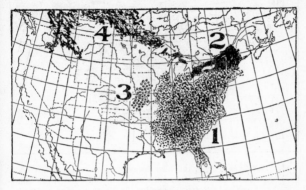

45. 1. *Tulip Tree*, pg. 177, also *Narrow-leaved C. Apple*, pg. 198.
north only from N. J. to Ill., west to Kan. and La., also
Shadbush, pg. 206, east to Me., west to Ia. and Kan., south
through Ga. to La.
2. *Crataegus submollis*, pg. 246.
3. *Crataegus pertomentosa*, pg. 248.
4. *Crataegus Douglasii*, pg. 252 (distribution imperfectly
known).

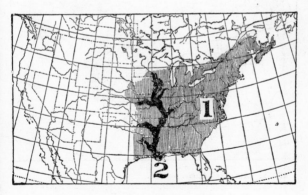

46 1. *Witch Hazel*, pg. 190.
2. *Western C. Apple*, pg. 198 (in black).

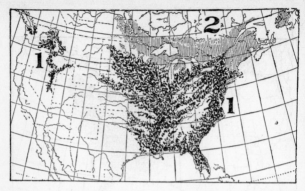

47. 1. *Hackberry*, pg. 166, also *Prunus americana*, pg. 265, north from Conn. to Col. only, also *Wild Bl. Cherry*, pg. 254, east to N. S. south including the Alleghany Mts. half-way into Fla.

2. *Canada Plum*, pg. 264, lapping in e. Mass., n. N. Y., and Mich. with No. 1.

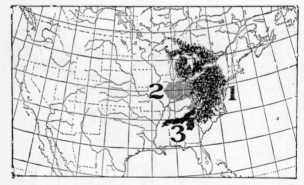

48. 1. *Am. Crab Apple*, pg. 198.

2. *Crataegus cuneiformis*, pg. 216, lapping with No. 1 in w. N. Y. and Pa., and south to W. Va.

3. *Crataegus collina*, pg. 218, lapping with No. 2 in south-western Va.

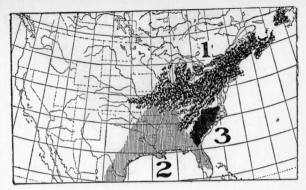

49. 1. *Amelanchier laevis*, pg. 208, also *Crataegus Crus-galli*, pg. 212, east only to n. N. Y. and Mass., also *Crataegus punctata*, pg. 216, east only to w. N. E. and Montmorency F. Que., and west to Ia., also *Crataegus succulenta*, pg. 250 east to N. S., only, west to Minn., south to Va., not including the middle west.

   2. *Mississippi Hackberry*, pg. 168, lapping with No. 1 in s. Ind. and Ill.

   3. *Crataegus flava*, pg. 226, lapping with No. 2 in Fla.

50. 1. *Crataegus Margaretta*, pg. 218.

   2. *C. viridis*, pg. 220, not including tract No. 4, also *C. spathulata*, pg. 232, also *C. Marshalii*, pg. 234, north to s. Va. only.

   3. *C. nitida*, pg. 220, lapping with No. 1 in s. Ill.

   4. *C. pallens*, pg. 222.

   5. *C. pedicellata*, pg. 222, lapping with No. 4 and with No. 1 in w. Pa. only.

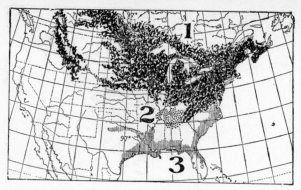

51. 1. *Crataegus chrysocarpa*, pg. 232, also *Staghorn Sumach*, pg. 282 west only to long. 97°.

2. *Yellow Wood*, pg. 270.

3. *Cassena or Yaupon*, pg. 290, also *Dahoon Holly*, pg. 290, south to Biscayne Bay, Fla. west to La.

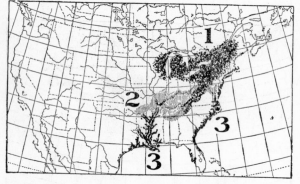

52. 1. *Crataegus roanensis*, pg. 236, also *C. villipes*, pg. 242, eastern half only from N. Y. and Pa. east to R. I., also *C. neofluvialis*, pg. 252, east to w. Vt. and west to Ia.

2. *Crataegus phaenopyrum*, pg. 248, lapping through the Alleghany Mts. with No. 1 and naturalized southward, also *Ohio Buckeye*, pg. 316, west to s. Ia. and east to cen. Pa.

3. *Am. Holly*, pg. 289, also *Swamp Holly*, pg. 292, farther westward and more inland.

430

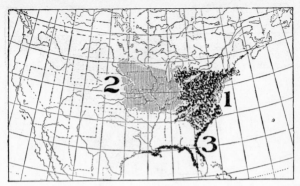

53.   1. *Crataegus Boyntoni*, pg. 220.
   2. *Crataegus mollis*, pg. 248, lapping with No. 1 from s. Ont. to Ky.
   3. *Loblolly Bay*, pg. 327.

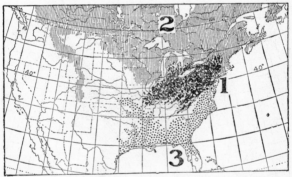

54.   1. *Crataegus pruinosa*, pg. 238, also *C. filipes*, pg. 240, southwest only to Pa. and Mich., also *C. coccinioides*, pg. 244, north to Montreal, east to R. I., and west to Kan., also *C. Pringlei* pg. 244, east to s. N. H., south only to lat. 40°, also *C. Brainerdi*, pg. 250, including all N. E., west to Ia., south only to lat. 40°, also *C. calpodendron*, pg. 252, east only to N. E. line, west to Minn., also *C. Jesupi*, pg. 242, west to Wis., south only to lat. 40°.
   2. *Wild Red Cherry*, pg. 257, lapping south through Alleghany Mts. with No. 1.
   3. *Chickasaw Plum*, pg. 260, also *Car. Buckthorn*, pg. 320, lapping with No. 1 from Long Island to Neb. to lat. 42°, also *Downy Basswood*, pg. 324, west to n. cen. Tex. but not north of La., also *Viburnum rufidulum*, pg. 399, northeast only to Va. and west including Ill. etc.

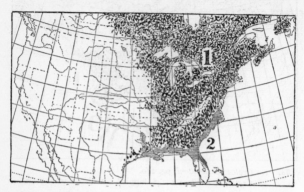

55. 1. *Choke Cherry*, pg. 256.

     2. *Water Ash*, pg. 378, lapping with No. 1 in w. Ala. and La.

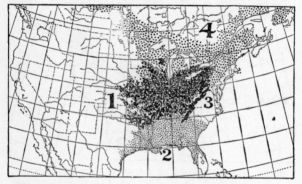

56. 1. *Ken. Coffee Tree*, pg. 266, also *Honey Locust*, pg. 268, not into N. Y. south lapping with No. 2 to the Gulf, also *Burning Bush*, pg. 296, west to Mont. along the Missouri Riv. and south to n. Fla.

    2. *Water Locust*, pg. 269, lapping with No. 1 north to s. Ind. Ill. and Mo.

    3. *Locust*, pg. 274, lapping with No. 1 in W. Va., also *Clammy Locust*, pg. 276, from s. Va. to Ga., only in the higher Alleghany Mts., also *Ilex monticola*, pg. 292, north to Catskill Mts. etc., and south to Ala.

    4. *Mountain Maple*, pg. 300, including all of No. 3 lapping in e. Ia. with No. 1.

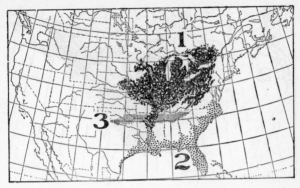

57. 1. *Toothache Tree*, pg. 277, also *Am. Bladder Nut*, pg. 298,
  east to N. E. and Que. south to S. C. and Mo.
   2. *So. Prickly Ash*, pg. 278, also *Leatherwood*, pg. 288.
   3. *Am. Smoke Tree*, pg. 288.

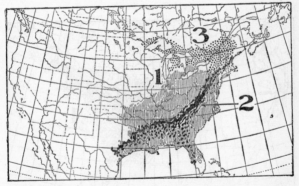

53. 1. *Redbud*, pg. 269, also *Hop Tree*, pg. 278, east to Long
  Island, west to Minn. and south to Mex.
   2. *Mountain Sumach*, pg. 284, in the mountains and rocky
  situations.
   3. *Striped Maple*, pg. 298, lapping with No. 2 southward to
  Ga.

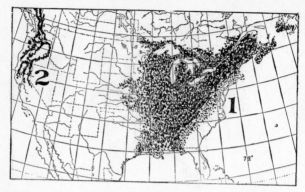

59. 1. *Sugar Maple*, pg. 302, also *Bl. Sugar Maple*, pg. 304, scarce
ly east of long. 72° south to n. Ala. Miss. and Ark., also *Red
Maple*, pg. 308, east only to N. S. west to Daks. and south
to mid. Fla., also *White Ash*, pg. 372, including coastal
plain to n. Fla.
2. *Vine Maple*, pg. 314.

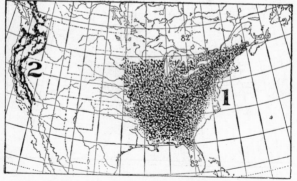

60. 1. *White Maple*, pg. 306, also *Flowering Dogwood*, pg. 332,
northwest to Minn., south to e. Tex., also *Rough-leaved
Cornel*, pg. 334, western half only, scarcely east of long.
82°.
2. *California Maple*, pg. 312.

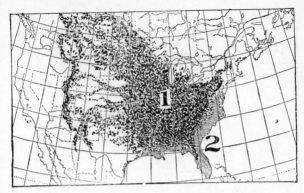

61. 1. *Ash-leaved Maple*, pg. 310, also *Green Ash*, pg. 376, east only to L. Champlain.
2. *Sweet Leaf*, pg. 370, slightly lapping with No. 1, also *Viburnum nudum*, pg. 398, east to Conn., thence southwest including Ky., lapping with No. 1.

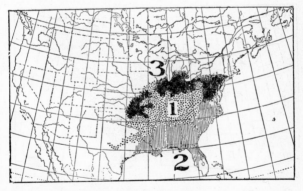

62. 1. *Sweet Buckeye*, pg. 316.
2. *Red Buckeye*, pg. 318, lapping north with No. 1 in W. Va. Ky. Tenn. s. Mo. and Ark. (distribution imperfectly known), also *Bumelia lycioides*, pg. 367, north to s. Ill.
3. *Viburnum prunifolium*, pg. 399, lapping with No. 1 except in La. Tex. and s. Ark.

435

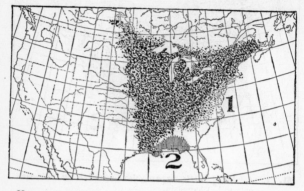

63. 1. *Am. Linden*, pg. 322, also *Red Ash*, pg. 375, south to n.
Fla., not including Miss. La. and Ark.
2. *Common Catalpa*, pg. 386.

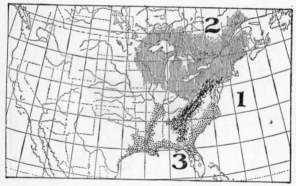

64. 1. *White Basswood*, pg. 324.
2. *Alternate-leaved Dogwood*, pg. 336, including No. 1 to Ga.
and Ala. only.
3. *Large Tupelo*, pg. 338, also Tree Huckleberry, pg. 359.
lapping with No. 1 in cen. Fla.

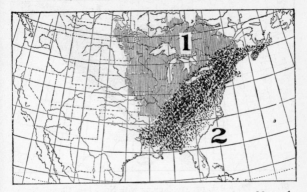

65. 1. *Nannyberry*, pg. 398, lapping with No. 2 from Me. and N. J. to Mo. and through the mts. to Ga.

2. *Mountain Laurel*, pg. 347, also *Rhododendron maximum*, pg. 343, south only to Ga. west only to O.

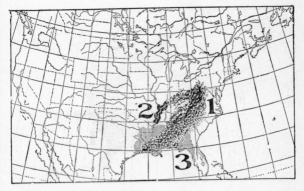

66. 1. *Sorrel Tree*, pg. 355.

2. *Hardy Catalpa*, pg. 386, lapping with No. 1 in s. Ind.

3. *Silver-bell Tree*, pg. 371, including No. 1 in the south and through the mts. north to Pa.

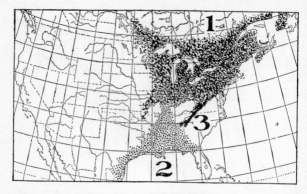

67. 1. *Black Ash*, pg. 379, lapping with No. 2 in s. Ill. and No. 3 in Va.

2. *Woolly Bumelia*, pg. 368, also *Swamp Privet*, pg. 380, including s. w. Ind. but not Fla.

3. *Rhododendron catawbiense*, pg. 344.

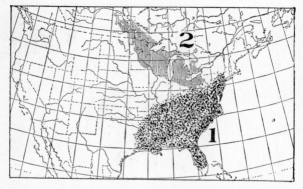

68. 1. *Angelica Tree*, pg. 331, also *Tupelo*, pg. 336, north to s. Me. Ont. and cen. Mich. and west to mid. Tex., also *Pumpkin Ash*, pg. 376, north to w. N. Y., west only to s. e. Mo. and e. Ark.

2. *Bailey's Cornel*, pg. 335.

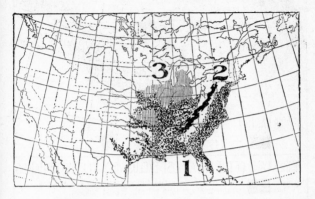

69. 1. *Persimmon*, pg. 368.

    2. *Biltmore Ash*, pg. 374, also *Rhododendron arborescens*, pg. 342, from s. Pa. to N. C. only.

    3. *Blue Ash*, pg. 378, lapping with No. 1 south to n. Ala.

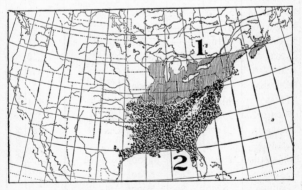

70. 1. *Ilex verticillata*, pg. 292, lapping with No. 2 on the coastal plain to Fla. and southwest to Mo.

    2. *Fringe Tree*, pg. 380.

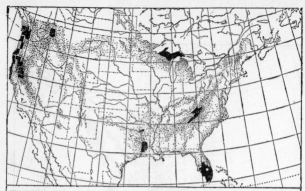

TIMBER LAND OF THE U.S. ALMOST EXCLUSIVELY IN PRIVATE HANDS

Areas of concentrated timber ownership; that is, the greater tracts of land with the fewest holders.

Areas of forest land comprising most of the lumber supply of the United States.

The 18 States possessing the greatest amount of standing timber are;

	Pine Etc.	Cypress	Hardwoods	Lumber cut in 1909	
1 Oregon	389.700	——	8.400	Yellow Pines	16.277
2 Washington	285.700	——	8.900	White Pines	5.400
3 California	236.700	——	11.400	Sugar Pine	97
4 Idaho	41.300	——	9.100	Lodgepole Pine	24
5 Montana	14.100	——	7.700	Douglas Fir	4.856
				Hemlock	3.051
6 Louisiana	67.700	15.700	36.400	Spruce	1.749
7 Mississippi	62.400	1.900	31.000	Cypress	956
				Redwood	522
8 Arkansas	6.000	2.200	50.500	Cedar	346
9 Texas	44.900	.200	20.900	Larch	421
				Firs	198
10 Florida	59.100	10.700	4.100	Oak	4.414
11 Alabama	38.000	.200	18.100	Maple	1.107
				Whitewood	858
12 Georgia (in part)	31.700	2.800	11.500	Chestnut	664
				Beech	511
13 N. Carolina (in part)	25.600	3.000	14.300	Birch	452
14 S. Carolina (in part)	19.200	2.600	8.900	Basswood	400
				Elm	347
15 Virginia (in part)	8.700	.200	5.000	Cottonwood	266
16 Michigan	22.200	——	25.400	Ash	291
				Hickory	334
17 Wisconsin	17.100	——	12.100	Tupelo	97
				Walnut	46
18 Minnesota	18.800	——	4.400	Sycamore	56
				Cherry	25

Various species 37

The annual growth of timber is approximately only 35 per cent of the annual cut; thus the annual depletion is about 28.471.300.000 feet.

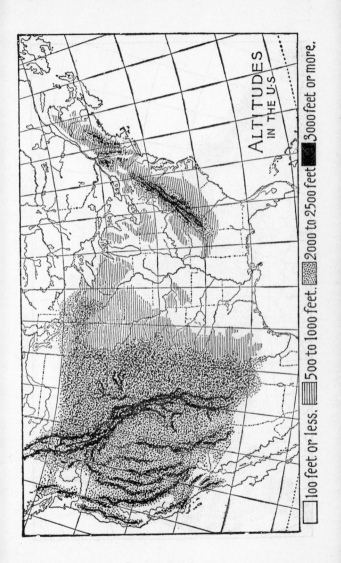

ALTITUDES
IN THE U.S.

100 feet or less.   500 to 1000 feet.   2000 to 2500 feet.   3000 feet or more.

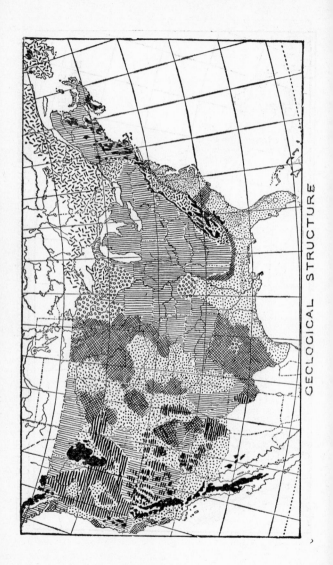

GEOLOGICAL STRUCTURE

GEOLOGICAL STRUCTURE

SHOWING FOUNDATION CHARACTER OF SOIL.

Volcanic Rocks. The Tertiary and later effusive igneous rocks showing from Greenland, Iceland, and the Aleutian Islands to Venezuela.

Volcanic Porphyritic, Granitic Rocks. The Post-Cambrian effusive rocks showing largely in the Cordilleras from Alaska to So. America.

Gneisses of the Appalachians, rare in the Rockies Undifferentiated Pre-Cambrian rocks including some Lower Huronian south of L. Superior; and much Laurentian in Can. and Lab.

Chalky Rocks. The Upper and Lower Cretaceous rocks including the marine deposits of the Permian, Jurassic, and Triassic periods, and western coal regions.

Limestones and Pennsylvanian Coal-measures. Including deposits of the Devonian, Mississippian, Silurian, Permian, and other periods of the Paleozoic age.

Sedimentary and Intrusive Rocks and Gneisses. Including the deposits of the Cambrian, Lower Ordovician, Huronian and other periods of the Proterozoic age.

Marine, Alluvial and Swamp deposits of the Tertiary Epoch. Including the Quaternary, Pliocene, Miocene, Oligocene and Eocene periods; covering the coastal plain.

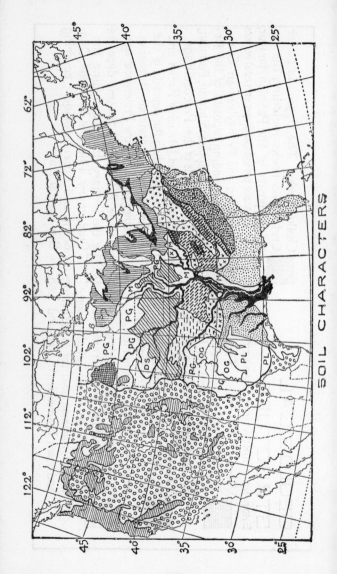

SOIL CHARACTERS

SOILS. GENERAL AREAS ONLY.

Limestone soil. Shenandoah Group.

Rich alluvial soil of river bottoms etc with the character of dark prairie soil.

M — Soil from wind-laid material (Aeolian) Mississippi Group.

PG — Undifferentiated soils from Glacial deposits allied to Aeolian Group.

OG — Sandstone and shale soils. Oklahoma group.

PL — Limestone soils, undifferentiated. Including many very small areas in Kan. & Mo.

Sedimentary soil of marine origin. Atlantic Group.

Timbered soils from crystalline rocks not including limestone.

Undifferentiated semi-arid soils. Eastern boundary very arbitrary, and therefore not altogether reliable.

Undifferentiated soils of sandstone, shale, and limestone.

Undifferentiated soils from Glacial deposits including drift and some Aeolian.

Undifferentiated soils from wind-laid material (Aeolian), incl' western timbered soils.

Dark-colored prairie soil from sandstone and shale.

Undifferentiated soils from wind-laid deposits incl' some loessial and glacial material

Cherty or silicious limestone soil, Ozark Group, light-colored, timbered soils.

Sandstone and shale soil including much timbered soil.

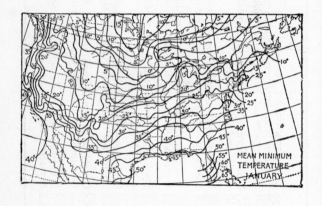

MEAN MINIMUM
TEMPERATURE
JANUARY

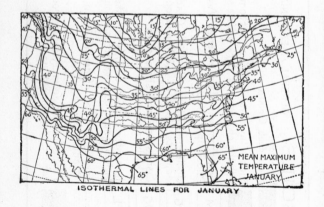

MEAN MAXIMUM
TEMPERATURE
JANUARY

ISOTHERMAL LINES FOR JANUARY

446

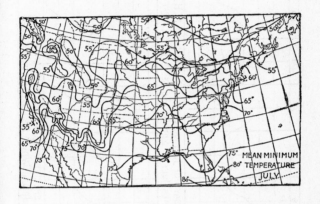

MEAN MINIMUM
TEMPERATURE
JULY

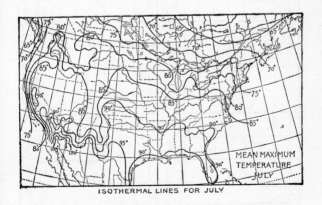

MEAN MAXIMUM
TEMPERATURE
JULY

ISOTHERMAL LINES FOR JULY

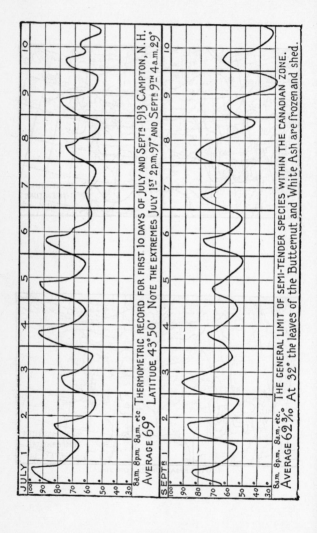

JULY 1   2   3   4   5   6   7   8   9   10

THERMOMETRIC RECORD FOR FIRST 10 DAYS OF JULY AND SEPT^R 1913 CAMPTON, N.H. LATITUDE 43°50′. NOTE THE EXTREMES JULY 1ST 2 P.M. 97° AND SEPT^R 9TH 4 A.M. 29°

8 a.m., 8 p.m., etc. AVERAGE 69°

SEPT^R 1   2   3   4   5   6   7   8   9   10

8 a.m., 8 p.m., etc. AVERAGE 62 3/10 %

THE GENERAL LIMIT OF SEMI-TENDER SPECIES WITHIN THE CANADIAN ZONE. AT 32° THE LEAVES OF THE BUTTERNUT AND WHITE ASH ARE FROZEN AND SHED.

448

BARK

A KEY FOR THE IDENTIFICATION OF A TREE BY THE CHARACTER OF THE BARK

It is by no means possible to recognize every species by the general appearance of the bark. The following eighteen illustrations are typically representative and the common species in addition may be grouped thus:

Bark with confluent ridges. White Pine—many Willows—several Poplars—Chinquapin—many Oaks—Black Walnut—Bitternut—Mockernut—Elms—Mulberries—Osage Orange—several Magnolias—Tulip Tree—Red Bay—Liquidambar—Redbud—Yel. Locust—several Maples—Lindens—Angelica Tree—Tupelo—Bumelia—Silver-bell Tree—Buttonbush—Fringe Tree—Paulownia—Ashes—Buckthorn.

Smooth Bark. Adelia—a few Poplars—Alders—Papaw—Yellow-wood—Rhododendron—Wax Myrtle—Cork-wood—several Ilexes—several Magnolias—Sweet Bay—Choke Cherry—Burning Bush—Hornbeam—Ailanthus (striped).

Smooth horizontally marked Bark. Birches—Mt. Ash—Cherries—Clammy Locust—Sumachs.

Smooth-warty Bark. Miss. Hackberry—Toothache Tree—Fir Balsam (blistered).

Small-scaled Bark. Spruces—Black Cherry—Catalpa—Rough-leaved Dogwood—Large Tupelo—Hop Hornbeam—Basket Oak.

Thin Scaly Bark. Most Apples—Planer Tree—Smoke Tree—Tree Huckleberry—Crataegus—Kentucky Coffee Tree—Locusts (sparingly so)—Ohio Buckeye—Horse Chestnut.

Broken-ridged Bark. Pignut—Post Oak—Live Oak—Sorrel-tree.

Shaggy Shredded Bark. Several Hickories—several Maples—Cedars.

Rough-scaly Bark. Plums—Soapberry.

Square-checked Bark. Flowering Dogwood.

Broad flat-ridged Bark. Loblolly Bay—Sweet-leaf.

Finely rough Bark. Pin Oak—Bl. Jack Oak—Laurel Oak.

INDEX TO MAPS

The numbers immediately succeeding the names are those belonging to the seventy maps of distribution of species.

INDEX TO MAPS

INDEX

INDEX

455

INDEX

INDEX

WHITE PINE   *Pinus strobus*

Reckless, inexcusable waste and inordinate cutting have brought this
valuable species to the twilight of existence.

POND PINE *Pinus serotina*

A picturesque species of southern swamp lands.

COLORADO BLUE SPRUCE *Picea Menziesii*

A Rocky Mt. species frequent in cultivation.

CALIFORNIA BIG TREE   *Sequoia gigantea*

The giant tree of the West, sometimes reaching an age of 5000 years.

RED CEDAR   *Juniperus virginiana*

A widely distributed dark bronze green evergreen with fragrant
brownish red wood.

BUTTERNUT   *Juglans cinerea*

An asymmetrical, wide-spreading tree with distinctly yellow green
foliage.

SWAMP HICKORY   *Carya cordiformis*

A common species of swamps or rich woodlands with slender branches
and yellow green foliage.

WHITE OR CANOE BIRCH   *Betula alba var. papyrifera*

The most common and distinguished Birch of the Northern States.

CHESTNUT   *Castanea dentata*

A wide-spreading tree with massive trunk unfortunately damaged
in recent years by a fungous parasite.

SCARLET OAK   *Quercus coccinea*

The foliage turns a brilliant dark cardinal red in autumn.

TULIP TREE *Liriodendron tulipifera*

It bears tulip-shaped pale yellow green flowers in May or June.

SHINING THORN   *Crataegus nitida*

As it appears early in October loaded with rich red fruit.

YELLOW WOOD   *Cladrastis lutea*

A symmetrical tree covered with cream-white drooping flower
clusters in late spring.

WHITE MAPLE   *Acer saccharinum*

The one Maple distinguished by an elaborately cut leaf with a silver
white back.

WHITE ASH   *Fraxinus americana*

A most valuable hardwood species largely used for the interior finish
of buildings and for furniture.

CATALPA   *Catalpa bignonioides*

A commonly cultivated tree bearing showy brown-spotted creamy
white flowers in June.

PITCH PINE   *Pinus rigida*

GRAY PINE   *Pinus Banksiana*

GEORGIA PINE   *Pinus palus tris*

Pinus ponderosa var. *Jeffreyi*

JEFFREY'S PINE

A stunted specimen on Sentinel Dome, the Yosemite Val., Cal.

A distinct variety of *P. ponderosa*, with dense, heavy, dark blue-green foliage, the

BLACK LARCH   *Larix laricina*

RED SPRUCE

Picea rubra

BLACK SPRUCE   *Picea mariana*

BALSAM FIR.   *Abies balsamea*

ALPINE FIR   *Abies lasiocarpa*

HEMLOCK   *Tsuga canadensis*

BALD CYPRESS   *Taxodium distichum*

COAST WHITE CEDAR   *Chamaecyparis thyoides*

ARBOR VITÆ

Thuja accidentalis

COMMON JUNIPER   *Juniperus communis*

GINKGO

Ginkgo biloba

YELLOW WILLOW

Salix alba, var. *vitellina*

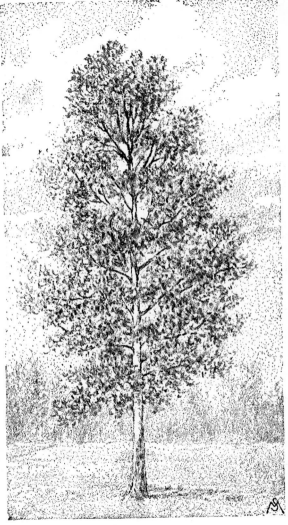

AMERICAN ASPEN OR POPLAR   *Populus tremuloides*

CAROLINA POPLAR   *Populus deltoides*
In cultivation, Laconia, N. H.

LOMBARDY POPLAR   *Populus nigra*, var. *italica*

BLACK WALNUT

Juglans nigra

MOCKERNUT

Carya alba

AMERICAN HORNBEAM   *Carpinus caroliniana*

GRAY BIRCH   *Betula populifolia*

YELLOW BIRCH   *Betula lutea*

BEECH

Fagus grandifolia

POST OAK

Quercus stellata

WHITE OAK

Quercus alba

LIVE OAK
Orton Plantation. N. C.

Quercus virginiana

ENGLISH ELM   *Ulmus campestris*

AMERICAN ELM   *Ulmus americana*

HACKBERRY   *Celtis occidentalis*

CUCUMBER TREE   *Magnolia acuminat*

SASSAFRAS   *Sassafras variifolium*

LIQUIDAMBAR   *Liquidambar styraciflua*

PLANE TREE *Platanus occidentalis*

ORIENTAL SYCAMORE   *Platanus orientalis*

MOUNTAIN ASH   *Pyrus americana*

SHADBUSH *Amelanchier canadensis*

ROAN MOUNTAIN THORN   *Crataegus roanensis*

WILD BLACK CHERRY   *Prunus serotina*

KENTUCKY COFFEE TREE   *Gymnocladus dioica*

HONEY LOCUST   *Gleditsia triacanthos*

AMERICAN HOLLY   *Ilex opaca*

SUGAR MAPLE   *Acer saccharum*

AMERICAN LINDEN   *Tilia americana*

TUPELO   *Nyssa sylvatica*

PERSIMMON   *Diospyros virginiana*

RED ASH *Fraxinus americana*

BLACK ASH

Fraxinus nigra

PAULOWNIA   *Paulownia tomentosa*

WHITE PINE
Small-scaled ridges

JERSEY PINE
Coarse plates

RED SPRUCE
Small scales

RED CEDAR
Spirally seamed

BUTTERNUT
Confluent flat ridges

SHAGBARK HICKORY
Shaggy strips

536

SYCAMORE
Thin scales, *buff* beneath

BIRD CHERRY
Horizontally lined

SHADBUSH
Dark brown striped

SUGAR MAPLE
Shaggy *flakes*

PERSIMMON
Rectangular plates

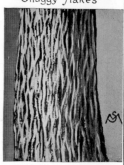

WHITE ASH
Narrow confluent ridges

CANOE BIRCH
Chalky white, horizontal lines

BEECH
Smooth, gray, mottled

CHESTNUT
Long confluent ridges

WHITE OAK
Long narrow flat scales

UMBRELLA TREE
Smooth, blisterlike

SASSAFRAS
Rough broken ridges